THE

COSMOS

OF

ARTHUR

HOLLY

COMPTON

# THE
# COSMOS
of
# Arthur Holly Compton

*Edited by* Marjorie Johnston
*with an introduction by* Vannevar Bush

*Alfred·A·Knopf*, Publisher, New York   *1967*

*Library of Congress Catalog Card Number: 66-11343*

THIS IS A BORZOI BOOK
PUBLISHED BY ALFRED A. KNOPF, INC.

© *Copyright 1967 by Alfred A. Knopf, Inc.*
All rights reserved under International and Pan-American
Copyright Conventions. Distributed by Random House,
Inc. Published simultaneously in Toronto, Canada, by
Random House of Canada Limited.

*Manufactured in the United States of America*

FIRST EDITION

*Portions of this work have appeared in whole or in part in earlier publications.
We hereby acknowledge with thanks permission to include in this edition material that has been previously published.*

Chapter 4: *Nobel Lectures in Physics, 1922–1941* (Amsterdam, London, and
New York: Elsevier Publishing Company; 1965), Copyright 1928 by The Nobel
Foundation; Chapter 7: *Proceedings of the American Philosophical Society*
(August 1956); Chapter 8: "Science and Man's Freedom" in *Atlantic Monthly*
(October 1957), © Copyright 1957 by The Atlantic Monthly Company; Chap-
ter 9: "Human Mind and Physical Law" in *Saturday Review* (July 12, 1958),
© Copyright 1958 by Saturday Review, Inc.; Chapter 11: "What the Atom
Looks Like" in *Scientific Monthly* (December 1931), Copyright 1931 by The
Science Press, by permission of *Science;* Chapter 12: *Scribner's* (January
1929), Copyright 1929 by Charles Scribner's Sons; Chapter 13: *Journal of the
Franklin Institute* (August 1940); Chapter 15: *Time and Its Mysteries* (The
James Arthur Foundation Lectures), Copyright 1940 by New York University
Press. Chapter 16: "Case Histories: Creativity in Science" in *The Nature of
Creative Thinking,* published by the Industrial Research Institute, Inc., New
York, 1953; Chapter 17: "Nobel Prize Winners in Physics: Michelson, Millikan,
and Richardson" in *Current History* (August 1931); Chapter 18: "The Progress

# Contents

# Foreword

This book is so full of the spirit of Arthur Compton, it gives such a fine view of the career of an outstanding American scientist, that my task is certainly not to elaborate on the text. Rather it offers an opportunity, and a very pleasant one, to emphasize three aspects of his career, which are indeed worthy of emphasis, not only to echo the sentiments of his host of friends, but also to remind young men entering the field of science that there is far more to a life devoted to science than intellectual accomplishment or even what is commonly regarded as genius.

The first of these points has to do with the Compton effect. There is no need to expound it; every physicist knows just what it is, and the experimental techniques used to establish it. They know, also, that its powerful presentation of the dual quality of light, as particle as well as wave, forced physicists everywhere to examine their premises, and to develop those far-reaching and seemingly bizarre theories which allowed physics again to proceed without being enmeshed in a quandary. It was undoubtedly one of the great discoveries, perhaps the key discovery, which led to the quantum theory, and revolutionized physics. It should also be emphasized that Arthur Compton's contribution was not just in precise measurement of the change of wavelength of X rays reflected at various angles from electrons. It included the then revealing concept that the momentum as well as the energy of a photon must be postulated if the observed effects were to be logically treated.

There is, however, another aspect of this great advance which I wish to emphasize. This country, located as it was initially in a wilderness, and long dependent for its prosperity upon the exploitation of the frontier and the production for its own use of relatively simple manufactured products, developed quite naturally an empirical, intensely practical attitude toward nature. This often spread before youth as an ideal the ingenious Yankee inventor, who knew very little about science, but who had a knack and a common sense which enabled him to get things done. All this was no doubt inevitable, but it had a sad side effect, for it was only too often accompanied by a scorn for fundamental or basic science, not universally of course, but which influenced the attitude of American universities, and decidedly influenced the attitude of the American public.

America hence lagged behind Europe on the basic sciences. In some areas it lagged so far behind that the American effort was negligible or nonexistent. And this was not good for science or for America.

A change occurred, slowly and painfully, for a generation. The primary stimulant appeared when a few American scientists produced results which were respected and admired throughout the world, results which could not be ignored by any truly educated man, and emphatically not by those who guided our universities. One thinks of Willard Gibbs, who was barely understood in this country at first, but who recast the methods by which physical chemists were bound to approach their problems with any hope of success; or Arthur G. Webster, whose exposition of classical dynamics opened a whole region which had previously been here hardly entered upon. But one thinks particularly of Arthur Holly Compton. For his great accomplishment was immediately recognized in that center of modern physics advance, Cambridge, where Rutherford, J. J. Thomson, and others had decidedly led the world. It gave at once a new posture to American physics in the eyes of that part of the world where opinion was most effective. So the Compton effect was far more than just another forward step in theoretical physics. It was in a very real sense a milestone on the tough path by which the United States finally grasped the deep importance of fundamental science, and strove to take a proper role in its development.

My second point has to do with Compton's work during World War II, and it has two parts, first his attitude toward the task, and second his conduct of a critical phase of the program on the release of atomic energy.

Scientists and engineers, in the war effort, were primarily motivated by a desire to aid their country in its peril. They knew the peril was real, they understood that science and technology could indeed make real contributions toward stopping the Nazi menace, and generally this was enough; they accepted their responsibility and went to work.

In the field of atomic energy, however, there was more than this to think about. For, to those who understood the power of the atom, a disquieting vista opened before them. If the atom were brought under control it might produce energy for man's affairs after he had exhausted his fossil fuels. But long before then it would present to mankind a new order of warfare, it might render warfare in its historical aspects obsolete, or it might wipe out mankind.

I think I understood Arthur Compton's point of view on all this. It was a conviction shared by nearly all the scientists I talked with, and it was simple. First, if the release of atomic energy were possible, it was also inevitable. If not accomplished by one group, it would most certainly soon be accomplished by another. Second, for the best hope for the world, it was essential that it first be accomplished by the true democracies, and not appear in the hands of any absolute monarch or dictator. No man could think far beyond this into the future; but that was enough to warrant the most intense efforts.

The second part of this point is more subtle. The whole range of effort on atomic energy had two phases. One was the scientific phase, to develop the necessary knowledge of the new physics and chemistry, to lay down the criteria and specifications which must be met for success.

The second phase was a broad engineering program, the assembly of materials, building of great plants, design and construction of explicit devices. These two phases called for very different types of organization and management. The scientific phase, for best progress, required much the same sort of organization as exists in well-handled university research, a maximum of freedom for gifted individuals, strong support of their efforts, a formulation of programs by consensus of opinion, and a minimum of direction in its rigid sense. The engineering phase required tight management, to control the efforts of thousands, to secure adherence to schedules, to be sure no detail was overlooked, to produce a fully integrated program oriented rigidly toward a closely defined objective.

With these two phases in a single over-all program there was bound to be conflict, and there was. This is not the place to discuss it. But it is the place to emphasize the contribution of Arthur Compton.

For it was his wise guidance, at the University of Chicago, of the group that produced the first nuclear chain reaction, which rendered that group a powerful team. It was his genial nature, his clear vision, his mature understanding of the ways of men of science, which drew about him that team of unmatched grasp and ability, and carried them to success in the effort which was the key to the whole complex undertaking. Many scientists and engineers contributed greatly, and received, at least among their colleagues, credit for magnificent performance. None will forget Fermi, whose key ideas were brilliant and essential. But Arthur Compton will always be remembered as the man who guided the key effort with wisdom and understanding.

My last point can be told briefly. The general public, and young people in particular, are likely to think of the scientist as eccentric, aloof, conceited, absent-minded, and given to idiosyncrasies of manner and dress. Many of Compton's students soon learned better. It would be salutary if youth all over the country would correct this false impression, and this book will help in that regard.

I will not try to characterize Arthur Compton. Those who knew him well need no such comments on my part. To those who did not know him it would be impossible to convey his human qualities of charm, simplicity, friendship, modesty. Let me just say that knowing him furnishes me with one of the most cherished of my memories, and that his friendship gave me an enhanced optimism as to the ultimate destiny of the human race.

VANNEVAR BUSH

# Introduction

Arthur Compton's mature thoughts on the relations of man, science, and society were expressed most fully to the students he taught during his later years. With them he discussed freely the ideas, the ideals, and the convictions that had ruled his life and had made him a towering figure in science and education. This book, which contains many of his views on science and its human implications, originated in response to the questions of his students. It is being published now so that others may have an opportunity to understand the thinking of one of our nation's distinguished citizens, a scientist whose influence has extended into virtually every aspect of American life and whose work has profoundly affected man's future.

In an apt characterization, a prominent British physicist once remarked that Arthur Compton was American to the roots of his being. It is true that his life was firmly rooted in the American tradition and reflected the rich and varied heritage that has shaped and is shaping our nation. More significant, however, is the role that he played as a powerful symbol of the future and of our nation's obligation to it. In fact, it would be difficult to find a figure of recent history who more clearly embodied the distinctive responsibility of the United States to the world.

Arthur Compton was personally involved in some of the most dramatic and far-reaching scientific developments of the century. His confirmation of Einstein's light quantum hypothesis provided an important foundation for quantum mechanics and the uncertainty principle, which have revolutionized physics and hold implications for other disciplines that are as yet hardly recognized; his personal achievements and scientific statesmanship contributed to the growth of American science from relative obscurity to world pre-eminence; and his direction of the key program in the wartime development of nuclear energy helped bring in the present age of tremendous opportunity and challenge.

Yet he was more than a major figure in twentieth-century physics, for his talents were directed not only toward the development of science but toward the larger task of service to man. The deepest aspect of his genius lay in the fact that he combined an unsurpassed knowledge of the leading intellectual movement of his age, a devotion to enduring principles, a sure grasp of the future, an unbounded confidence in man's capacities and creative possibilities, a youthful enthusiasm and zest for living, and a compassionate Christian humanism that motivated and inspired his efforts.

To Arthur Compton science was an intellectual adventure of compelling interest and beauty, one that he could have followed with pleasure and devotion throughout his life. But he knew, as many of the greatest scientists have always known, that the ultimate values of life are beyond science and that the highest purpose of science itself is to elevate and enrich human existence. He therefore turned with enthusiasm from the pursuit of science to the more practical matters of university administration when he saw an exceptional opportunity to help influence man's social and human growth.

He viewed the university as the most dynamic institution in American life and American college students as potentially the most vital force in shaping the future of the United States. Because of the uniqueness of the American experience, he felt that these students represent also the group whose aspirations will ultimately be most effective in shaping man's destiny. He was convinced that nothing else he might do could be as important as helping college students to find the integrating perspective and shaping vision that would permit them to pursue lives of personal significance and human meaning in a scientific world.

He saw higher education's great need as a unifying concept that would enable the student to integrate the various fragments of ideas and specialized knowledge to which he is exposed in college. Without such a concept, unless the student is a veritable genius, it is virtually impossible for him to relate his increasingly specialized courses to his vastly enlarged capacities for constructive participation in the life of the world. And only as a student comprehends his own individual responsibility for the values, the ideas, and the actions that shape and control his world will he be led to make the discriminating choices that will constitute an affirmative response to life, a response at once critical and imaginative.

In his search for such an integrating perspective in higher education, Arthur Compton eventually developed a course for undergraduates on the theme of science and human responsibility. He hoped that a similar course, which would examine science both as an intellectual activity and as a means of accomplishing human objectives, would one day become part of every college student's orientation toward life in a scientific age.

As he presented it, the course was not a mere exercise in academic thinking on the relevance of science and technology to human affairs. It was an informed effort to translate the idealism of today's college students into practical attainment of the important human goals that have become newly accessible through the advance of science.

He had special qualifications for this task. His principal contribution to science, made almost at the outset of his career and before American science had reached notable achievement, had gained him a reputation that enabled him to move easily among many of the groups that strongly affect our national development and to take an increasingly important part in their activities. As one examines where he chose to place his effort, one is chiefly impressed with the constant and effective role that he played in stimulating a greater degree of synthesis and integration in American life. The most conspicuous example is his part in the development of nuclear energy. He considered the true significance of the atomic project to be its powerful demonstration of the strength that results from the cooperation of diverse and specialized groups when they are united upon a common objective. Moreover, he believed that the growth of knowledge, of which science is but one part, demands a commensurate growth in cooperation, with a consequent lessening of traditional tensions and antagonisms and a developing sense of community of interest, not only within our nation but throughout the world.

Arthur Compton's careful examination of the relationship of man to science led his students directly to the central question of the purpose of man's existence, for he believed that only in terms of such an ultimate purpose is it possible to assign a meaningful scale of values to scientific knowledge and technological developments. The purpose of life, as the central theme for his course, also provided an opportunity to examine the nature of the goals that have inspired worthy and satisfying lives, to discuss the social and human objectives of special significance to people who are part of a scientific and technological civilization, to evaluate the various aspects of our present culture in terms of our national purpose, and to consider what can best be done now toward achieving that purpose. Among the many approaches to the purpose of life that he felt must be considered and weighed are those of such disciplines as anthropology, history, biology, psychology, sociology, philosophy, economics, politics, and religion. He believed that the significance of every type of course offered in a college curriculum can be explained in relation to the purpose of life, and that in this context the coherence of the total college program becomes apparent. An interdisciplinary course devoted to a thorough examination of the relationship of man and science, he felt, provides an opportunity to give the college curriculum the unity it has lacked since the introduction of the elective system.

Arthur Compton was eager that his students should understand both the powers and the limitations of science. He taught them that man has now reached the stage of development where he has the scientific knowledge and the technological tools consciously to direct his own cultural evolution and to shape his future as he wills. But he also taught them that the scope of science is sharply limited and that it does not interpret the spirit of man. From a thorough knowledge of modern physics, he explained the shallowness of the pseudoscientific philosophies that would use science to deny the effectiveness of human volition, purpose, and values; and he encouraged his students to consider the nature of the humane goals that can direct and inspire individual effort. From a long involvement in humanitarian causes, he taught them that progress in such tasks will not come as the automatic result of advancing science but only as the result of hard work and sacrifice by trained and dedicated individuals of high aspiration who will devote their minds, their hearts, and all their strength to meeting human needs.

He prepared his students to look upon science in its true light, not as an abstract force but as a human activity that unites in a remarkable way man's highest creative abilities of intellect and imagination. He explained the futility of trying to escape the pervasive influence of science and suggested that only in seeking a satisfying relationship with the dominant intellectual movement of the age and active participation in the attempt to apply its gifts for human ends can an individual find either freedom or happiness.

He warned his students of the danger of thinking that mankind as a social organism is of prime value, for he believed that the ultimate good lies in meeting individual needs and that the individual's prime social responsibility is to cultivate the growth of society toward a structure within which people can pursue lives of fullest meaning. He taught them to recognize the narrowness of the popular view that equates human welfare with material security and comfort, and he encouraged them to measure human well-being by a standard of human potential.

He taught them to see in American democracy an unusual combination of knowledge, idealism, and practical experience directed toward the liberation of the individual in order that he might reach his full development. But he also guided them toward the realization that the United States, as measured by its goals of freedom, justice, and open opportunity for all, remains an underdeveloped country. He suggested that the obstacles to human achievement represent the unsolved problems of American society, each offering an opportunity for constructive action. And he explained that those things considered rights in a comparatively selfish sense become, from the point of view of altruism, vital to the individual in order that he may perform his proper service to society. So he encouraged his students to see that in an increasingly complex society our greatest freedom no longer lies in independent action but in cooperation, which multiplies the individual's effectiveness.

Above all, he taught his students, and richly demonstrated by his own life, that only a sense of commitment and hope can release man's creative energies and generate the imaginative solutions to human problems that will assure for mankind an increasing destiny.

In a course presented by a leading scientist that emphasized not science but man, it was perhaps inevitable that many of the students were as greatly interested in the teacher as in what he taught. In response to their questions, he frequently referred them to statements that he had prepared on science and its broader implications, and he sometimes modified or expanded earlier articles for class discussion. From these materials the present text began to emerge.

The plan of the book is simple. It opens with brief personal reminiscences, followed by a section on the general relevance of science to human affairs. After an examination of several aspects of the philosophical background of science, there follow examples of the intellectual adventure of scientific pursuits, as seen in the author's work and in that of other scientists. The last half of the book is devoted to specific social and political issues in which science plays a role.

Some portions of this book have already appeared in published form, and the major previous publications have been credited in the acknowledgments. Such publications did not always have the benefit of Mr. Compton's final scrutiny, and many of them differ somewhat from his preferred or revised texts, which have been used here.

We must point out that we have added the several papers dealing directly with Arthur Compton's work, as it was characteristic of him to find examples of creativity in the work of others, and we believe the reader might like to know how a little of his own scientific achievement. We have also attempted to provide sufficient annotation to identify his allusions both for the nonscientific reader and for the specialist. We cannot urge too strongly, however, that the reader postpone all reference to footnotes until he has read what Arthur Compton himself has written, and then consult the notes only if questions remain. We believe that his own words express his ideas and character more completely than could those of the most skillful annotator; and constant attention to footnotes, as Samuel

| xix |

Johnson once remarked, only refrigerates the mind and causes the reader to throw away the book that he has too diligently studied.

As friends and associates of Arthur Compton, we were pleased and honored to accept the invitation of Chancellor Thomas H. Eliot to oversee the preservation and possible publication of the Compton papers, which now constitute a permanent archive at Washington University. Chancellor Eliot's constant support of our work was greatly encouraging. While as trustees of the papers we bear the responsibility for this publication, we should like to acknowledge our indebtedness to the friends and colleagues who have helped advance our work. To list every individual would be impossible, and we trust that all who have helped us will accept this general expression of our cordial thanks.

Our largest debt is to Mrs. Betty McCloskey Compton, the author's wife, who encouraged our work from the beginning with the same enthusiasm and devotion that she displayed for all her husband's varied activities throughout his lifetime. We cannot adequately express our thanks for her constant interest and concern. Among others who have assisted us we should like to thank especially Professor Richard E. Norberg, chairman of the Department of Physics at Washington University, and each member of the physics faculty for their willing help in confirming many details as well as for their patience, courtesy, and understanding of our work. Among the many scientists, students, and friends of Arthur Compton who took time to read and comment we must mention particularly Richard L. Doan and George E. Pake, whose contribution of time and effort extended far beyond the bounds of friendship.

Preparation of this manuscript was financed by grants from two of Arthur Compton's closest friends. Mr. James S. McDonnell, Jr., gave the work its initial impetus through his generous provision of the financial support that enabled us to formulate our plans. This support was later augmented by a generous gift from Mr. Edward Mallinckrodt, Jr.

Throughout the preparation of the book, we received invaluable assistance from Mr. Angus Cameron of Alfred A. Knopf, Inc. We owe him a special debt for his unfailing help, wise counsel, and discerning criticism.

Mrs. Janet S. Biegelsen not only typed the manuscript and its numerous revisions with skill, patience, and meticulous attention to detail, but made many thoughtful and helpful editorial suggestions. Miss Shirley Funk capably assisted in compiling and checking the bibliography as well as in skilled typing and proofreading from time to time. Mr. Bhola Mehrotra copied much of the original manuscript material and helped with bibliographical searching.

Arthur Compton's contributions to science will remain as part of man's permanent heritage. To those who knew him, however, his greater achievement lay in the nobility of character that illumined and informed all he undertook. His qualities of character, joined with lofty aspiration and keen intellect, led him to a progressive embodiment of the highest ideals of scholarship, citizenship, and service and enabled him to demonstrate something of what man might aspire to become. Such men as he, more rare even than genius, were once described by Louis Pasteur as *allumeurs d'âme*—kindlers of the spirit. If modern man might catch a little of his spirit and his vision, the Compton effect could become known not simply as one of the supremely lucid laws of physics but also as an example of the accepted standard of human relations in a world transformed by science in the service of man.

JOHN J. COMPTON
EDWARD V. CONDON
THOMAS S. HALL
MARJORIE JOHNSTON
HOWARD LOWRY

# I

---

# A Life
# in Science

Relying upon a faith that our universe is not a chaos but an ordered cosmos,

I believe that through sincere and courageous effort man can learn what is true.

I believe that inherent in what is true is that which will serve creation in its highest form, which is humanity.

I believe that truth shall make men free—free from the ills of the flesh and the spirit.

I rely upon an unfolding knowledge of the truth to provide a solution for the problems and conflicts that vex humanity.

I therefore dedicate myself to the task of seeking the truth, fearlessly and zealously, and to the application of what knowledge I may gain for the establishment of a peaceful, just, and orderly civilization on earth.

ARTHUR HOLLY COMPTON

# 1. Personal Reminiscences

Arthur Compton was not among the small number of men of science who have left relatively complete autobiographies. Though he himself possessed a keen sense of history, his orientation, like that of most scientists, was toward the world of the future. He especially enjoyed being with young people. Their enthusiastic interest in his ideas and accomplishments prompted him to speak on occasion of some of the highlights of his own career. Because he could not take part in as many of these informal student gatherings as he wished, he planned to develop some of his comments into a short essay for other students who might be interested.

As was his habit, he first compiled some of the material he had used on these occasions to provide a framework for further elaboration and refinement. A considerable portion of this material was written and revised with some care and frequently repeated. A smaller part consists of informal remarks that were spoken extemporaneously. The latter should not be considered to be in the nature of impromptu remarks, however, as they were based on carefully prepared outlines and they, too, were repeated more than once. Nevertheless, it is idle to speculate how these notes might have been altered if Mr. Compton had revised them as he intended.

It is with Mrs. Compton's permission, and after some early hesitation, that we publish these informal notes for an autobiography that was never to be completed. Only slight alterations have been made, chiefly in the arrangement of some of the sections. The informality of the language has been preserved. It is hoped that the reader will understand the fragmentary nature of the essay and that he will realize the remarks were intended chiefly for high school and college students, with whom Mr. Compton had often shared reminiscences about science and scientists. Some, but not most, of these students were themselves planning careers in science.

## REFLECTIONS ON SCIENCE

When I was invited to become chancellor of Washington University, in the spring of 1945, I warned the chairman of its board of directors that

| 3 |

I did not know what people's attitude toward me would be when they learned what I had been doing during the war. Either they would think of me as representative of the scientists who have saved civilization or of those who are threatening the destruction of mankind. A few months later the atomic bomb fell on Hiroshima, and people learned what we scientists had been doing. Today, after two decades of the turbulent peace that the bomb forced upon the world, the scientist remains a center of controversy. There is no doubt that he is one of those whose actions are changing the world. But sentiment remains divided about whether the scientist represents the dragon who will consume the earth or the knight who is slaying the dragon.

To give some basis for shaping your opinion on this matter I would like to tell you something about science and the scientists I have known as friends. I shall not consider merely those scientists I see every day but also those of other lands and of earlier times who made possible today's science, for they, too, through long familiarity have truly become my friends. What I really want to do is to explain to you why I have confidence in these scientists, and I want to help stimulate in your minds a similar kind of confidence. One way of doing that is simply to tell you about some of my own experiences.

It happens that I am a somewhat representative American scientist. My family background and my educational pattern are those that statistical studies show have been the most favorable for the development of our native-born American scientists.* My father was a professor at the College of Wooster, which is a small, denominational, liberal arts college in the Midwest. It was at Wooster that I received my own college education. My professional study was carried on at one of the eastern schools, Princeton University. Shortly after receiving my doctor's degree, I spent a year in research in a foreign university. Each of these statements is typical of the background that has been found to be most favorable for the development of our American men of science. It is thus reasonable to suppose that what has happened to me is more or less representative of what has happened to many other scientific men.

I am proud to be a man of science. I value science because it is helping us to understand the world around us and it is making it possible to shape the world to our desires. The first is the philosophical function of science; the second, its practical use. Many very sincere scientists, in their endeavor to simplify the universe, overlook the subtle but rich implications of science for the matter of living. Science, viewed broadly, is more than a matter of test tubes and electrons. Fundamentally, it is a discerning approach to the problem of living satisfyingly in an environment of materials, men, and events that do not of themselves conform readily to our desires. It is a search for truth.

The part of my scientific study that I have most enjoyed has been this effort to discover new truth. Nothing has given me greater satisfaction than such research. From childhood until I was forty-eight years old the uncovering of truth about the world of nature was my life commitment. And I am sure that few people have found greater enjoyment in the quest for truth. A second part of my research has gone into the supplying of new means for the development of industry. A third part has gone into the defense of the nation. Such research for the nation's defense is simply one man's share in fulfilling his duty to his country.

The scientist is commonly thought to be a man apart from the main body of citizens. This is an error made by critics of the scientists and not infrequently by certain of their defenders. The fact is that science as the growth of knowledge is an aspect of life shared in differing degree by all moderns, and respected by nearly all. Scientists are merely those citizens whose lot it has been to make especially close study of certain aspects of knowledge and, in most cases, to use the knowledge of science as a basis for living.

My own special field of science is physics, a rigid, rather exacting discipline of considerable practical value, but confined to a limited aspect of human knowledge. As Sir William Dampier reminds us, science can never represent the whole of experience: ". . . to see life steadily and see it whole we need not only science, but ethics, art, and philosophy." [1] To these my sister, Mary, would not fail to add common sense.

My sister reminded me of this rather forcefully some years ago when she was guest of honor at a luncheon in Chicago. On that occasion she was introduced as "the missionary sister of Professor Compton, a scientist of the University of Chicago." To me, seated at the opposite end of the table, it was obvious that Mary did not particularly like the idea of being introduced as the sister of her younger brother. So she told a story.

Looking pointedly across the table at me, Mary told of the time when she and her husband had moved from one Indian mission house to another. In their new house in Allahabad she found that one of the tall windows was badly out of repair, so she called in an Indian carpenter to repair the window. She explained to him as well as she could what she wanted done and then went about her other duties. When my sister returned she found that the carpenter had misunderstood her instructions and had pretty well ruined the window. In fact, it was going to be rather

[1] William Dampier: *A History of Science* (Cambridge, Eng.: The University Press; 1944), p. xxiii.

| 5 |

difficult ever to make it look right again. Mary was thoroughly exasperated and expressed her displeasure most emphatically. In reply to her questions the carpenter said: "But why didn't you explain more accurately what you wanted done?"

Her answer was to exclaim: "Why didn't you use your common sense?"

The carpenter's rejoinder was to raise himself to his full height and say: "But common sense, madam, is a very valuable thing. It is a gift of the gods. I have technical knowledge only!"

That was my sister's way of getting back at this scientific brother of hers who had technical knowledge only. And perhaps that incident may have provided part of the inspiration for me to take some interest in aspects of life other than strict science, although the background of science is one that gives a good and firm basis to build on, and I am very happy to have it.

Science is founded upon a belief that the world is reliable in its operation. Strange as it may seem today, this view was not widely current a century ago and scarcely conceivable two thousand years past. To believe that the world is reliable takes us away from the old conception that things just happen or the very persistent belief that capricious and whimsical gods dispose of men and events according to fancy. The characteristic attitude of the past is shown in the case of the farmer who offered sacrifices to the gods so that his barn would not be struck by lightning. Now we know that the thing to do is to put up lightning rods. We not only protect ourselves from outlaw electricity in this manner, but we have domesticated the force, as we did cows and horses, and have compelled it to draw our loads and carry our burdens. We can do this because we think of the world as a reliable, orderly thing, a cosmos and not a chaos.

Thomas Huxley expressed this change in our attitude in his essay "On the Advisableness of Improving Natural Knowledge," in which he recalls that men blamed the Great Plague of 1665 on God and the Great Fire of 1666 on the Papists. Now when plague strikes men do not flock to the churches, they look to the drains. ". . . we have no reason to believe that it is the improvement of our faith, nor that of our morals, which keeps the plague from our city . . . it is the improvement of our natural knowledge." [2]

By the method of science is meant simply that the truth of every supposed fact, the validity of every theory or hypothesis, must be tested by reliable evidence. Negatively, this means not to accept anything without adequate evidence. A truly scientific attitude is to be bold in hypothesis

[2] Thomas Henry Huxley: *Lay Sermons, Addresses, and Reviews* (New York: D. Appleton & Company, Inc.; 1903), p. 8.

but always to be patient and meticulous in verification. It is frequently overlooked that scientists show with their lives a faith in the value of the search for new knowledge and the trying of new techniques for which the evidence is suggestive rather than conclusive that would be condemned by scholars of more academic mold. Thus the Wright brothers demonstrated their faith in the value of human flight by trying their airplane before there was conclusive evidence of its ability to fly and even less evidence that it would remain right side up if it once rose in the air. The determination with which the little band of nuclear physicists pressed their development of the American atomic project in the middle years of World War II is a historic example of scientific faith: faith in the value of atomic energy and in the ability of their scientific techniques to solve as yet unforeseen problems.

I believe it is fair to say, among all the professional groups in today's society, that it is the scientific technologists who exhibit most clearly the faith that makes things happen. The biblical reference to the "faith that moves mountains" is frequently quoted as the acme of effective faith. But note that this is precisely the type of faith that is held by the engineer or the physician. He sees something that should be done to meet man's needs and, using whatever means may be available, proceeds to undertake the task and frequently accomplishes what had long been considered impossible. He thus performs in the true sense a miracle.

One usually marks the beginning of modern science from the period of Galileo [1564–1642]. The central point, I think, is that Galileo emphasized the importance of experiment as distinguished from the attempt to get at things purely by reasoning without checking the reasoning here and there. Galileo's use of the telescope illustrates in a striking manner the importance of experiment. Copernicus [1473–1543], who was born some years before Galileo, had revived an old theory about the motions of the planets. The idea that the sun is the center and the planets revolve around it had been well known in earlier times. Aristarchus [fl. 280–264 B.C.] had held this theory. It was replaced by Ptolemy [ca. A.D. 90–168] with the theory that the earth is the center. At the time of Aristarchus the evidence for his theory was quite inadequate. It was a choice; and you could take whichever view you wanted. That man is the center of the universe was the view that looked more reasonable. There were Greeks who knew that the sun was much larger than the earth, but this view was not very popular. Copernicus is said to have turned up this theory of Aristarchus and to have seen how simple it was. He wrote a book about it, which created a considerable amount of discussion in a small circle, but it was not widely accepted.

Then came Galileo. You cannot say that Galileo proved that the earth revolves around the sun. What he did do was to look up at the sky through his new telescope and see a planet, Jupiter. Galileo saw this planet and saw around it four moons. Then when he looked again a few hours later the moons had moved. You can see them hour after hour, night after night, and you see that they are revolving in orbits around that central planet. Galileo realized that here on a smaller scale was precisely what Copernicus had been talking about. Could anyone longer doubt that our earth and its moon form a similar system, or that the earth and its companion planets revolve around the sun as Copernicus had argued? To a scientist this is one of the great events of history. Julian Huxley was giving a lecture at Washington University a few years ago, and we invited him to our house for dinner. When he saw my telescope he pointed to it and said: "Do you ever use that? Let's get it out." So I took it outdoors and pointed it at the moons of Jupiter. He was as thrilled as could be.

Galileo's work naturally provoked hostility among the people who considered the earth as the center of the universe. Galileo said, "If you don't believe me, just look at the sky." They refused to look. They did not want to see. That the facts were otherwise was not what they wanted to believe. They believed that man was God's chief interest, and that he therefore was the center of the universe. It took a long time to adjust people's thinking to the fact that it does not work in quite that way.

It was from this point, however, that things began to happen. I would emphasize the power of observation in getting at knowledge and also in adjusting people's thinking to their place in the universe. This was just one thing that Galileo did.

In this connection, it may be worthwhile to repeat what we mean by the scientific method. So far as our logic is concerned, it is no better than it was at the time of Aristotle [384–322 B.C.]; but our science is very much better. The test comes in one case through logic. But the true scientist is always suspicious of his results, and because of his suspicions he insists that his results be tested before he has confidence in them.

Galileo had reason to believe that a heavy body would fall faster than a lighter body, and he had a good reason. He thought of testing his theory, and he found that the lighter body fell just as fast as the heavier. As he went back over the reasoning, he found a flaw not in the reasoning but in some of the assumptions of Aristotle. The point is that in the scientific method one relies primarily on observation of facts, and uses the methods of reasoning to relate one set of facts to another set, always checking the reasoning where possible on the basis of experiment. We do use reason, but we use it qualifiedly, always suspicious of the results. That is the thing that is most characteristic of our period of science.

Today we find a culture based on science in a dominant position in the

| 8 |

world. Science has proved its value in enabling people to do the things they want to do. It has opened to us new possibilities for a healthier and more abundant life. It has given us a new view of ourselves and of our relation to our world, a view that we recognize as more reliable because it is based on tested truth. From the rate at which this scientific culture is growing, it seems inevitable that it will rapidly become the worldwide heritage of man.

It may be of value to give an illustration of the way science does its work to shape our lives. The discovery of electromagnetic induction is typical. Michael Faraday, something over a century ago, noticed that when a magnet was moved near a coil of wire an electric current was produced in the coil. This remarkable discovery of a connection between magnetism and electricity excited the scientific world. Faraday became the talk of London. But then came the inevitable question, "Of what use is your discovery?" To an elderly lady who asked the question, Faraday countered: "Madam, of what use is a baby?" * More pointedly he told Gladstone: "Sir, someday you may tax it." What a bold suggestion! Electricity did not appear to be related to people's needs for food, for clothing, or for shelter. In fact, for fifty years the most valuable application of Faraday's great discovery was in making parlor shocking machines for entertainment. Then came Thomas Edison with his electric light and his system of distributing electric power. At long last, electricity began to fill a human need. Gradually, the use of electricity became widespread, until now our cities would be helpless without it and life as we know it could not exist. And millions of dollars in taxes on the electrical industry flow into government each year.

When Michael Faraday did his work, at the Royal Institution of London, he was almost unique as a professional in scientific research. For the most part, knowledge of nature grew in an accidental fashion. Today, the search for new knowledge is a conscious objective of many thousands of trained minds, and the resultant explosion of discovery and invention causes strikingly rapid changes in our mode of life. If we compare the millions of years of man's existence to one year, the past century of scientific research would be encompassed in the last hour; and, on this time scale, the published results of research during the last ten minutes would equal those of all previous history.

## DAWN OF SCIENTIFIC INTERESTS

Science has been my interest since childhood.* This interest found its earliest expression in my hobbies, but later science became my vocation. My chief scientific hobbies in my youth were astronomy and airplanes, both of which I pursued avidly for several years. The period of this activity was undoubtedly very important to me in my personal as well as in my professional development. In fact, I can see germinating during those years most of the ideas and emotions that have driven me during my later career.

## Astronomy

I was twelve years old when I became actively interested in astronomy, and I remember the circumstances vividly. I was sitting on the front porch of our house in Wooster, Ohio, on a cold evening in early February of 1905. A clear view was open toward the sky over the schoolhouse, and as dusk fell I watched the stars appear. Among them were three stars arranged in a row, and to the east of them an unusually bright star. At supper I told the family about seeing the stars come out. When I mentioned the three stars in a row, Father asked me a few questions about their location and then said, "That was the constellation Orion which you saw, with the dog star, Sirius, off to the east." After supper he brought out a star map that he had used in college and pointed out the constellation I had seen. I could recognize Orion, and I understood how it would be possible for me to locate the other principal stars in the sky. Then my older brother Karl went to the bookshelves in the library and pulled down a copy of *Sun, Moon, and Stars* by Agnes Giberne. He said he had read it and found it very interesting, but he did not undertake to tell me any of its contents. I do not remember just when I finished reading this book. I was a slow reader, however, and it probably took me several months. But I quickly sensed that I was on the track of something that I wanted to follow in greater detail. With the next order that Father and Mother sent to Sears, Roebuck for supplies, I put in my order for a telescope costing $3.95. As usual, I needed their approval before I could place such a large order, but the money came from what I had earned from time to time by doing chores.

I did not spend much time that spring trying to identify the stars, although I did spend several evenings sitting in our garden with a pair of binoculars that Father used for watching the birds and searched the face of the moon until I became thoroughly acquainted with its more familiar markings. As soon as the telescope came from Sears, however, I was very busy trying it out in every possible way. The telescope did not include a tripod for its support, and I had to make a crude one out of wood. Having thus a stable mounting, I found that I was able to read the time on the town clock a mile away and to make out details on the distant hills to the south. I also found that I could make out the craters of the moon and some of the details about which I had been reading. I was able also to locate the moons of Jupiter. I was quite thrilled when, finding that one of the stars I was examining was not a simple round point of light and trying to account for its angular shape, I determined that it was the planet Saturn, whose rings my telescope could not resolve. I also found, by putting in front of the telescope a piece of plate glass that I had blackened with soot from a lamp, that I was able to look at the sun and to make out the sunspots. Considering the way I experimented, I think I was rather lucky not to have ruined my eyes. But in the process I not only learned much about the planets but also about how the telescope worked and what it could do. My observatory was a vacant lot north of our house. Frequently, the boys from the missionary home in Wooster joined me there in the afternoon and evening to look at the stars, but neither they nor either of my brothers showed the fascination that I had in keeping up the observations hour after hour.

There is no doubt that I had at that time a strong emotional stirring that developed into an enthusiasm for scientific work. To become an astronomer was an obvious answer, and some years later I talked about this possibility seriously with Professor Gable, who was our professor of astronomy at the College of Wooster. At first, of course, my thoughts were not so definite. My interest seemed more like that of a child who has just received a Christmas box and wants to see at once all the things that are in it. A new world had been opened to me, and I was exploring it. Who could tell where it would lead? Father and Mother were sympathetic with my interests, but they were more inclined to put on the brakes than to drive me faster. They were aware of the possibility that I might develop too narrowly. I think that was the major reason why Mother would not let me stay up late at night to find stars that I wanted to identify.

During these early years at Wooster I do not remember that there was anyone else who showed any marked interest in astronomy. To Professor Gable astronomy was only a side issue. My chief counsel came from my father and my brother Karl, who were interested in astronomy at this stage primarily because they knew of my own rather intense interest. My interest was to be a continuing one. In fact, although physics became my vocation, astronomy has remained a major avocation.

I still have a photograph of Halley's Comet that I took in May 1910. In the meantime, however, my interests had developed considerably. I had bought myself a camera with which I had earned some reputation as a youthful photographer. I had made several cameras consisting of home-made wooden boxes with light-tight plateholder compartments and lenses of whatever type I could find available. The climax of this activity was the construction of a wooden equatorial mount with a homemade slow-motion attachment and alarm clock drive for one of my cameras and my well-torn telescope. I mounted this on a post in the vacant lot that I used for my observatory. With this equipment I took a photograph of the constellation Cygnus. My print of this photo says "September, 1908, exposure one hour." I also have a diagram dated October 14, 1907, showing the appearance of the stars in the Pleiades, which indicates something of the continuity of my boyish interest in the stars.

In 1910, of course, everyone was interested in the appearance of Halley's Comet. The college observatory was in those days almost unused, and I was free to work in it as I wished. I had by then begun my college work and was janitor of the physics laboratory. So I had access to means for keeping the telescope in repair. Through the courtesy of one of the professors, I also had access to the college darkroom.

For taking the photograph of the comet, I made up a new camera, consisting of a wooden box painted black inside and with a compartment for my own plateholder. For the lens I borrowed a projection lens from the physics laboratory. I fastened this camera onto the tube of the observatory's telescope with straps and used the telescope itself merely to keep the camera pointed at the head of the comet, which was moving so fast that correction for the earth's rotation was not adequate. My wife, who was a college classmate, recalls my taking her to the observatory and showing her the camera adjusted for the photograph and explaining the adjustments that would have to be made while the photograph was in progress. I do not recall that anyone was with me for the long period (one hour and forty-five minutes) in which I had to keep the telescope accurately pointed toward the comet while the exposure was in progress. I did not feel that any of my friends would have the patience needed for such an observation. Immediately after taking the photograph I went to the college darkroom to develop it. This was a familiar process to me. I do not recall any special feeling of elation at the successful result, though the fact that I made a supply of prints to sell at the college bookstore indicates that I took some pride in this accomplishment. I have no doubt that my family was pleased.

## Airplanes

To a considerable extent my interest in astronomy overlapped that in airplanes. I was fifteen, and a second-year student at Wooster Preparatory School, when one of my fellow students, Arthur Swan, showed me an article in *McClure's Magazine* telling about the early glider flights of Glenn Curtiss and the Wright brothers. Stimulated by this article, I became very much interested in these machines and I read everything about flying that I could find. Then I started making model airplanes of various types. The first ones I made did not work at all well. I remember one big one, with wings five feet across, that I spent about three weeks on, and it simply refused to fly. Shortly after that, though, I thought of a way to make my flyers go right, and from that time on all my models worked. Some of these were made simply of paper, while others were made of paper on wooden frames. Of course there were no airplane kits at that time, so I had to work out all the designs myself.

When I started this work the planes that were being flown were not stable. The Wright brothers, for example, described riding their airplane as like riding a bicycle, in which one gets the feel of the guiding motions necessary to keep one's balance. For making model planes that would fly successfully, it was necessary that they have inherent stability so that they would fly smoothly without a pilot to drive them. A major point of these early model experiments of mine was to determine the conditions necessary to maintain stability. By a systematic series of experiments that I devised, I determined a way in which the various surfaces of the wing, elevators, and rudder could be arranged and the weight distributed to give the airplane a maximum of stability. I also got a report by S. P. Langley of his experiments at the Smithsonian Institution on the forces of wind on moving surfaces. When I discovered that nearly all the real airplanes worked on the principle that I had figured out for myself, I was quite tickled to think I had found it without anyone's telling me about it.

After making literally thousands of model airplanes, I next set out to plan a glider that would carry me. Father was by then in London, studying at the British Museum, and at Mother's suggestion I wrote him of my plans and hopes for the projected glider, asking his permission to proceed with its construction. I was almost seventeen, and he had enough confidence in me to let me go ahead. With his approval, I began the work in June, 1909, using the barn at the rear of our house as a shop and hangar. That summer my brother Karl and my sister Mary were in charge of the household while Mother joined my father in Europe. By the time she came home in later summer, my construction job was nearly complete. I did not attempt to fly the machine, however, until after Father came home.

The structure was a triplane with wings of 27 feet spread and 3 feet 4 inch width and an over-all length of just over 12 feet, total weight about 150 pounds. The framework was yellow pine, braced with piano wire, and the surfaces were covered on both sides with muslin, the underside being paraffined. The plane was mounted on broad wooden runners to make the landing easy. The runners in turn rested on a two-wheeled truck, which ran along a wooden track, the wheels in tandem like a bicycle. When the plane became airborne the truck fell over and stopped its motion, while the plane went on. It was necessary to have someone at the end of the wing run along with the plane to keep it balanced until the wind took hold. The only special feature of the glider was its balancing system, which consisted of two horizontal rudders, one 7 feet in front of either end of the main wings and a steering rudder 3 feet in the rear, and controlled by a single steering gear. This balancing mechanism was the subject of a patent application that brother Karl helped me finance. Finally, a patent was allowed, but the claim had been so restricted that we agreed the patent would not be worth taking out. This was the only part that K. T. took in this venture of mine, but he continually gave me encouragement by discussing my progress with me.

In building the glider the only help that I had was some mechanical suggestions from a fellow student, Ceylon P. Strong, whose father was a piano tuner and who gave me some advice about handling the steel piano wire that I was using for bracing the structure. I did all the work and the sewing of the muslin surfaces myself. My tools were Mother's scissors and sewing machine, Father's plane and try square, and my own pliers, screwdriver, and pocketknife. The total cost of the machine was between $30 and $35. I took this from the savings that according to our family practice I had been able to put aside from chores that I did for the neighbors.

By July 22, 1909, I had completed the machine, and I made a test flight down a nearby hill (the local golf course) with a fifty-pound sandbag in lieu of an operator. The glider took off into the air, rising to some 15 feet, but due to a faulty adjustment of the center of gravity, stalled, and then pancaked to the ground. The landing skids were weak and crumpled when the glider landed. Accordingly, I spent some weeks in readjustment, followed by a second flight without an operator on December 24, 1909. This time the stability was perfect. The glider sailed evenly for 125 feet before striking the ground. It then glanced up and flew another 75 feet. The landing caused some structural damage and no further flight was attempted until April 3, 1910. On this day with myself as operator, two flights were made.

The first time, as the wind was not strong enough, I was unable to obtain sufficient speed through the air, so that when the rudders were turned up the flyer barely rose and quickly settled down with the truck under the right wing. I was able to balance the machine, however, and it alighted easily. The second flight was made in a stronger breeze. Being unused to the action of the balancing system, I caused the glider to pitch and strike the ground lightly. It immediately arose from the ground again and sailed for another 110 feet, about 185 feet total. Father and two or three of his faculty friends helped me that day in carrying the glider to and from the hill where the flight was made. And Father ran alongside to balance the wings.

Having demonstrated the validity of the balancing system and my ability to get off the ground, Father and Mother urged me to stop further work on the project. By that time I had myself come to feel that as a field of engineering development aeronautics was too far in the future to be of active interest to me. So in later April I burned the plane in a great bonfire and called it a day. Except for some later work with gyroscopic stabilizers and some air-navigation instruments, I never returned to airplanes as a field of major interest.

As I think back on these early experiments, one matter strikes me forcibly. It is the contrast between my first airplane experiments, which were done entirely with my own hands and with a minimum of contact with others working in the same field, and my last major engineering or scientific job. This was the atomic reactor, where thousands of people were engaged using the best available tools, and my part consisted largely in organizing the activities and the thoughts of the scientists who were concerned with getting the job done. In the thirty-three years that intervened my own scientific work, like that of the nation, went through all the stages from primitive pioneering, where one's own individual skill and resourcefulness, not only in ideas but also in handcraft, was the basis of success, to what has now become a vast enterprise in which each individual contributes a small but expert part, but in which, nevertheless, the originator of the idea has still to take the responsibility for it.*

CHOICE OF CAREER

When I was ready to begin my work in college, I was increasingly troubled about the choice of a life work. The idea that the good life is devoted to service had been a strong part of our family tradition. My father was not only a professor of philosophy but an ordained minister in the Presbyterian church who had himself given serious consideration to entering the mission field. My mother was the corresponding secretary of the foreign missionary society of our church. It was her responsibility to keep in touch with the many missionary families whose children were studying at Wooster. The missionary motivation was also to find expression in the work of my sister, who with her husband was to spend forty years as a missionary in India and Pakistan. At this stage I felt that perhaps I should myself become a missionary. Evidently my father saw my uncertainty, for he gave me then the only counsel along this line that I can recall having received from him.

"Arthur," he said, "to my mind there is no calling as high as that of the ministry, and no service that is as important to the lives of men and women as that of the missionary; but you seem to me to have unusual facility as well as special interest in the field of science. If I am not greatly mistaken, it is in science that you will find that you can do your best work. Your work in this field may become a more valuable Christian service than if you were to enter the ministry or become a missionary."

This was just the guidance that I needed and gave me confidence as I set my life's course. It was for me a venture of great faith, however, when in 1910 I elected to follow the path of science in the hope that it would be found to be of practical human value. Were not the great discoveries already made? What could the future of science bring that would be comparable with the great contributions of the past? Would it be possible even to find employment other than to teach others the useful facts and principles that I had myself been taught? Today the world's growing recognition of the practical value of scientific research is indicated by the fact that there are at least a hundred times as many scientists employed for finding new knowledge as there were when I was beginning my own scientific work.

By the time I reached the age of twenty my interests had become closely confined to research in physics with special regard to the nature of matter and radiation. This continued as my chief interest for about ten years. My work in this field was a combination of experiment and theory, about equally divided. In my theoretical studies the mathematical aspects appeared to me of less relative importance than the physical significance. My experiments were aided by more than usual manual dexterity and a liking for a certain amount of hand work and drudgery. My youthful interest in machines and invention definitely carried over to this type of research interest. In fact, I can see now that my scientific work developed in a continual and connected manner from my early enthusiasm for astronomy at the age of twelve.

It was as a youth at the College of Wooster that I did my first work with X rays. Wilhelm Roentgen had discovered these highly penetrating rays in 1895, a discovery for which he was later awarded the first Nobel prize for physics.* Very soon after Roentgen's discovery, Dr. William Z. Bennett, then professor of physics and chemistry at the College of

Wooster, purchased X-ray equipment for the physics laboratory. This was used later by my brother Karl in working out his master's thesis during the winter of 1908–9. His thesis was related to a part of the electrical equipment, a so-called Wehnelt interrupter, that was used in connection with the induction coil that operated the X-ray tube. Incidentally, this work led to the first scientific research publication that I know of having been sent out from the College of Wooster.* I first saw this X-ray equipment when I went with Karl to the laboratory where he was at work on his thesis. Later as a college student, about 1911 or 1912, I used it myself in laboratory experiments, an introduction that was of substantial help to me when I went to Princeton a few years later to do my graduate study.

### BROADENING HORIZONS

## Graduate study at Princeton University

My first real introduction to the scientists occurred when I went as a graduate student to Princeton University. I entered Princeton in 1913 as a fellow in physics, intending to transfer to engineering after one year. Instead, I continued graduate study in physics, being appointed in 1914 as a student assistant and in 1915 as Porter Ogden Jacobus Fellow, which was then the highest fellowship awarded by Princeton. It may be of interest to mention some of the influences upon a young man who was about to enter the field of physics.

At Princeton the first person I met was Andrew West, dean of the graduate school. West was not a scientist, however; he was a noted classicist. He and Woodrow Wilson engaged in quite a memorable controversy in which Princeton sided mostly with Andrew West. As a result Woodrow Wilson left the presidency of Princeton and eventually became President of the nation.

The best scientist that I found at Princeton was undoubtedly O. W. Richardson. He was the man who developed the law for the emission of thermoelectrons from hot wires. He also investigated and found the laws controlling the emission of photoelectrons from metals struck by light. In the latter work he was testing and established a law that had been indicated previously by Einstein.* He worked out the law of thermoelectrons for himself. This is a phenomenon that had been discovered by Thomas Edison but had not previously received any explanation.

Richardson was not the kind of person, as a scientist, who would trouble to make inventions or develop the things that he learned into practical applications. That remained for Sir John Fleming, the Englishman who made the first electron tubes, and others who developed the electron radio tubes as we now know them. But Richardson continually performed experiment after experiment to find new laws and to discover the facts. He was a great inspiration to his students to follow in his footsteps.

Richardson was one of those lecturers who never has his lecture outlined but who starts writing on the blackboard and works out his outline as he goes along. The result was not a very well organized lecture. Sometimes he would stand in front of the blackboard for a full minute without saying a word or without writing down a letter with his chalk, and then he would go off on a line that showed what he had been thinking, developing the explanation in mathematical form while he was there in front of the class at the blackboard. It was really very illuminating and helpful, but it was not always a very stimulating lecture. My brother Karl had studied with Richardson and had taken meticulous notes of his lectures. So when Richardson decided to publish his book on *The Electron Theory of Matter,* he utilized Karl's notes for his outline.

There were others around Princeton who were likewise following the field of pure science. One of the most interesting of the other men was Augustus Trowbridge. He had studied in Germany and France, and also some in Italy, so he brought to us a coloring of what the European physics was like. It so happens that I had in my Sunday School class of the First Presbyterian Church at Princeton Gus Trowbridge's two sons, Cornelius and George. Both of them became ministers in the Episcopal church, but I don't think they got that from me in my Sunday school class. Gus Trowbridge's comment to me when the second boy went into the seminary was: "Arthur, I don't see why lightning has to strike twice in the same place."

It might be worth mentioning in that connection that in the setting in which I found myself then, the large majority of the scientists with whom I was in contact had a high respect for religion. Most of them were men who were active in the various Christian churches. Of course, the interpretation of the relationship between science and religion was different from one to another, but that is something one learns to understand.

William Francis Magie was another of the physicists we had who had been trained in Europe. A good part of our training came indirectly from Germany and France, but some came also from England because Richardson was trained in England. Magie had studied in Germany, especially under Hermann von Helmholtz, who is given chief credit for establishing the principle of the conservation of energy. So you see that dates the discovery of the principle of the conservation of energy as being about two lifetimes back from me.

Another interesting scientist at Princeton was Professor E. G. Conklin. He was not a physicist but a biologist, and he was concerned with expounding the principles of genetics as discovered by Mendel. Mendelian genetics was new then, and it was something that Conklin was trying to develop. As this was a subject of live scholarly concern, Conklin opened up to us who were graduate students an interest in an exciting development in a whole new field of science.

I cannot leave this group of scientists without speaking of Henry Norris Russell, who was perhaps the greatest astronomer that the United States has produced. When I was at Princeton he was full of the idea of the life history of the star. After making a special study of this, he had come to the conclusion that the stars had existed for a very long period of time and that the energy that gave the stars their heat was too vast to have its origin even in the radioactivity of uranium or radium. At about that time Sir Ernest Rutherford, later Lord Rutherford, came over from England on a visit and gave a talk before our physics colloquium. He told us of his new discovery [1913] that the atom has a nucleus, much smaller than the atom itself, in which most of the mass resides. He also explained that the energy of this nucleus shows itself in radioactivity. Russell was in the audience, and the discussion between the two of them about how the nucleus of the atom might possibly have supplied the energy for the pouring out of heat from the stars was a thrilling event for a young physicist. It was then that I really became interested in this matter of the energy that is stored in the atom, but I had no idea that I would have anything personally to do with its release.

## Collaboration with Karl Compton

When I was in my final year of study for the Ph.D. degree, my brother Karl returned to Princeton as an assistant professor. To me as an aspiring young physicist it was an unusual privilege to share intimately the experiences of an older brother as he undertook his new work. I saw K. T. accept the responsibility for guiding the research of a competent group of young graduate students. He began by exploring systematically the various new fields of physics research that were then opening up, and selecting certain promising fields in which he judged that particular research problems might arise that would be suitable for attack by the small group he would collect as his team. The field he selected was that of the phenomena connected with the passage of electrons through gases. This field he broke down into more elementary events, such as the elastic and inelastic collision of electrons with molecules and the related questions of ionization and excitation of atoms. It was thus that K. T. entered into the field that was at the same time being opened up by James Franck and Gustav Hertz. His examination of these problems led to a series of papers in the *Physical Review,* which were of value chiefly as guides to his students in understanding the background and the significance of their experiments.

For these studies Karl saw the need for use of an electrometer of higher sensitivity than the Dolezalek electrometer then in common use at Palmer Physical Laboratory. With the help and suggestions of Professor H. L. Cooke, who was supervising my thesis, I had built such an electrometer for use with an X-ray spectrometer with which I was to make my thesis study of the intensity of X-ray reflection from crystals.* This instrument served as a prototype of the one Karl wanted. But here occurred an incident that illustrates the difference between K. T.'s approach and my own. I had set up the original electrometer without great care, and by trial and error had achieved the very high sensitiveness that was needed for my work. Karl liked the general design and built a similar one, but with real care as to symmetry and mechanical perfection. The result was disappointing, for he was unable to achieve a sensitiveness approaching that of my much less carefully built instrument. Karl was thus inspired to make a thorough examination of the theory of the operation of the electrometer. This study revealed the fact that the unusual sensitiveness of the instrument was the result of an assymmetry of the needle and the quadrants. With this understanding it was possible to introduce the desired departure from symmetry and to attain an electrical control of the stability of the needle that made available a wider range of sensitivity. We thus had an instrument that was much more flexible and versatile than had previously been available. This improved electrometer became the subject of the only technical paper on which Karl and I ever collaborated.* The instrument was never patented as we preferred to publish the details of its construction and make them available to any who wished to use them. It was put on the market both in the United States and in England, and for many years it was the most sensitive available instrument of its type.

Eventually the time came for me to receive my diploma for my doctor's degree, and Dean West called me into his office. He said: "Now, Compton, how much Latin have you had?"

I explained that I had had my prep school Latin, four years of it, but I had not had any in college.

Then came the next question: "How much Greek have you had?"

I told him I had not had any.

He then asked me: "Do you think that you are a proper representative to go out from Princeton with that background and understanding of the classics?"

I replied, "That's up to you, sir."

He was not very happy about that, and so this sturdy defender of the classics called my attention to the importance of some of the things to be found there. I would like to pass on a few of the things that I learned from him.

One of them was an idea attributed to Pythagoras [fl. sixth century B.C.]. You may remember Pythagoras as the man who invented the geometric theorem of the sums of the squares of the sides being equal to the square of the hypotenuse. Another thing he did was to develop the eight-note scale in music, which is called the Pythagorean scale. The important thing about Pythagoras in the present story, however, is his instructions to his disciples. Pythagoras was really a physicist, so his statement is quite a relevant one. He said to his disciples, or his students as I suppose we would now refer to them: "Search to find of what and how the world is made, in order that you may find a better way of life."

Now the first part of that is straightforward science: ". . . of what and how the world is made." That is a major objective of science at the present time. But why? "in order that you may find a better way of life." The way of life was the thing that he was concerned with. So, you see, science from a very early time was connected with the life of man. Scientists today in their acceptance of the principle that the proper function of science is to enrich the life of man hold for their profession a similarly high ideal. As Albert Einstein has remarked: "Concern for man himself must always constitute the chief objective of all technological effort." [3]

Another quotation that comes out of the classics is that of Democritus: "Rather would I find the true cause of one fact than become king of the Persians."

If you ask why people do science, there is your answer. They do it because it is so interesting to find new information. I want to understand, to find the true cause of the facts, and I would rather do that than become king of the Persians. Some of you may remember from the stories of Herodotus what it meant to be king of the Persians. It was really the

[3] Address to students of California Institute of Technology, February 16, 1931, used with permission of the Estate of Albert Einstein. An accurate translation of the address appears in Otto Nathan and Heinz Norden, eds.: *Einstein on Peace* (New York: Simon and Schuster; 1960).

greatest position of power and wealth that one could hope for anywhere in the world.

In spite of my lack of knowledge of the classics, Dean West decided to let me have that doctor's degree, so I came away happy with that.* But he said to me, "Compton, I hear you are planning to get married." I agreed that I was. He said, "Well, I wouldn't do that now if I were you. We have a traveling fellowship waiting for you to take you over to Europe. If you don't go now, it is doubtful whether you will ever get that trip to Europe. I would strongly suggest that you postpone your marriage until after you have had a year in Europe. It will be good for the broadening of your education." I didn't agree with him very well, and I guess I let him know it.

From Dean West's office I went over to the physics laboratory, and while I was there one of the other deans, William Magie, came around. West was dean of the graduate school, but Dean Magie, whom we all came to know as the "noble" dean because of his outstanding character, was dean of the faculties. He looked me up and he said, "I hear that Andy West has been trying to persuade you not to get married." I admitted that he had been trying to persuade me in that direction. Then Dean Magie said: "Don't you listen to Andy. If you want to get married, go ahead and do it. Keep your eyes open for some other opportunity to go abroad. You'll find it." Two weeks later, Betty McCloskey and I were married, and not so many years passed before we found our way across the water.

## SCIENTIFIC RESEARCH

### Electronic structure of the atom and properties of X rays

After leaving Princeton I went up to the University of Minnesota for about a year.* I still recall what a wrench it was to my wife's parents when I took her with me to Minneapolis. Minnesota then seemed much farther from her home in Ohio than Europe seems to most of us now.

An incident occurred at Minnesota that proved to be one of the most illuminating experiences in my science career. I had my first job as an instructor, and it was the first time that I was really on my own to do scientific work. I tackled a job to see whether when iron is magnetized the atoms in the iron are turned around by the magnetic field. This was an old theory of the elementary magnet by a German named Weber. For many months I had worked in a dark basement laboratory, often late into the night, to set up the sensitive apparatus that would affirm the theory. A special X-ray tube had been built for my experiment, and I had a variety of spectrometers, electrometers, and electromagnets. Finally, everything was set to carry out my experiment. According to the test that I had devised, when I turned on the magnet the intensity of reflection from two magnetized crystals should differ and I should get a deflection of a spot of light on a scale. When everything was ready I turned on the magnet, and nothing at all happened. The spot of light stayed right where it was. Again and again I tried, checking the instruments one by one. Still nothing happened. I could hardly believe the fact before my eyes. My heart sank. Just then the chairman of the department wandered in. He was a tall, slender gentleman with the good Minnesota name of Henry Erikson.

"How is the experiment coming along?" he asked.

"It isn't," I answered. Even then it seemed unbelievable that the beautiful theory I had hoped to verify could be false.

Erikson must have noticed that my face was rather long as I explained the state of affairs. Here was something that not only I but also the physics department had gone to considerable effort to get ready. And it had not worked out.

"Well, Compton," he said, with a friendly slap on my shoulder, "the way things are is always more interesting than the way we thought they were."

I don't know what I replied, but I don't think I said very much. He did not stay long, and I was left to mull over his remark. All this was back in 1916. But the more I have thought about that incident, the more I have realized that it was one of the best lessons in the understanding of science that I have ever had. The mistaken notion is to get some idea and then try to prove it. That is a false impression of what a scientist tries to do. The real thing that a scientist tries to do when he is faced with a phenomenon is to attempt to understand it. To do that he tries all the possible answers that he can think of to see which one of them works best.

In this case the answer that I tried did not work out well. The answer was obviously something else. My experiment went almost unnoticed.* It took years for the answer to be found. Eventually, it was found by two scientists at the University of Leiden, Samuel Goudsmit and George Uhlenbeck.* They found that the thing that was really the elementary magnet inside the iron was not the atom but the electron, and the electron is what is turned around. That was too small a thing for me to detect with my experiment. I might have detected the turning of the atom, but I could not detect the turning of the electron.

What I learned from the genial Erikson lies at the very heart of the scientific approach: "Get at the absolute truth, without regard for the

| 23 |

consequences." Back in 1860 Thomas Huxley gave a classic description of this scientific attitude when he said:

> Science seems to me to teach in the highest and strongest manner the great truth which is embodied in the Christian conception of the entire surrender to the will of God. Sit down before a fact as a little child. Be prepared to give up every preconceived notion. Follow humbly wherever and to whatever abysses Nature leads, or you shall learn nothing. I have only begun to learn content and peace of mind since I have resolved at all risks to do this.[4]

That is just how Henry Erikson might have put it if he had been in a more literary frame of mind, for it is exactly what he meant.

From Minnesota I went into the research laboratory of the Westinghouse Lamp Company as a research engineer for two years. The director of the laboratory had shared my hope that in the setting of this newly created laboratory * there would be an opportunity for me to do basic research in my own field of atoms and X rays, as well as to cultivate the body of knowledge from which better lamps would be built. Because of the need of the laboratory to establish itself with the company, however, it was soon evident that the former more general type of research had no essential place. Nevertheless, when my interest in the advance of knowledge for its own sake led me later to take a research position at a university, I found that my experience in the industrial laboratory was a great help. In this laboratory the techniques were highly developed. There was an effort to make an efficient balance between the cost of the time of the research man and that of his assistants and equipment. Still more important to me was familiarity with an organized research program in which different parts were assigned to specialists highly qualified for their particular tasks.

After leaving Westinghouse there followed for me some twenty years of university research dealing with X rays and cosmic rays, carried on chiefly at Washington University [1920–3] and the University of Chicago [1923–45]. Such studies were a proper part of a university's scientific program, for they were aimed at the understanding of the basic physical principles of the universe. It would have been difficult indeed to justify such studies in any industrial laboratory. I could have given no reasonable assurance of a profitable return even on a longtime basis to the industry that would support them. The incentive to do such research was the pure love of knowledge.

[4] From a letter to Charles Kingsley, in Leonard Huxley: *Life and Letters of Thomas Henry Huxley* (New York: D. Appleton & Company, Inc.; 1901), p. 235; reprinted in M. Lincoln Schuster, ed: *A Treasury of the World's Great Letters* (New York: Simon and Schuster; 1940).

From the national point of view, however, even such pure research has its practical value.* The knowledge thus obtained was a part of the background that led to the discovery of uranium fission. Those trained in the techniques of X-ray and cosmic-ray research included such men as Luis Alvarez, who during World War II invented the ground approach system for bringing airplanes to safe instrument landings. Most of the scientists who during the war headed the development of new instruments at the Radiation Laboratory in Cambridge, Massachusetts, and at the various atomic research laboratories were the products of such research training.

## Research at Cavendish Laboratory

In October 1919, I sailed for Cambridge, England, to do research with Professor Ernest Rutherford, who had discovered the atomic nucleus. I had never before been out of the United States, but I had my Ph.D. degree and several additional years of experience. My prime objective was to make progress on a job of scientific research that seemed to me important. With Professor Rutherford was the best place that I knew to do the work. The famed Cavendish Laboratory at Cambridge University was to me simply the place where he was stationed, so I went there.

It was not easy. At first my application for a fellowship was declined. My wife said, "Arthur, you must go anyhow. I'll stay home with the baby." My reply was that I would not go without her. I knew that the experience would give her as much to bring home as it would give to me, and I feared that if I went alone our outlooks on life would tend to grow apart instead of toward a common family goal. Her reply was that we must borrow the money then, so that all three of us could go. We were all set to do this, when at the last moment a fellowship was granted.* As I recall it, the fellowship gave us $2,200, which covered about half our year's expenses. As an investment in our own future there was nothing that could have paid better dividends—in financial rewards, in professional achievement, or in the understanding and meaning of life.

I have always considered Dean William Magie of Princeton to have been my wisest adviser regarding my personal development. He told me he knew that I would do my part in my professional studies at Cambridge. But, he commented, the time would come when I would have a hand in shaping American education. "It is very important," he said, that you should know what the cultural values are that are to be found in other countries. Don't confine yourself to the laboratory. See the universities of Europe and visit the art centers. You are among those who will be responsible for helping American students to know the best there is to know. And I'm glad," he added, "that you are taking your wife along. For what she brings back will be just as important in building American life as what you will bring."

He could not have spoken truer words, as our experience has shown us. When I was at Cambridge University, I found something else that I had not anticipated, and I know that Betty found it, too. I was already devoted to my scientific studies. That was why I left my good job as a Westing-house engineer to return to the university. What I found at Cambridge was a whole community to all of whose members the growth of under-standing was the greatest possible achievement. In this atmosphere my studies took on a new measure of meaning, and what advances occurred in my own understanding became a greater joy. I am sure that this did much more than give added meaning to the scholarly life for Betty and me. It has made it possible also for us to pass on something of our own enthusiasm to the students and faculty with whom we have worked.

When we went over to England, World War I had just ended, and all the young men were pouring back into Cambridge to take up their studies again. It was the first time for six years that they had been free to attend college, and they returned in unprecedented numbers. Among them were those who had been crippled and blinded. The class room was rare that did not have crutches leaning against a chair. But what sank most deeply into my soul was the awareness that so many were not there who should have been. It was the very finest of the British young men who in 1914 and the years that followed had thrown themselves into the fight to save their country. Most of these young men now lay in fields in Flanders.

Before leaving for England, I had written to Rutherford to ask if I might be received in his laboratory. He wrote back to the effect that I would be very welcome, but he was afraid I would not find any place in Cambridge to live because of the great influx of students. Fortunately, I never received that letter until I got to Cambridge. In the meantime we had arrived and were struggling to find a place to live. There were my wife, our son Arthur Alan, at that time fifteen months old, and our niece, a young lady in her early twenties. It was quite a job; but, anyhow, we were there.

When we reached Cambridge, we first looked up a lady who had been introduced to us by means of a letter. She was Lady Darwin, who was originally from Philadelphia and who was the mother of C. G. Darwin. She was very good about showing us our way around. She said, "First, you must look up Lady Thomson, who can help you look up some of the other people." So we went around to Lady Thomson. She asked us immediately: "How are you fixed?" We told her we were having difficulty in finding a place to stay. Next she asked: "What about your child?" Before we left her, we had a crib for the young man and also what they called a pram. An English pram is built like a mail cart, but nevertheless it served very well as a baby carriage to put our young son in. While we were in Cambridge I often took the carriage and rode Arthur over across the street from our hotel, the Blue Boar, where there was quite a pleasant little place to walk. It was a bit wild, but we didn't meet any wild boar!

The Thomsons did everything possible to help us become comfortably settled, and Cambridge proved to be a thoroughly delightful experience. J. J. Thomson, the famous discoverer of the electron, was then Master of Trinity College. He was one of the truly great figures in physics. When I was in Cambridge he was giving some lectures on "Positive Rays," which I attended. Our paths crossed a great deal, as he was the person who had much to do with the scattering of X rays and I was working specifically in that field. Thomson's son, G. P., who is my age, was at the time a student at Cambridge University, and he was also our close friend.

On one occasion when we called on the Thomsons at Trinity College we had quite an afternoon tea. I remember Lady Thomson's turning to me and asking, "Oh, Mr. Compton, will you give us one of those weird college cries that you are famous for over in the United States?" She wanted me to give a college yell. I elected not to do that, as I thought a drawing room at afternoon tea was not quite the time or place. Besides, it might have brought the neighbors running if I had.

When our next son was born we called him "J. J." after Professor Thomson. Some years later we stopped at Trinity College for a visit while we were in England with Johnny, who was by then six or seven years old. While we were having tea, J. J. Thomson took our young son out into the garden. After walking around with him for a while, Professor Thomson drew a gold half sovereign out of a little coin purse and gave it to Johnny, cautioning him to have his mother take care of it for him. Johnny treasured that coin long after he was grown.

We made other very good friends in England. C. G. Darwin, later Sir Charles, who was slightly older than I, was giving some lectures at Cambridge on the quantum theory. We had many things in common. We had been working in our research on similar problems, and for forty years we have had dealings with each other. Just a few years ago my wife and I were living for the summer in a little apartment at his home in Cambridge. But the closest thing we had in common was when I had come to write up my Ph.D. thesis at Princeton. I found that I had worked out almost exactly the same problem that Darwin himself had, and for a time it was questionable whether I was going to be able to use that as a thesis. In working it over, however, I was able to make a few additions and changes that made it acceptable. But, in doing so, I struck out on a new line that led me to write up a new paper, which I submitted to the British journal *Nature.* The editor of *Nature* in turn submitted it to a referee. The referee was Sir William Bragg, who was then professor of physics at the University of London. I never had a more pleasant experience than I had as a result of that.

Bragg went over my essay and made his recommendation as referee that it should be published. Then he wrote me and explained that this was precisely the subject that he had been working on himself, and that he had come to somewhat the same conclusion that I had as to a method of approach to the problem. He then referred me to a paper that he had written but had not yet published in the *Philosophical Transactions* of the Royal Society. So, as a result of that, I went ahead and published my paper,* and I developed it a little further in the *Physical Review* afterwards.

Some ten years later when I came to write a book on X rays * I found that one of the problems I was considering was very closely related to Bragg's work. Bragg was known for having discovered how X rays can be used for interpreting the arrangement of atoms in crystals, and I tried to show in my book how you could determine by means of X rays the arrangement of electrons in atoms. By that time [1925], the technique for doing this had not yet been fully developed, so I devoted a chapter to how to determine from experiments with X rays the arrangement of the electrons in atoms. I sent this chapter to Sir William Bragg's son, W. L. Bragg, now Sir Lawrence Bragg. He wrote me back a letter of thanks and explained that this showed him just exactly what he needed for developing the ideas he was working out for further study of the arrangement of the atoms in crystals. Recently I was talking with one of Sir Lawrence Bragg's students, who told me that this technique has now become the basis for the formal interpretation of all the X-ray plates. Of course, that was a great booster for my morale as regards my work in science. But it is also interesting to see how that active interchange among scientists, lasting over a period of almost fifty years, indicates how science advances, by exchanging ideas of one person with another.

Also at Cambridge in 1919 was Sir Arthur Eddington, one of the most brilliant and imaginative individuals I have ever had the pleasure to work with. Eddington was greatly concerned with the principle of relativity, which was something quite new then, and he was giving a series of lectures at Cambridge on the theory of relativity. When I was at Cavendish the first test of Einstein's theory, by studying the deflection of the starlight by the sun at the time of eclipse, had just been made. Eddington had taken an active part in that work and reported the conclusion that the deflection of the starlight by the sun's gravitational field could be measured in accord with Einstein's theory and not in accord with the obvious interpretation to be drawn from the principles of Newtonian mechanics. That was something of very live interest to the scientists.

For me, however, the greatest of the physicists was Ernest Rutherford, the pioneer of nuclear science. The nucleus of the atom had been discovered by Rutherford in 1913. Just at the close of World War I he had made the startling discovery that when an alpha particle (a helium nucleus) strikes the nucleus of a nitrogen atom a proton (a hydrogen nucleus) is sometimes emitted. Here was artificial transmutation, the changing of one chemical element into another. What is more, nuclear energy was released. This was shown by the fact that the proton escaped with an energy greater than that of the incident alpha particle. On writing to an American friend about this experiment, Rutherford commented that its influence on history might eventually be greater than the war that had just been fought. I had heard of this incident just before sailing to England.

I found that Rutherford had an intuitive feeling for what was there. He was apt to be right without knowing he was right. When you came to find something ten years later, you found he had sensed it without having proof. I believe that Rutherford had this intuitive insight with regard to laws of physics because I have a certain modicum of that insight myself, and I can understand how he got it. I did not have as much. I could not see as clearly. But I could see what he meant.

Rutherford was a remarkable human being. He personally went out of his way to provide for me, as a young research fellow, all the research equipment that I needed during my stay at Cavendish. Stories of Rutherford's nimble wit are legion. One occasion that I have reason to recall was when I was invited to address the Cambridge Physical Society in 1920. Rutherford introduced me, and he said: "This is Dr. Compton, who is with us from the United States to discuss his work on 'The Size of the Electron.' I hope you will listen to him attentively. But you don't have to believe him!"

Many years later, in 1934, I found myself in Oxford as Eastman Visiting Professor. Oxford, peculiarly enough, did not give much thought to science at that time, as they were chiefly interested in the classics and in politics. Some of my friends had heard that I was to be in England and, assuming that I had returned to Cambridge, had sent letters to me there in care of Lord Rutherford. Shortly after I reached Oxford a packet of letters arrived from Rutherford with a little note, very brief and to the point: "Dear Compton," it read, "I hear you are at Oxford. Whatever can you be doing there?"

I should say that I did find some good scientists at Oxford, though not so many as in later years. Among the scientists at the Clarendon Laboratory with whom I became well acquainted was Frederick Lindemann, who as Lord Cherwell was the chief scientific adviser to Winston Churchill during World War II. On the scientific side he had developed some important things with regard to quantum theory and, incidentally, had made one of the most satisfactory recent electrometers. I had also invented some electrometers, though of quite a different type, so we had several things in common.

One of our best friends at Oxford was Sir Alfred Egerton, one of our English friends with whom we later had many dealings, especially in India. Egerton was in India as an adviser when I was also out there in an advisory capacity. His particular concern was with the sources of power that India might use because of her shortage of fuel.

Returning to my experiences at Cambridge for a moment, however, I should add a word specifically about the atmosphere at the Cavendish Laboratory while I was there. The general equipment of the laboratory I found to be good, though not as complete as that of several of the better university laboratories in the United States. The laboratory was, moreover, rather overcrowded with research students. Nevertheless, for work on all aspects of radioactivity the facilities were excellent. The library facilities for research in physics were equal, though not superior, to those of the better university libraries in the United States. It was in the opportunity for frequent personal consultation with men who were working on similar aspects of physics that I found Cambridge as a place for conducting research to be exceptionally stimulating. The spirit of such men as Thomson and Rutherford can only be described as contagious. On the whole, for the particular work on which I was then engaged—a study of the phenomena of gamma-ray scattering and absorption—I doubt if better facilities could have been found anywhere. Furthermore, as a place for the intellectual growth of one with a fairly thorough knowledge of physics, I considered Cambridge to be unsurpassed.

## Resumption of research in the United States

From Cambridge I went to Washington University. After World War I, some of the wiser heads on the faculty had urged upon Chancellor Frederick A. Hall the importance of building a strong physics department as essential to the healthy growth of the university. They invited me to undertake establishing such a department. I brought in one other man, G. E. M. Jauncey, and took the unprecedented step of setting up a budget of some $4,000 per year for research equipment and expense. We were fortunate during our first few years in obtaining some striking results in research, and the department has maintained a strong research activity to this day.

From the time that I first became a serious student, finding a place to do thinking has been a central problem personally for me. During the years 1920 to 1923 at Washington University I found probably the best conditions in this respect that I ever found anywhere. It may be worthwhile to look back to see why that was so.

In 1920 Washington University, at least so far as its college of liberal arts was concerned, was a small kind of place. I went there, frankly, because I did not want to become confused in being in a center where there was so much going on along the line in which I was involved that I would be led away by the thinking of the time. At Washington University there were small but reasonably adequate facilities to do the kind of work that I wanted to do, and I was far enough removed from such places as Chicago, or Princeton, or Harvard, where I felt I would have been thrown into the pattern of thought of the period and would not have been able to develop what I had conceived of as my own contribution.* That was my choice as compared with what would then have been called a great university, or as compared with an industrial research laboratory, which I had left in order to get into this kind of work. Somewhat the same kind of opportunity had been presented at Cambridge, where as a research fellow I had no responsibilities other than research.

At Washington University in 1920 I found several outstanding scientists, chiefly connected with the medical school. Among them were such distinguished men as Evarts Graham, the surgeon; the biochemists Philip A. Shaffer and Edward Doisy, and Joseph Erlanger and Herbert S. Gasser, the physiologists who later received the Nobel prize for work on the electric current carried by nerves. Outside the medical school I think especially of George T. Moore, head of the Henry Shaw School of Botany, and Benjamin Duggar, the botanist who later did such remarkable work on aureomycin.

While we were in St. Louis during that period of three years, C. G. Darwin, whom we had known earlier in England, came through the city, and I had him go with me over to the famous Missouri Botanical Garden with Dr. Duggar. One of the most interesting experiences that I have ever had was that visit when Benjamin Duggar took such great

| 31 |

interest in showing Darwin the orchid collection. Darwin was particularly interested in seeing the mechanism whereby the orchids are fertilized. Darwin, though a physicist, knew enough botany to ask the proper questions of Duggar, and Duggar was explaining to Darwin the botany of it in such a way that a physicist such as I knew exactly what he was talking about. I was simply an onlooker, but I felt that I was very well rewarded by having had the privilege of listening in on that discussion.

I might follow that little incident by the observation that scientists are not always one hundred per cent accurate in their predictions. Some years later, about 1930, C. G. Darwin was invited to give an after-dinner speech at a meeting of the American Physical Society in Washington. In his address he stated that, since all the problems of chemistry and most of those of physics had been solved, it would be a good idea if the physicists got out of physics and went into biophysics and studied biological structures. This was just before the discovery of the neutron, the positive electron, and a group of other discoveries that almost upset the whole field of physics. As a result the field in which Darwin thought that all the problems had been solved opened up as a field in which I suppose there are now more problems than it appears we have ever had in the past. That just shows that the scientists sometimes get only a part of the whole picture.

## Nobel prize work

To return to my own study of physics, I should explain that for the first twenty years my central objective was to determine how electrons group themselves in atoms. For this purpose I used X rays, somewhat as light is used with a microscope, for X rays are like light but of much shorter wavelength. But in using the X rays to "look at" the electrons, I found that these rays had certain properties that had not been noticed before. They knocked out of the atoms the electrons I was trying to locate, and in the process the X rays themselves were increased in wavelength. This phenomenon became known as the "Compton effect," * and for its discovery I was awarded the Nobel prize for physics in 1927.

It was a paper by C. G. Barkla, which I had read when I was working at the Westinghouse Lamp Company, that eventually led me by a circuitous route to the disclosure of the corpuscular aspects of X rays. Barkla had reported the results of experiments he had performed that did not fit with certain theories that had been developed to account for the scattering of X rays. I began to busy my head over what could account for these results of Barkla that were departing from theory. Not having X-ray equipment at hand, but sensing that Barkla had hold of something of fundamental importance, I undertook to find some theoretical explanation consistent with classical electron theory that would account for his results. After several years of work trying to find out what was wrong with the theory that might explain these unusual experimental results, I settled down at Washington University and started a set of experiments that I had had in mind for some time.* Because I am so often asked about it, I will include a brief account of some of this work for those who may be interested.* The discussion will be somewhat technical, however, so the reader who has not studied physics may prefer to pass over these pages.

In the first place, I would like to explain that from the time X rays were discovered by Roentgen in 1895, the dominant hypothesis has been that X rays are light rays of very short wavelength. But the question of whether X rays are waves or particles has been a matter of perennial discussion over many years, and we are not yet ready to give a positive answer to that question. The answer we can give is that X rays have the properties of both waves and particles. That is different from saying that they *are* either waves or particles. The fact is that they have the properties of both.

To explain what I mean by that, I will need to review just briefly the principles of a theory of J. J. Thomson to account for the scattering of X rays. Thomson supposed that X rays are electromagnetic waves that, in passing over matter in which electrons are present, accelerate the electrons in the same direction as the electric vector acting upon them. Precisely as the antenna of a radio transmitter, with the electric charge surging up and down from the antenna to the ground, radiates the electric waves that we call radio waves, so an electron being set in motion by the electric wave of the passing X ray would in turn radiate an electric wave off in all directions. This phenomenon is known as scattering. According to Thomson's electron theory, the radiation being re-emitted from the electron is taken from the primary beam of X rays, resulting in a loss of intensity. Thomson worked out theoretically the formula to represent the loss of intensity due to such scattering and came out with a perfectly definite amount of energy that is lost.

Barkla had used Thomson's formula as a means of determining how many electrons there were in a bit of matter over which the rays passed and which scattered the X rays. By this means he calculated that the number of electrons in an atom is equal to what we now call its atomic number. As a matter of fact, he published these results in the same number of the *Philosophical Magazine* in which Ernest Rutherford published his paper showing that the charge on the nucleus of the atom is equal, in electronic units, to the atomic number.* At that moment we thought we had a very fundamental result so far as the nature of the atom is concerned. We had a nucleus with a charge on it equal in electronic units to the number of the atom, also that the number of electrons in the atom surrounding the nucleus was equal to the atomic number, giving a nice balance and leaving the atom as a neutral atom with electrons and a nucleus.

When Barkla proceeded to extend his experiments he found that the scattering for X rays of very short wavelength becomes less intense than indicated by Thomson's theory. That was the problem that was worrying me. How could it become less intense? So I tried to find some interpretation of Barkla's result but without much success. Finally, I hit upon the idea of supposing that the electron, instead of being a point charge of electricity, is a diffuse mass of electricity occupying a certain volume, roughly a thousand times larger in size than had been supposed. On that basis I found that I could account, in terms of the interference between the rays scattered from different parts of the electron, in a fairly satisfactory way for the intensity of the scattering of X rays of short wavelength.

That had been sufficiently encouraging to me to determine to set my sails in the direction of going to Cambridge. I wanted to study with J. J. Thomson and Ernest Rutherford and to make a detailed investigation of the scattering of X rays and gamma rays, which are another type of short wavelength electromagnetic radiation. The most productive part of this work proved to be an examination of the secondary radiations produced in light elements by gamma rays. By the time I had spent that year in Cambridge, I came to the conclusion that my studies could be carried through to better advantage in my own laboratory, where I would be able to set up equipment especially designed for my experiments * and where I could pursue my research according to the way in which one experiment leads to another.

Accordingly, when I went to Washington University in 1920 we tried a number of experiments on the scattering of X rays under a variety of conditions. I was fortunate to find some colleagues, particularly Charles F. Hagenow and G. E. M. Jauncey, who joined me in this study. Together we went into the effort to find out what X rays are like. We polarized them, we diffracted them, we reflected them from polished surfaces, and we found some results that ultimately led to some rather interesting conclusions.

The first of our experiments were simply to make sure that the X rays that we called scattered really were scattered. I must say that this had been pretty well demonstrated before, but anyhow we tried a number of experiments to test the wave idea of X rays, and these experiments did show that X rays have the same wave properties as light. Following these experiments, logically, one would put our experiments on the polarization of X rays. Such experiments were first done by the same man, Barkla. Our experiments were carried out by Charles Hagenow, and he improved by a factor of at least ten—perhaps a hundred—on the accuracy of Barkla's experiments and showed that the degree of polarization we get in the scattering of X rays is almost complete.

These two experiments, the one showing the wave character of the rays and the other showing the polarization of the scattered X rays, indicated pretty clearly that we were dealing with truly scattered waves. But that did not help me at all in my effort to get at the reason for the reduction in the intensity of the very short wavelength scattering. So I tried a series of experiments in which I confirmed the previous experiments made by A. W. Hull, Barkla, and later by J. A. Gray. I found that the intensity actually *was* lower than Thomson's theory had predicted and, further, that in the scattering process the wavelength of the X rays had in some way been increased.

The next problem was to go into some rather serious theoretical study. I found that the scattered X rays showed a predominance in a forward direction, rather than at right angles or in a backward direction. Then I hit upon the idea that the observed distribution of the scattered rays could be quantitatively explained if the electrons were considered to be moving in the direction of the primary beam at about half the speed of light. This would mean that each electron had a momentum equal to that of a quantum of energy of the frequency of the primary X rays. But, after all, every electron in the scattering material was fixed right in the apparatus, so it was rather difficult to suppose that all the electrons were moving forward in that fixed bit of apparatus at such a velocity. This led me to examine what would happen if each quantum of energy were concentrated in a single particle and would act as a unit on a single electron. Thus I was led to the now familiar hypothesis of an X-ray particle colliding with an electron and bouncing from it with reduced energy, the lost energy appearing as the recoil energy of the electron.

It was at that time that we acquired a very sensitive kind of X-ray spectrometer in order to facilitate our measurements. In taking the readings I used a technique that may be of interest. I was afraid of being influenced by finding what I was looking for, so I got to help me in the laboratory an assistant who did not know at all what I had in mind. I made the spectrometer settings while he took the readings. Not knowing what we were looking for, he felt that the readings were very erratic.

After the experiment was over, he remarked to me: "It was too bad, wasn't it, Professor, that the apparatus wasn't working so well today?" He was disturbed by the fact that the readings went up and down, and he had no idea that they were just the kind of thing I wanted. The data that he took have since been published most frequently as showing the typical changes in wavelength of X rays for different angles of scattering.

When I first came out with these results, I was a member of a committee that had been assigned by the National Research Council to make a report on scattered X rays. The chairman of the committee was William Duane of Harvard. The third member of the committee was A. W. Hull of Schenectady. The three of us sat down together to see what we could report. I had been assigned the job of writing the report, and I included my revolutionary conclusion that the wavelength of X rays was increased in the scattering process. Duane said, "We can't include that. You haven't got firm enough data on it." But Hull said, "This is really important; we've got to include it." The result was that with Hull's support these results were included in the report.*

Incidentally, very shortly after that report appeared in print, Peter Debye, then working at Zürich, came out with a theory of the scattering of X rays that was essentially the same as the one that I had described, and with a mathematical calculation that was identical. Obviously he had had that in mind before my results were published.

When I presented my results at a meeting of the American Physical Society in April 1923, it initiated the most hotly contested scientific controversy that I have ever known. After all, it is not easy to believe that scattered rays of any kind can differ in frequency and wavelength from the primary rays. If you whistle in front of a barn door, the echo you get back sounds just the same as the sound that goes out. It has to be because as many waves come back as strike the door. In the case of scattered X rays, you would expect the echo to be thrown back similarly with the same wavelength as the incident rays. That kind of reasoning sounds rather convincing, but when you find in experiments that the wavelength is actually changed you can see that there must be something wrong with the wave theory.

At the meeting of the American Physical Society during the following Christmas holidays, there was staged a rather formal debate between Duane and myself about whether the evidence for this change in wavelength of scattered X rays was real. I had repeated the experiments literally dozens of times, so I entered the debate with confidence. Nevertheless, I was very pleased to find such men as P. A. Ross of Stanford and Maurice de Broglie of Paris coming out with confirming photographs in which they had found the same thing. Still, the result was inconclusive.

About that time, Duane did something that I like to think is characteristic of the true spirit of science. He came to Chicago, where I was by then continuing these experiments after leaving St. Louis, to see how my experiments were done, and he invited me over to his laboratory at Harvard to see how his experiments were done. Neither of us could see what was wrong with the other fellow's experiments, but it turned out that my apparatus was more sensitive than his and more specifically designed for the particular measurement.

The following summer the British Association for the Advancement of Science met at Toronto, with Sir William Bragg presiding over the physics section. At this meeting a special session was set aside for the debate to continue. After discussing it for a solid afternoon, we decided to call the debate a draw. The result was summarized by a comment of C. V. Raman, who was visiting Toronto at the time. As we left, he said to me, "Compton, you're a very good debater; but the truth isn't in you." Just the same, I think it was probably these discussions that led him to discover the Raman effect two years later, which was essentially a very similar phenomenon that was observed in the field of light.

Duane followed up this meeting by a new interpretation of the change in wavelength that he attributed to what he called a "box" effect, explaining that by surrounding the scattering apparatus with a lead box I had in some way altered the character of the radiation. This interpretation I answered by repeating the experiment outdoors with essentially the same results. Not long after that Duane discovered that he could find the same spectrum of the increased wavelength I had been reporting, and he came out with a very good determination of that change of wavelength. I do not know whether he was actually converted by his own experiments or by those of other people who were active in the field, among them particularly C. T. R. Wilson and W. Bothe. In any case, since that time there has not been any question that the change in wavelength actually occurs, and the theory has been pretty well confirmed. It has thus become evident that though X rays have the characteristic optical qualities that identify them as waves, they nevertheless move and do things as particles. It may be fair to say that these were the first experiments to give to physicists in the United States a conviction of the fundamental validity of the quantum theory.

Now that the properties of X rays were better known, I could use them reliably for locating the electrons in the atoms, a task that I had begun back in 1914 as my Ph.D. thesis. With the help of my associates, by the

| 37 |

early 1930's this had been done for helium, neon, argon, and mercury vapor. The theory of atomic structure had been developed so far by this time that there remained little doubt about how the electrons grouped themselves. By 1934 it was possible to say the problem was satisfactorily solved. My experiments gave merely one more confirmation of the quantum theory. Thus the main result of my twenty-year research program was less dramatic than was the unexpected by-product of new information about the X rays themselves. *

## Further research on X rays and cosmic rays

Beginning in 1923 my experiments had been conducted at the University of Chicago. The most stimulating of the scientists I found there was A. A. Michelson, the first American scientist to receive the Nobel prize. As a college student I had studied Michelson's book, *Light Waves and Their Uses*. This was one of my first contacts with the work of a truly great American scientist. Again, shortly before I went to Chicago to become a member of Michelson's remarkable team that was the physics faculty of the University of Chicago, I attended the meeting of the American Physical Society where Michelson told of his measurement of the diameter of Betelgeuse. One of the physicists from another city leaned over and made a remark to me that caught the spirit of the occasion: "He's the king of us all!" That remark tells truly the position that Michelson held in the minds of his colleagues.

Michelson is chiefly known for his precise measurements of the speed of light. He once told me that during a dinner with some Chicago businessmen his neighbor to the right asked him condescendingly what type of work he was doing. Michelson replied, "I have been measuring the velocity of light."

"Is that so?" his dinner companion rejoined. "How fast do you find that it goes?"

"About a hundred and eighty thousand miles a second," answered Michelson.

"What, a hundred and eighty thousand miles?"

"Yes."

"In a single second?"

"Yes."

"I don't believe it."

And it is almost unbelievably fast.

In Chicago's Ryerson Physical Laboratory, where Michelson conducted these exacting experiments, as in other scientific laboratories, precision measurement is the basis of reliable knowledge. This knowledge in turn gives us new hope for man's future. Something of this spirit was captured in these lines about Michelson in "The Ballad of Ryerson": [5]

. . . when from the plunging planet he spread out a hand to feel
How fast the ether drifted back through flesh or stone or steel,
The fine fiducial fingers felt no ethereal breath.
They penciled the night in a cross of light and found it still as death.
Have the stars conspired against him? Do measurements only seem?
Are time and space but shadows enmeshed in a private dream?
But dreaming or not, he measured. He made him a rainbow bar,
And first he measured the measures of man, and then he measured a star.
Now tell us how long is the metre, lest fire should steal it away?
Ye shall fashion it new, immortal, of the crimson cadmium ray.
Now tell us how big is Antares, a spear-point in the night?
Four hundred million miles across a single point of light.
He has taught a world to measure. They read the furnace and gauge
By the lines of the fringe of glory that knows nor aging nor age.
Now this is the law of Ryerson and this is the price of peace—
That men shall learn to measure or ever their strife shall cease.
They shall measure the cost of killing, and measure the hearts that bleed,
And measure the earth for sowing, and measure the sowing of seed.

. . .

Now if they slay the dreamers and the riches the dreamers gave,
They shall get them back to the benches and be as the galley slave.
But if they be wise to measure the star beneath their feet,
Intense with tissue of power and woven with waiting heat,
There are starry uses of stars. Let them love their planet and see
How it longeth to bear the burden and let the slave go free.
They shall loose the lightning gently, the granite shall bloom with grain,
And under the rainbow glory young Eden shall come again.

## First visit to India

In 1926 I was invited to give lectures at the University of the Punjab, at Lahore in what was then north India. At first I was reluctant to go, as I was busy with my work at the University of Chicago. But, at my wife's urging, I took a year off to make the trip.*

We had planned to do a little sightseeing before settling down to my duties at Lahore, but my contacts with the Indian scientists were destined to begin as soon as I reached India. When we arrived in Calcutta, I sent

[5] Reprinted from *University of Chicago Poems* by Edwin Herbert Lewis by permission of The University of Chicago Press. Copyright 1923 by the University of Chicago.

a wire to my brother-in-law, Herbert Rice, telling him that we intended to make a little trip up to Darjeeling instead of going immediately to Lahore. He wired back that I should go directly to Lahore because I was expected to lead an expedition into the Kashmir to study cosmic rays there, and everything was arranged for the trip. That was news to me, so I replied by telegram asking about arrangements for the expedition. I found that they had arranged for the proper number of coolies and the necessary food and transfer, but they said nothing at all about any apparatus that was to be used to measure the cosmic rays. So I asked them to look into it a little further, and I quickly learned that they had made no provision to take with them any apparatus. They expected me to supply that. I immediately went around to the professor of physics at the University of Calcutta, C. V. Raman, whom I knew only very slightly at that time. But he invited me into his laboratory, and turned his mechanic over to me during the next few days while I was in Calcutta to make up for me an electroscope of the kind that I needed for my emergency use. In order to get the apparatus ready in time we had to round up somebody out of the bazaar, who provided us with a hookah bowl. A hookah is a water pipe shaped like a pear. I was a bit surprised to find myself using a common, ordinary hookah bowl as a scientific instrument; but, as my wife says, the remarkable thing about it was that it worked. It was the one instrument that we had up on the mountain at that time that measured the cosmic rays.

That was really a memorable expedition. Its members included Nazir Ahmad, a young professor from Islamia College, the Muslim college at Lahore; S. S. Bhatnagar, then professor of physical chemistry at the University of the Punjab; Martin Benade, the professor of physics from Forman Christian College, an American mission college; and young Indian graduate students from Kashmir, Agra, and Patiala. These included Kashmiri Lal Buddhiraja, whose father was Chief Justice of the High Court, and H. R. Sarna, who became Associate Director of the National Physical Laboratory. It was a very interesting group representative of completely different religions and cultures. My wife was the only woman in the party.

We started up the mountain from the foothills of the Himalayas with a string of horses and coolies to help get the luggage up to the high mountain lake where we were to make our measurements. It turned out that my wife and Nazir Ahmad were the two best horsemen, so they usually kept in front of the party while I brought up the rear to be sure to pick up any of the packages that fell off the horses. In that manner we went up the mountain. When we stopped at night we would stay at what

was called a dak bungalow, which is a sort of shelter house. It is nothing
very fine, but at least you are out of the wind. We would button up at
night in our sleeping bags to keep warm. But before we did that we would
sit around the fire and swap yarns.

I remember very well one story that Nazir Ahmad told. I have frequently spoken of the scientist's role as a catalyst among the peoples of
different nations. The scientist fills this role simply because the laws of
nature transcend international boundaries, and one's scientific colleagues
are more apt to be found in another country than on an adjoining street.
Nazir Ahmad's story, ascribed to one of the wise men of ancient Persia,
illustrates the value of a catalyst through the tale of an old Arab sheik
who makes use of a catalyst to resolve a dispute over division of an estate.*

As we were coming down the mountain after we had made our measurements, Nazir Ahmad drew me aside and said, "Compton, you don't
know how lucky you are."

I asked, "Why, Nazir?"

"To have a wife who understands what it is that you are doing," he
replied.

Betty had been taking her turn in making the readings on the cosmic
rays along with the rest of us. I said, "What's so unusual about that?"

"Consider my case," he said. "When I returned to India after obtaining
my Ph.D. in physics at Cambridge, my family said to me: 'Now, Nazir,
it's time for you to get married.' So my family looked around for a suitable
wife, and they could not find anyone of the proper age and family who
could read and write. I protested that it was rather severe for a young
man coming back from graduate work in England to discover that no
one could be found for him to marry who could even read and write.
But there was nothing to be done about it, so I was married." That was
the end of that conversation.

But the next day he came around to me and said, "You know what I am
going to do? I am going to see that Indian women get an education."
When we were next out there in 1939 I found that he had been making
real progress in encouraging education among Muslim girls.

That gives a little picture of an Indian scientist. After the partition of
India and Pakistan, Nazir Ahmad became an influential member of the
government of Pakistan, and has represented his country at the United
Nations. Other members of this expedition also held important positions
in India and Pakistan in later years. Here was a bridge of mutual understanding. But for me the experience of this year in India was to open
my eyes. Years later I told my friends that it was the beginning of my
education. It seemed to me that for the first time because of my foreign

experience it was possible for me to see in new light the meaning of my own heritage. Here was the basis for comparison. The new values that I found unsuspectedly hidden in Oriental culture were balanced by a new depth of insight into the values of life in my own country.

As a result of this trip my interests soon began to broaden into related sciences and the humanities. When I was a college student I had taken an active interest in philosophy, especially ontology, as taught by my father.* During intervening years this interest had lain dormant. But my studies of physics had led me into developments of quantum theory that seemed to have interesting philosophical implications. This, together with my broadening culture interests, made the philosophical implications of science occupy a considerable part of my attention in later years. One aspect of this was to try to determine whether physical laws are sufficient to account for the actions of living organisms. This study led also to a consideration of the relation of science to religion, a problem with which my father had wrestled, and which we had frequently discussed in my college days.

As of about age thirty-seven, my experimental research began to be done more and more by others under my direction. It was always true that when I got down to a research job I could do it myself faster than I could tell someone else how to do it. But there is the matter of plowing back into your job what it is that you learn. So it was my custom when engaged in research to have anywhere from half a dozen to a dozen research students around working with me on tasks that I was doing. In this way they were being trained. The first results were less, but now those students are carrying on research far more effectively than I would be able to carry it on. Gradually my function became more of an organizer of research enterprises and a stimulator of men to carry them through. I continued, however, to spend careful thought on the theoretical interpretation of the results. This, indeed, had been my chief scientific interest from the very beginning.

During the early 1930's, when my X-ray studies were nearing completion, I turned my main attention to the properties of cosmic rays. These are highly penetrating rays that come into the earth's atmosphere from outside and produce effects similar to those of X rays. My experiments with cosmic rays really began in 1921, but they entered a much more active phase about 1930 when we began to develop improved instruments for their measurement.

My first experiment in cosmic rays was done because Sir Ernest Rutherford had started me wondering why radium was radioactive. Mme Curie had suggested that this might be due to the capture of cosmic rays by radium. So in 1921 I put a little radium in an electroscope, and carried it with me on muleback down Bright Angel Trail to the bottom of the Grand Canyon. There the cosmic rays were much feebler than on top, but the radioactivity of the radium remained unchanged. Mme Curie's guess was wrong. But not all our guesses have been wrong.

In the 1930's the central question concerned the nature of cosmic rays. Some thought they were like X rays or light, but of yet very much shorter wavelength. Others believed they were electrical particles, perhaps electrons. If such was their nature, these rays should be affected by the earth's magnetism. Fewer rays should reach the earth near the equator than near the poles. Some investigators had reported such a difference. Others had looked for such an effect and had failed to find it.

Organized loosely around my laboratory at the University of Chicago, a dozen scientific expeditions, involving roughly a hundred physicists, undertook a series of cosmic-ray studies using identical instruments in different parts of the world. We studied cosmic rays in every continent: on top of the Himalayas, the Andes, the Alps, and the Rockies; in tunnels and coal mines, in airplanes and balloons, and on the high seas. My wife, our fourteen-year-old son Arthur Alan, and I comprised one of these teams, traveling some forty thousand miles, from Australia to northern Canada. The net result of this world survey of cosmic rays was quantitative and convincing data showing lower intensity near the magnetic equator, and hence showing that the rays are electrical particles.* It is fair to say, I think, that these studies marked the turning point of our knowledge of the nature of the cosmic rays.* Further studies that this survey stimulated have shown that the cosmic-ray particles that come into the earth's atmosphere are the nuclei of atoms, chiefly hydrogen, moving at tremendous speeds.

But there were also personal results from this world survey of cosmic rays. My wife and son and I met scientific associates wherever we went. Our son went to school in north India, in Switzerland, in England, and in New Zealand. He learned that people in other lands are as human as we. We should not have been surprised that instead of following a scientific career he later found his place as a foreign service officer in the State Department. My wife came to know the interests of scientists and their families. We were just starting our cosmic-ray studies when we met Laura and Enrico Fermi in Rome. Fermi, as a young professor of physics, had brought together at the University of Rome in 1931 the first international conference on nuclear physics. Here began a friendship that many years later was to help make the wartime atomic task a success. But how little we dreamed then, visiting with the Fermis in their pleasant Rome apartment, that we should one day be welcoming them to Chicago to help preserve the world's freedom. As for myself, my cosmic-ray studies, though not dealing directly with the properties of atomic nuclei, kept me conversant with such studies and acquainted with many who were active in the field.

## Atomic research during World War II

In 1940, my forty-eighth year, I began to feel strongly my responsibility as a citizen for taking my proper part in the war that was then about to engulf my country, as it had already engulfed so much of the world. I talked, among others, with my minister in Chicago. He wondered why I was not supporting his appeal to the young people of our church to take a stand as pacificists. I replied in this manner: "As long as I am convinced, as I am, that there are values worth more to me than my own life, I cannot in sincerity argue that it is wrong to run the risk of death or to inflict death if necessary in the defense of those values."

A short time later the president of the National Academy of Sciences needed someone to assess the possible military value of energy from atomic nuclei, and he thought of me.* I already knew something about the subject, but I was not into it so deeply as to have a vested interest. He asked me to head a committee that would report on the potential usefulness of atomic energy in the war then in progress. This was a task of critical importance, for the recommendations of such a committee would in all likelihood serve as the basis for the government's action regarding the military use of atomic weapons. It was a task that could not be declined. But with its acceptance I myself became completely involved. For more than four war years every ounce of my strength and virtually every thought day and night was concerned with insuring that atomic energy would be used to save lives and to bring increased freedom to man.

When this work was just getting started, one of my students came to me with the question: "How do you satisfy your conscience with working on such a horrible weapon as the bomb we are making?"

"Remember," I answered, "that we in this laboratory are the only persons in the world who can possibly prepare this weapon before the Nazis may have it. If we do not do our part the world is exposed to the mercy of the Nazis. Can we be responsible for that risk?" Truly, knowledge means power, and the fact that one learns new truths gives one an inescapable responsibility.

My mother was born a Mennonite, whose grandparents had come to this country to escape the militarism of Europe with the hope of finding peace. Now the world has become so unified that wars anywhere become our wars, and peace is impossible here without world peace. My forebears did their best to give peace to me, by setting up their home and adding their strength to a peace-loving community. Here was the test. Did that peace-loving community, together with others like it throughout the world, have the strength to preserve the world's peace in face of the nations that wanted war? If we failed the test and let the war-bent peoples maintain their armies, neither we nor the world could hope for future peace. Only by carrying through the struggle to place decisive control of the world's military strength in the hands of peace-loving peoples could we pass peace on to our children. Because I shared with my Mennonite forebears the confidence that Americans will remain lovers of peace, I wanted control of the world's fighting power in the United States.

Here I shall not go into the story of our wartime quest for atomic energy.* By now the story has become a familiar one: how the nuclear chain reaction was developed, how the bomb was used against Japan, and how it brought the war to an early close. By demonstrating the effectiveness of its atomic bomb the United States made it possible to avoid any disastrous world conflict during the years many political observers have considered the most dangerous of our century.

Some years after the war, business took me to Japan. I found the reporters waiting for me as I walked into my hotel in Tokyo. Their first question was: "Why did you drop the atomic bomb on Japan?" I replied that it had been our expectation that the shock of such a terrible new weapon would make it possible for the Japanese to resign with honor from a disastrous war and effect a net saving of millions of Japanese and American lives. It was evident from the stories these reporters wrote for their newspapers that the answer they had wanted was that I was sorry we had used the bomb. But, having seen the fighting men suddenly released from the need to invade Japan's main islands returning happily to their homes, I could not say I was sorry.

A week later at a press conference in Kyoto the same question was asked. This time I was better prepared: "Would you have preferred," I asked the questioner, "that we should have let the war run its normal course without using the bomb?"

After a long pause, the reporter turned the questioning in an entirely different direction. He came to me to apologize after the interview. "I am sorry I asked you that question," he said. "If it had not been for the atomic bomb, we would have kept fighting until the bitter end. In that case, I would not be here to ask why you used it."

What happened at Hiroshima and Nagasaki will, in the perspective of time, become but incidents in history books. Yet, as I try to view these events in historical perspective, I doubt whether even Columbus's discovery introduced as great a change as did the events that came to dramatic focus in the release of nuclear power. Columbus opened the way to new lands for us to use. The release of nuclear power gave new urgency for us to accept our fellow man. The atomic experiment stands as convincing evidence of the value of world cooperation and marks the commencement of a new human epoch. Henceforth the interests of all men are one.

One commentator has remarked, not intending to be sacrilegious, that there have been two great events that have divided history into eras. The first of these was the coming of Jesus, whose doctrine of love of God and man gave mankind the basis for a life of meaning. Hope came, and the world could not be the same again. As the second great event he named the release of the atom's energy. With the advent of atomic weapons man's attitude toward war was changed overnight. Major war must not be allowed to happen again.

It may be that history will show that this is an exaggerated estimate of the meaning of the atomic age. But as one who has seen the birth of this new age at first hand, I am convinced that the meaning of this dramatic event is to be found in its awesome demonstration that our survival in a scientific and industrialized world depends ultimately upon the growth of the human spirit.

## EDUCATIONAL LEADERSHIP

With the success of the atomic program and with military victory assured, I reasoned that my efforts were no longer needed to help in maintaining the nation's scientific strength. This continued to be a great need, but the nation's leaders were by now well aware of its importance, and there were many scientists who were continuing vigorously to develop this aspect of our strength. The less evident need seemed to me to be the much greater one. I saw the United States emerging to a position of world responsibility that it had not sought and for which it was ill prepared. The freedom of the world and, in particular, the safety and welfare of my country seemed to me critically dependent upon whether we in the United States would develop adequately our industrial strength, our understanding of our world responsibilities, and our will to grow in freedom. In none of these respects did I consider our situation satisfactory for continued safety. It seemed to me further that the most dangerous period of our relations with Russia would be for a generation or so after about 1960, when Russia would be recovered and the United States would very possibly be lulled into a feeling of false security. During this critical period the survival of our free society would depend largely upon the wisdom and leadership of the men and women we would train in our universities. A group of leaders must be developed in our country who would have a better understanding of the realities of the world situation than was possible to us of an earlier American generation. Such leaders could be developed only through education, and an education based on wide understanding. Of course, every period in the nation's life is critical, but to me, sound educational guidance during this period seemed to be of utmost importance.

As of about the close of the war I had the choice of heading several educational institutions. My concern for scientific research had kept me from accepting similar offers at an earlier period. Before the war I had reasoned that my highest function in society was in learning the truths of nature and in interpreting these truths for man's welfare. I had been given the best of training, both for searching the secrets of the physical world and for comparing the values of modern civilization with those of more traditional cultures. If I were to leave the task on which I was engaged, would I not be deserting that which seemed to me to hold the hope for man, the disinterested search for truth? There was something almost unique in the position with regard to science, religion, and society in which the fates had placed me. As a professor of science in a free university atmosphere, representing no organization having its own cause to promote, and subject to the criticism of my intellectual peers, I found myself sharing the thinking that must shape the attitudes of our growing culture. It was to this end that society had trained me, and I felt that I must keep this as my goal.

Having come to feel, however, that no aspect of our life is more important than is higher education in building the safety and welfare of the world's free people, I came to see in Washington University a truly unique opportunity for strengthening the nation. It was an opportunity that amounted to an obligation; and so, in 1945, I left my scientific work to become chancellor of this Midwestern university.

The development that Washington University knew that it needed was in technology. While I was sympathetic with developing the engineering school, the great need that I saw was for first-class liberal education, where young men and women could learn to guide wisely the powers of their nation. I was particularly concerned with seeing that the students should learn to know what freedom means and be willing to assume the responsibilities that go with freedom.

Washington University had been started in 1853, at a time when St. Louis was the focal point for the growth of the United States into a nation of continental dimensions. At this focal point of growth there was urgent need for education that would fit men and women for the leadership that our great new nation would require. Now Washington University again found itself in a key position, but a position even more critically important to human destiny than it was a century ago. For now mankind is on the march, and it is to the United States that the world perforce must turn for its leadership in that grand march. Whether this great movement leads man into the abyss or toward unprecedented heights depends in large degree upon the wisdom of the leadership that the United States can provide. Who will provide such leadership? Obviously no one city, no one university can do this task alone. It is a part of the American genius that we shall do it together, that each part of our country shall help every other to do its part effectively. But the central position of St. Louis, its industrial and commercial leadership, the fine balance of its religious, its cultural, and its educational activities: such factors as these led me to see in Washington University an exceptional opportunity to provide an important share of our country's leadership. I felt that this was the place where a given amount of educational effort would have the maximum effect in shaping the thinking of the United States, and hence on the survival of free society.

In 1949, a few short years after I had accepted my new assignment, there came into my office Ernest Lawrence, professor of physics at the University of California. It was he who had come to me in 1940 and had called attention to the very serious hazard that might develop from the growing power of Germany; it was he who came to me a little later to suggest the possibility that Germany might be developing an atomic bomb and how important it was for us to get there first.

When Lawrence came into my office in 1949, he was just returning from Washington, and he was oppressed by the current news. We tried to estimate how long it would be until the Russians would be prepared to attack us. It was of course evident that they were working mightily on their military development. I estimated five years. He thought I was unduly optimistic, and he said he was going back to his laboratory and turn his efforts toward the scientific approach to certain new weapons that he hoped would be helpful in the approaching struggle. I told him how I felt about it, and I said, while of course that was very important, as far as I was concerned my task no longer lay in science but in the development of men and women to meet the issues of peace, to build a strong society that could and would see all that was worth defending.*

## REFLECTIONS ON SCIENCE AND SOCIETY

Today mankind is concerned with three basic problems: safety from military disaster, an economy adequate for survival, and an inspiring meaning for life. Each of these problems is related to the others, and together they provide the framework within which freedom can exist. What happens in the United States is of distinctive significance regarding each of these problems, and what happens here depends to a large extent upon the wisdom of the leaders trained in our colleges and universities.

Taken in the longer view, there is nothing as important to the world's safety as is the wisdom of our country's leadership. For upon it depend not only a substantial share of the military defenses of the free world, but also the confidence and the hope for the future that win support for an ordered and stabilized world. Competent and informed men and women, of broad human sympathy and devoted to the advancement of the common welfare, must be of prevailing influence here if the world is to be safe.

The great world event of this century has been the demonstration by the United States that freedom from destitution and disease is possible for a large, confined mass of people. Such freedom has been present here to an unprecedented extent during the last two generations. Living within limited geographical boundaries, our population, our life expectancy, and our means of living have all increased. Throughout the world people see this situation and are demanding that they, too, shall share this continued improvement in physical well-being.

If the hope is not to prove false that man can free himself from the age-old specters of destitution and disease, it is of prime importance that we who have blazed the trail to such freedom shall carry on with increasing success. If we in the United States can maintain our own health and prosperity over the generations without preying upon the rest of the world, our example will be a beacon light to the rest of mankind. This is the great human significance of a successful American economy. And to maintain its success will require our full effort in the development of new methods, not only in technology and in medicine, but also in business procedures, in administration and in government—in all of those aspects of life where the work and needs of one person must be coordinated with that of others.

But, as I see it, it is for the health of the spirit of mankind that what happens here is of greatest significance. It is not only that our thoughts are important in shaping the dominant American attitudes. It is also that the world looks to us for guidance in finding human meaning in modern technological life.

## Crucial role of American leadership

It has been said that the industrial revolution began in Britain. In one sense that is true. But it was in the American Midwest that the industrial revolution became a pattern that raised the level of life for all the people. Starting with the iron stove that was needed to warm the cabins of the pioneers, extending to the reapers that greatly reduced the time needed for harvesting, and continuing through the railroads and the automobiles and the telephones that have made us an integrated and interdependent society, mechanized industry has been the backbone of our society. We have known no other. With the growth of technology in agriculture, in industry, and in medicine, we ourselves have grown. There is a certain rawness in such a world, but in the continual striving for a better way there is also an enormous vigor. Because of its vigor and vitality, the culture that we know is fast spreading throughout the world, including people who are far less prepared than are we to live amid kaleidoscopic change. Wherein lies the enduring value of such a life? Who can hope to find the answer if not we to whom this life is native?

It was my old friend, Sir Shanti Swarup Bhatnagar, who impressed this upon me in a way I shall never forget. I had gone to India some years after the war as chairman of an India-America Relations Conference,* and Bhatnagar invited me to be his house guest in New Delhi. Many years earlier we had spent months together in north India when he was a young professor of physical chemistry at the University of the Punjab. At that time he had helped me make measurements of cosmic rays in the Himalayas, and I had carried on X-ray experiments in his laboratory. Bhatnagar later did remarkable work in his own field of science. His outstanding studies of magnetic chemistry won him the signal honor of a fellowship in the Royal Society of London. He made some advances in the method of extracting oil from shale that resulted in a fortune that he put at the disposal of the Indian government. He had devoted an intense life effort and a very considerable fortune toward the development of India's technological strength, and he had become one of her most effective exponents of the usefulness of science in improving India's productiveness and her scale of living. In this effort he had visited me at the University of Chicago as leader of an Indian scientific mission.

Bhatnagar was appointed secretary of the first Indian Ministry of Science, and thus, after a lifetime of his own productive research effort, he became the leader of India's program of science and technology. When I visited him after India gained her independence he was engaged in the project of building a dozen or more national science laboratories, one of which, the National Chemical Laboratory, I was to help dedicate at Poona within a few weeks.*

After several days spent in renewing our old friendship and discussing our various interests, Bhatnagar opened to me what was closest to his heart:

"Compton," he said, "I am really worried. We know that we are going to have to follow the example of you in the West and proceed with the development of a technological society in India. It is our only way for economic survival. But there is one thing above all others that you can do to help us."

"What is that?" I inquired. I expected him to ask for some economic aid or technical counsel; but that was not what was on his mind.

"We are concerned with what a technological and industrial society will do to our way of life. Can life really be good to live in such a society?"

Bhatnagar had studied in Europe and Britain. He had visited the United States on several occasions, and he knew, at least from the outside, what life in the West is like. He was aware of our relative economic prosperity. But he knew also of the stress and strain with which we live.

"To us, when we see how you live in the West, with your tensions and pressures, the disillusionments and fears, widespread frustrations, frequent divorces and occasional suicides, it does not appear that you have found a happy life. Is this what we must expect as we follow where technology leads? Can you not show us that life can be good to live in such a world? If you can do this, you will give us heart as we follow you along the technological road. If we can be convinced that life is good to live in a world of science and technology, we and all the world will follow your footsteps."

It is impossible to transmit the depth of emotion with which Bhatnagar was making this appeal. From his youth on he had followed a life of science. Yet deep in his heart remained the question, would the type of life into which he was leading his nation be found good once it had been attained?

The question was too big and of too great significance to my friend for me to turn it lightly aside or to answer with platitudes. So I did not immediately attempt a reply, but I assured him that I would return to it on my next visit to India.

Several years later, I received a letter from the secretary of the International Federation of University Women asking me to address their organization in London on whether there are human values to be found in technology. Here in the midst of the industrialized world, as in India that was looking forward to industrialization as the world of the future, appeared the central question: "Show us that life can be good in the world of technology that beckons us."

I worked that address over rather carefully. In the course of my remarks I pointed out that science and technology are of themselves morally neutral. They can be either good or bad according to the use to which they are put. They simply constitute effective tools with which we can perform the tasks we set ourselves. If we are men of goodwill, determined to help our neighbors to attain better lives, I know of no more powerful method for achieving our desired goals than through the use of science.*

This was essentially the thought that I repeated at the University of Delhi on my next visit to India, in 1954. Bhatnagar was in the audience. I concluded that life can be good to live in a world of science and technology if, but only if, one's great concern is the welfare of men and women. Then one finds joy in developing the power that science offers, for it enables one to help people to grow more fully. After the lecture Bhatnagar came to me and said, simply: "I believe you have there the only answer."

### EPILOGUE

As I look back on an eventful life, my thoughts turn again to airplanes, for life itself is like an airplane flight. Recently I flew from New York City to my home in St. Louis. There were thunderstorms in the air and the course was a devious one. We circled and climbed through the clouds to avoid the worst, but there was a period of rough going before we were in the clear. Then we sped straight toward our destination. Approaching St. Louis, the plane's nose dipped down. Smoothly and rapidly we headed in toward the airport. It was midnight as we approached the field. The flaps at the rear of the wings bent downward to brake the speed and the plane leveled off to a comfortable landing. A short drive, and weary but at peace with the world, I found myself welcomed by my wife at home.

Not all of my life's flight has been smooth. But from childhood, while I was climbing until I could see my way, on through the rough as well as the smooth weather, my life has been a thrilling adventure. My interest in science led me on a glorious quest that was richly rewarded with new discoveries, exciting experiences, and the satisfaction of feeling that what was found would someday help men and women to live more fully.

Now I realize that I am making rapid progress toward home, where welcome and rest await me. In many ways the short period leading to the landing is the best part of the flight. It is the time when one makes most rapid headway toward his goal. And the vision of the goal itself becomes more clear. Truly Solon was right, in his words to Croesus, when he said that one cannot know whether one's life is happy and good until the course is complete.* Now, though the challenge of adventure is still present, progress is rapid, and the restful end of the journey with its welcome at home is greatly to be desired.

# 2. Science and the Discovery of Human Values

## 1953

~❦~ "Human Values in a Technical World," was the theme selected by the International Federation of University Women for the Eleventh Triennial Conference of its thirty-one national member associations. The conference was held in London, England, and Mr. Compton gave the main address, on August 8, 1953.

As the invitation from the IFUW coincided with his announced intention to resign as Chancellor of Washington University, in order to begin an intensive study of the relation of science to human affairs,* Mr. Compton considered the address to be somewhat in the nature of a beginning to his new work. In these remarks he states his conviction that the human value of science is to be found in the opportunities it provides for men and women to achieve their full potentialities. Many of the ideas expressed here are developed more fully in later addresses.*

### SCIENCE AND THE VISION OF EXCELLENCE

There is no doubt that the great initiators of science have seen in its development an important step in the fulfillment of man's destiny. Pythagoras is quoted as explaining that "we seek to learn of what and how the world is made in order that we may find a better way of life." Francis Bacon puts into the mouth of the Father of Salomon's House the words:

> The end of our foundation is the knowledge of causes, and secret motions of things; and the enlarging of the bounds of humane empire, to the effecting of all things possible.*

As the effects of advancing science become apparent, however, we find many difficulties, raising serious questions about whether this advance is truly working for man's good.

| 53 |

These difficulties were expressed to me a number of years ago, rather wistfully, by the Master of Balliol College at Oxford. "I look with dread upon the encroachment of your technology," he remarked. "Our social life is the product of many centuries of adjustment and refinement. Each person knows his place, accepts it, and is satisfied. All this is being destroyed by the so-called improvements that spoil the pattern. I see that the coming of your 'modern world' is inevitable, but I don't want to live in it. When one drives down a hard highway in a powerful motorcar, how can one enjoy nature as one does when rambling at ease over the beautiful English countryside?"

The fact is, of course, that science is engaged upon tasks that we all want to have done, and it is doing these tasks with remarkable effectiveness. But, in doing these welcome tasks, science brings about change in our way of life. As is always true, such changes produce maladjustments. That these maladjustments are of a secondary rather than a primary character is evident when we note the major changes that have occurred in the parts of the world that have been most directly affected by science.

In its major effects, the growth of science has brought substantial gains, as illustrated by what has happened in the United States and is closely paralleled by much of western Europe. From 1900 to 1950 while the population of the United States approximately doubled, life expectancy rose from forty-six to sixty-nine years, real wages increased on the average by roughly 200 per cent, and the fraction of our young people receiving a college education multiplied fivefold. Moreover, all of these advances are continuing. Thus, as a matter of statistics, in its broad biological and human aspects mankind is prospering where advancing science is affecting life most strongly.

The questions that we ask ourselves regarding the human value of science, even though they may be of high importance, are nevertheless concerned with matters that biologically and even intellectually are secondary. We note complaint and unrest, a growth of nervous tensions, frequent crimes, a new appearance of destructive wars, a break from traditional beliefs that have stabilized the social pattern. We must question whether with all our improved health and more extensive education there results any general increase in human satisfaction. There is no doubt that science and modern industry have given us much of what we have wanted. It is almost as a footnote that we renew the old observation that getting what one asks for does not bring happiness.

It is not my intention, however, to dwell upon these difficult problems, troublesome though they are. I want, rather, to focus attention on the central objectives of science, i.e., organized knowledge of man and his world, as related to the great goal of the scholar, the vision of excellence. For the significant fact in our present discussion is that with the new opportunities that science opens to us the effort to attain excellence takes on added meaning. I am convinced that it is in our loyalty to this vision of excellence that we must discover the basis of human values.

## SCIENCE AND FREEDOM

The great significance of science to man is that it encourages his growth as a free agent. Science does this by placing before us ever higher goals, by showing us more effective means for reaching these goals, and especially by emphasizing the importance of working to promote human welfare and thus bringing into prominence a goal that gives meaning to the lives of those who accept it.

It has been said that it is such things as truth and beauty and freedom that give meaning to life. Increased freedom is a gift that science offers to all who are a part of the modern age. I consider this, therefore, to be the great contribution of science to human life. To that relatively small number who are themselves students of science there are other gifts perhaps even more precious. These gifts are concerned with the truth and beauty of nature. Whether he studies the elemental particles of matter or the glorious expanding universe, the growth of a living cell or the grand expressiveness of a simple mathematical equation, to every sincere student of science these truths carry a deep inner meaning. The psalmist who sang, "The heavens declare the glory of God; and the firmament showeth his handiwork," expressed a sentiment that has become of even greater meaning to the increasing numbers of men and women, and especially of youth, who have caught the spirit of science.

Added to the appreciation of the beauty and wonder of the truths of nature there has been found also a new form of active and meaningful self-expression. It is that of sharing in building the structure of science. Just as over the centuries many have found high personal satisfaction in creating beauty through art or music, so now we realize that the search for new, reliable knowledge is in itself a richly rewarding experience. For those who are themselves builders of the new world of science, these are the great values that they are experiencing and that nothing can take away.

But tonight we are concerned primarily with what science means to the vastly greater number of people who find themselves outside the working team of scientists but who are drastically affected by what this team is doing. To this group I want to make one point. It is this: The advance of

| 55 |

science is making it possible for us to work more effectively and with greater hope toward achieving true excellence in the lives of men and women.

I can think of no illustration of our modern situation that fits more accurately than the ancient parable of the tree of knowledge of good and evil. Science is making this tree vastly more productive of fruit. Having eaten of this fruit, we can no longer be blind to the consequences of our actions. To a new degree we see our responsibilities as men and women. We cannot be at peace except as we work to enable those who depend upon us to grow to their best. We may long for the paradise of innocence where these responsibilities were unknown, but the angel with the flaming sword is barring our return. We have no choice but to strive to give full opportunity for growth to those about us. Yet, as we put our hearts into that effort, God in his mercy has granted that we shall find ourselves growing toward a certain excellence.

*The quest for the good*—in this quest itself is to be found the distinctive human meaning of modern life. Here is the essence of freedom. If the goal that is sought is wisely chosen its realization brings certain satisfactions. Yet it is in the endeavor to attain the goal that much of the value lies. It is characteristic of the modern world that our major sources of enjoyment are not to be found in contemplative appreciation of beauty and perfection but rather in the active effort to create beauty and to attain a condition of higher perfection. To us moderns it is in the growth toward perfection that our lives take on their most valued meaning.

Thus, if we are looking for the meaning of science in its broader human significance, this meaning must be discovered in what science does toward enabling and encouraging us to select worthy goals and in helping us to work more effectively toward attaining these goals. That is, it is only insofar as we have a vision of excellence for men's lives that science has a human meaning. If we aspire to such a goal, science becomes our valued servant. Through the power of scientific knowledge we have greater freedom. Through greater service to our fellows we become more worthy men and women.

## VISION AND ACHIEVEMENT OF GREATER GOALS

Let us note then how it is that science opens to us wider possibilities and gives us more powerful means of attaining the goals we desire.

In the first place, we note that science broadens our perspectives. It supplies us with a reliable and expanded view of our limitations and our possibilities. We recognize with new force the vastness and complexity of our universe. With our increased awareness of man's physical insignificance comes a new appreciation of the unique value of the human spirit. We have learned also the reliability of nature's laws and how these laws may be turned more effectively to serve our purposes. At the same time that we have been freed from fear of superstitions and the whimsies of daemons, we have learned new respect for the powerful forces of physical nature and of the human mind that shape the conditions of our lives. Thus new possibilities for our development are opened to us.

Let me illustrate what I mean by these new possibilities opened by science. Consider the effect of our increasing life expectancy, which has approximately doubled during the past century. First of all, this longer life means a greater likelihood that we shall attain the maturity of experience that is necessary for our full development. This in turn places new emphasis on the importance of an education that will enable us to use our experiences for the enrichment of life. Moreover, we can afford to devote more time to education and training because we anticipate a longer period of working years. Thus we have before us an expanded opportunity for the cultivation of our human possibilities. We have to choose not only whether we shall use this added opportunity for our education but also what the character of our education shall be.

Or consider the effect of our greatly facilitated travel and communication of ideas. How shall these be used? The answer is: for our business, for our enjoyment, and for aiding our understanding. In each of these areas of our lives new vistas are opened, new opportunities appear, new possibilities are presented that can affect profoundly for good or ill the lives of those for whom we care. Our moral choices thus become more insistent and of greater intensity. This is not only because the course of our lives no longer follows a traditional routine. It is also because the effects of our choices are of greater consequence.

In speaking of the new possibilities opened to us by the modern world, I am using the word *science* in a representative sense. Actually, the growth of scientific knowledge is only one of several factors that are responsible for the rapid and widespread changes in our modern way of life. Of comparable significance are improvements in technology and developments in the organization of society. Included among the significant modern organizational developments are those of industry, education, and government. These three agencies—science, technology, and organizational procedure—have grown side by side and have stimulated each other to more rapid growth. Science is thus symbolic of several great forces that are working together to change our world.

We also sometimes refer to the present period symbolically as the *atomic age*. In this phrase we crystallize somewhat fearfully the drastic significance of our choice of the use to which we put our new powers.

Whether it is the destructive possibilities of atomic weapons or the educational potential of television, we realize with new urgency that what we do affects deeply the lives of others. We cannot keep ourselves blind to what has become of such far-reaching import. Moreover, because rapid change has moved our lives out of the traditional routine, new choices of what is good cannot be escaped. We are impressed by the need to know surely what are the human values toward which our new powers can best be used. That the excellence toward which we aspire shall be wisely chosen becomes to us a matter of prime and urgent importance. Thus it is that we are encouraged, perhaps even forced, by science to accept greater responsibilities and greater freedom.

## SCIENCE AND THE PROMOTION OF HUMAN WELFARE

Toward what values then must we aspire if we are to thrive in the modern world? Knowledge of science itself has little effect on human life. Something more is needed.

A significant hint about what this something more must be is given by comparing what has happened in places where knowledge of science is present but where the accepted ideals of society are different. Among the highly civilized nations, the contrast becomes most evident in comparing what has happened in the United States with what has happened in India. During the past fifty years the major developments in science have been known to the leading scholars of both countries. Over this period of half a century the population of both nations has approximately doubled. But the striking contrast remains that in the basic measures of well-being—life expectancy, per capita real wages, and average education—India has not changed substantially while the United States has moved strongly ahead. Why this difference?

One answer is that as a people the Indians have not willingly accepted advances in technology and in industrial organization whereas Americans have accepted these advances eagerly. But this is only a superficial answer. The basic difference lies much deeper.

The typical American accepts as an opportunity the possibility of making new knowledge effective in the service of man. It is not only that in the United States financial rewards come to the inventor and the industrialist who make widely available the benefits of science and technology. It is also that the high prestige of such men reflects a universal American regard for the person who enriches the lives of his neighbors. The scientist, the pioneer in medicine, the inventor, and the industrialist are men who are honored. In the United States no man is respected by his peers or by the public unless he works for the common welfare. It is characteristic of Americans that the person whom they count as greatest is he who renders the greatest service to his fellows.

Not so in India. There to the typical citizen service to one's fellows is considered rather demeaning. Action of any kind is of value as it is reflected in one's own growth and satisfaction. To the Indian not only is service to the public of minor importance, but the temptation offered by science to turn one's attention to material matters is positively harmful, for its effect is to distract one from the all-important matter of growth of the inner spirit. This Hindu attitude is closely related to the Christian admonition to keep oneself unspotted by the world, but its direction differs in that attention is directed not toward love of God and man as expressed in the service of man but toward the absorption of self in the Infinite. Where this is the form of excellence toward which one aspires, it is difficult indeed to find any value in the contributions of science. In such a setting the influence of respect by one's fellows gives scant stimulus toward accepting responsibility for persons beyond one's immediate ken. The appeal of widespread human benefits that may come from the applications of science brings little response.

In this contrast, it seems to me, we find the key to the ideal toward which we must aspire if our lives are to have full human meaning in the world that science brings. Our goal must be that of giving men and women an opportunity to grow to their best. With such an ideal science appears as a blessing, for it helps us to see how such human growth can be advanced.

But, if the goal of promoting human welfare burns bright before us, note also how science and her sister agencies induce the fuller growth of our own personality. We have emphasized the greater responsibility that we bear as we wield these mighty modern powers. Is not this the very essence of being a person, that one shall choose regarding matters of human significance, that one shall make his choice effective, and that one shall accept the responsibility for the consequences of one's choice? By accepting the increased responsibility that science places before us, we thus grow to greater manhood. Our lives grow in value to ourselves and to our fellows.

## VIRTUES DEMANDED BY SCIENCE

It remains to show that as a condition for survival the forces of the modern world are making it necessary for us to cultivate certain high virtues.

It is evident that success in science means loyalty to truth, a concern for reliable knowledge, a desire for understanding. Technology calls for the skilled expertness that comes from experience, combined with specialized knowledge whose useful applications become apparent from a broad perspective. Effective participation in any social organization requires willingness to cooperate, consideration of one's fellows, and a desire to promote the task on which the group is engaged. These are, moreover, attributes of high importance for growth of the human spirit: loyalty to truth, understanding, technical competence, and a love of one's fellows.

As an indication of the importance of these virtues to survival in our modern setting, let us consider a person for whom the vision of excellence burns bright. We shall suppose that our citizen is loyal to the best he knows and has his heart in its advancement. He examines his vision carefully to make certain that what he considers good stands the test of promoting the welfare of others as well as of himself. He equips himself for service to his ideal as effectively as he knows how: by maintaining vigorous health, by learning useful knowledge, and by acquiring skills. He puts into the achieving of his ideal all of his strength. In short he devotes all that he has and can attain to the promotion of the great good toward which he aspires.

I believe we should agree that a person with such a spirit would be a notable asset to the society of which he is a member. Even though his ardent effort to promote his high ideal might well lead him into troubles with those of lesser vision, we should expect him to find his life a rewarding one. Certainly he would be an exemplar of freedom, one who works eagerly and effectively to make his world what he considers good.

But note how the spirit and actions of this noble man are precisely those that are best adapted for survival in the modern world. First of all there is loyalty to the best one knows, interpreted in terms of the welfare of one's fellows. Here is the basis for joyfully taking one's place where one can be most useful in cooperation with others for the common good. Whether that goal be expressed in terms of the material things produced by industry or, for example, in terms of the intangibles that come with education, if it can best be reached by coordinated effort within an organization one will seek to fit himself to his proper place. There is similarly the knowledge and skill and also the willingness to do well the menial tasks that are represented by technology and the healing arts, those tasks by which we live and prepare ourselves for worthy living. And there is the vital, unbiased search for understanding in the true spirit of science; first of all to make sure that one's vision of the best is adequate and valid, and then to gain the power of knowledge in order that one's efforts may be most effective.

It is such spirit and action that modern society recognizes with rich rewards. It is the nation with such citizens that is fitted to meet the challenges of our changing world.

A few years ago I spent a week with an Indian friend in Delhi. I asked him: "What are the chances that India can preserve its democratic freedom and not fall under the domination of a dictatorial Communism?" He replied with cautious hope, recognizing however that dangers lay ahead. Then he added, "There is a way that you in the West could help us immensely."

"How is that?" I asked him.

"By showing the world that life can be good in the kind of society that you are making inevitable for us," he answered. "It is clear that we also shall have to accept technology and highly organized industry in order that we may survive. But we look on such a life with dread. For what we see in the West does not encourage us. In our ancient Indian culture each person is a member of a family where he belongs and has a human place. Even if he starves his plight is shared by others who care. In the West we see relative prosperity but many signs of human tension. There is routine factory employment that removes the human meaning from one's work. There is nervous breakdown, frequent divorce, occasional suicide.

"If only you can show us that life in the modern democratic world can be good to live, that it has real human meaning, you will give us new courage. The world will follow your lead."

Here was a most significant observation. At the very least it showed that we of the West, with all our confidence in the superiority of our social order, have failed to convince even our friends in other cultures that we have found the good life. The really troublesome thought is that we have not even convinced ourselves. We see all too clearly that what we have leaves much to be desired. Yet we are embarked upon an epochal adventure, and we cannot turn back. We have raised the hope for all men everywhere that the age-old specters of starvation and premature death from disease can be the exception rather than the rule. We have raised the vision of widespread education that will open men's minds. Among large segments of our populations these conditions are already in existence. What do we need that will answer the question of my Indian friend?

I believe the answer lies simply in accepting the basic premise of democratic freedom. That premise is that it is men and women, our individual citizens, who are the basis of value. We believe that persons are of themselves important. We call this concept the dignity of man. It is an idea that all free peoples want to have recognized, whether they be Asians or Europeans or Americans.

| 61 |

If we take this idea in earnest, and plan our lives and our society accordingly, the answer to finding the life of human meaning is apparent. For if we truly take men and women as our measure of value we can do nothing less than direct our efforts toward giving them the opportunity to grow to the fullest stature that is possible to them. We know that such growth comes only as they themselves contribute as best they can to the life about them. Our civilization thus acquires an accepted goal—the goal of a social order where every person is enabled to contribute his part, is recognized for how he does it, and by contributing his part can grow to his own fullest development.

The vision of such a social order all too often becomes dim and uncertain. It is nevertheless the heritage of all who understand freedom. As that vision becomes clearer, and as our citizens hold it more definitely as their own, science, technology, and the organization of our society will all take on human meaning, for it is through the use of these agencies that we must endeavor to give to men and women the opportunity for growth.

The goal is thus human excellence, the best that is possible to us. What the age of science demands is that the aspiration toward this excellence shall be open to all who will accept the goal.

The task of organized society thus becomes that of making conditions possible for every person to work effectively toward the common welfare. Such is the truly free community, where each individual can put his heart into making his world what he wants it to be and where government and industry and education and religion are working together to the end that such a vision and such an opportunity may be open for all.

The task of technology becomes that of supplying the techniques of living, of preserving health, of communicating ideas. Thus technology endeavors to provide the physical conditions such that every person can make an effective effort to achieve his best.

The task that science shares with other fields of scholarship is the search for understanding and knowledge. The effort to understand one's world parallels the search for beauty as an ultimate aspect of the good life. But, as experience has shown, it opens also new possibilities for human adventure. In its applications, the knowledge of science will serve more widely the needs of man, giving him new strength as he endeavors to enable his fellows to live more fully.

Stated in another way, the great problem of finding human meaning in life in the modern world has a simple answer. It lies in losing oneself in the effort to give one's fellows an opportunity to attain lives of highest value. This is an ancient doctrine that now takes on new meaning because it becomes a condition for survival.

I doubt whether there is any other adequate answer to the quest for human values in a society based on technology. Our setting requires that each of us shall serve his fellows. Full human value comes from this service only when we give it freely because we want our fellows also to grow to their best. As we lose ourselves in such service, our lives attain a certain nobility. We find our own souls.

Science and technology and the organizations of government and industry thus become the agencies whereby we work to achieve the open opportunity for men to grow. Far from blocking the way to a life of human meaning, these powerful agencies that are shaping modern society become the way toward greater freedom. Whether they do, in fact, impart added value to human life depends upon the spirit with which we use them. For those who are inspired by the vision of men and women reaching their full stature through living for their fellows, science is a blessing that opens the way to a life of full human meaning.

# II

## The Human Meaning
## of Science

If you want your life's work to be useful to
mankind, it is not enough that you understand applied science as such. Concern for man himself must
always constitute the chief objective of all technological effort . . . to assure that the result of our
scientific thinking may be a blessing to mankind, and
not a curse.

Never forget this when you are pondering over
your diagrams and equations!

ALBERT EINSTEIN

# 3. The Significance of the Discovery of X Rays

## 1938

One of the great milestones in the history of science is marked by Wilhelm Roentgen's discovery of X rays in 1895. The value of this achievement was widely recognized at once, and Roentgen soon received numerous honors and awards, among them the first Nobel prize in physics, which was presented in 1901. In this lecture, which was given on several occasions during 1938, Mr. Compton appraises the importance of Roentgen's discovery.*

Mr. Compton's own field of research was for many years the study of the properties of X rays and other ionizing radiation.* His work was recognized by the award of honors from scientific and learned societies, including the Nobel prize, the gold medal of the Radiological Society of North America, and the Plakette of the Roentgen Museums at Roentgen's birthplace in Lennep, Germany. The author of a highly regarded textbook on X rays,* Mr. Compton was also actively concerned with the physiological effects of radiation. He was one of the initial members of the National Cancer Advisory Council (1937–44) and helped to organize the Chicago Tumor Institute. During World War II, he was called upon to direct the development of the first nuclear chain reaction and the first quantity production of plutonium, with an attendant responsibility for guarding against the possible health hazards associated with such an undertaking.

In this prewar address, as in those of later years, is to be found Mr. Compton's characteristic and conscious emphasis upon the constructive aspects of man's development and a hopeful view of man's ultimate destiny.

Never has a scientific discovery so thrilled the world as when the news came of rays that showed the bones of living men. Wilhelm Conrad Roentgen, an obscure professor in the little German university of Würzburg, had electrified a group of his scientific colleagues by demonstrating his discovery at a small gathering in November, 1895. The news spread like wildfire. Within a month his experiments were being repeated throughout the world. Public and scientific press alike hailed the discovery as epoch making. And correctly. For here was the match that lit the torch that is modern science. Within a year X rays showed ions in gases, leading to the discovery of the electron and with it new knowledge of matter, new chemistry, and new industries. Within the same year *natural* X rays were found in uranium. Radium and radioactivity were the result. A considerable part of the difference of our lives from those of our parents is indeed traceable to this discovery of X rays.

Yet, such is human memory, when I was asked to read a paper last winter before a national scientific society on "The Physical and Biological Consequences of the Discovery of X Rays," * the subject must have seemed hopelessly academic. Where now can one find human interest in X rays?

In my effort to find an answer to this question, I soon saw that I was presented with a first-class example of the power of science. We frequently hear of the growth of knowledge as the central thread of history. On the foundation of what has been known the structure of new knowledge is built, and each new finding stimulates others. But it is not always easy to grasp the full human import of this increased understanding of nature. Here the example of X rays may be helpful.

What is the most important event that has happened in the world in your lifetime? "The world war," many would answer. Let us then set the discovery of X rays beside the world war for comparison. Will X rays be hopelessly outweighed? As a basis of judging relative importance we shall compare human values: life and death, health and disease, manner and means of living, the worthwhileness of life.

Life and death! The total number of people killed in the four years of the world war was about nine million. Of the people now living in the nations that fought the war, statistics show that five or six times that number will die of cancer. X rays and radium supply the best treatment that we know for alleviation and cure of this disease. Millions of those who were living in these warring countries will in fact be saved from death by cancer through X rays and radium. The numbers would be much greater if we were to count also those who are being saved from death by the accurate diagnoses made possible by X rays. It is thus a fair estimate that X rays and radium will save more lives of those now living in Europe and America than were killed in the great war.

But think of the many wrecked lives of those injured in the war, and the wastage of disease that followed the war. As against these, let me ask who among you does not have a close friend whose health has been aided by X rays? The setting of a broken bone, locating tooth infections, diagnosis of tuberculosis and other internal disease, relief and cure of growths of various kinds—all are aided by X rays. Among the soldiers themselves, the X ray was one of the most effective tools for healing the wounded. Because of X rays we live longer in a healthier world.

But what of the vast political and economic changes that the war has caused? Whole nations bending their energies toward the single goal of victory; the economic upheavals that have followed? Such effects are truly tremendous.

Scientific achievements such as the discovery of X rays work in a more quiet way, but are none the less effective. Science grows like a living plant, extending its roots and tendrils into the very fiber of our lives. If we are to gauge the significance of a scientific discovery, we must follow its consequences in some detail.

One of the first fruits of the discovery of X rays was the finding of radioactivity. Through use of X rays, ions became known, which led to the understanding of electric currents flowing through gases. It then became possible to identify and to use electrons, those miracle workers of modern technology. All that has to do with electrons is thus the direct descendant of the discovery of X rays. This includes, of course, X rays themselves; many electric devices, such as current rectifiers; electron tubes, such as are used in radio, long-distance telephony, and submarine-cable telegraphy; photoelectric cells, for exposure meters and various automatic machines; the possibility of airplane flight through fog and over seas on a radio beacon; the safety of ships at sea. Fundamental to all of this is knowledge of the electron, and hence of X rays.

But the really great significance of such a discovery as X rays is yet more indirect. It provides a great stimulus to scientific advance in all fields. Insofar as our lives are dependent upon science, we thus owe an accumulating debt to such discoveries.

When the discovery of X rays electrified the scientific world, literally thousands of people who could find the necessary equipment repeated Roentgen's experiment and told of their results. In our country Thomas Edison, Michael Pupin, W. F. Magie of Princeton, and Albert Michelson of Chicago were among the many who made contributions. The science of physics that had been dead was made alive, and that life has increased steadily in vigor through four decades to our present day. Here was an opening for keen-eyed young men with adventurous spirit to seek for and find new discoveries. J. J. Thomson, Ernest Rutherford, Peter Debye, Irving Langmuir—each contributed his share.

The vigorous new science of physics inspires her sister sciences. As X rays give certain proof of ions and bring into clear light the structure of crystals, molecules, and atoms, chemistry has a firmer foundation for her own growth. The distinction between polar and nonpolar molecules is clarified, valence forces between atoms become electrical forces, and with increased knowledge of its fundamentals, chemistry grows to new heights of scientific and technical achievement.

In biology, the possibility with X rays of studying the anatomy of living men and animals likewise stimulates important advances, such as knowledge of the growth of bones and the cure of rickets. The tragic effects of X rays on the early roentgenologists showed the possibilities for curing disease through destruction of organisms. The artificial production of mutations, that is, the making of new varieties and species by exposure to X rays, opened up new developments in genetics. As in physics, however, these direct consequences of the use of X rays have had their greatest effect in stimulating advances in associated fields.

While it would be obviously unfair to ascribe to the discovery of X rays the entire credit for the rapid growth of science during the present century, it is probably fair to say that, since Darwin's development of the theory of evolution, no single contribution to science has had an equal effect. The discovery of X rays serves as a landmark that divides the old from the new in physics, and it has thus been directly or indirectly of great influence in other fields. At the same time, Roentgen's discovery itself was made necessary by the development of the science of his day. Some had previously produced X rays without observing them; others had noted their effects without finding the cause. If not Roentgen, certainly someone else within a year or two would have found the rays, for the time was ripe.

In a similar way, it would be unfair to ascribe to the world war such major effects as the development of Communism in Russia, which already had a background in the political and religious intolerance of the country and in the teachings of Marx. National Socialism in Germany may owe as much to Nietzsche as to Kaiser Wilhelm or Adolf Hitler; at least, the war was but one determining cause. Or to come closer home, is our sequence of periods of prosperity and depression the result of a war twenty years past, or is it a by-product of a more closely knit industrial organization that has resulted from improved communication, transportation, and technical methods of production? Important as the war may have been, it becomes clear that it was only one of many factors now determining our political, economic, and social life.

In making a fair relative evaluation of the significance of these two major events, we must note that the everyday life of most of us is dependent primarily upon the technology that has come to us through science. From our conversations over the telephone to the drinking of pasteurized milk, it is obvious that without this science urban life as we know it could not exist. Our social conditions are determined by science to an extent far greater than by any past wars. We may add that even our political structure, whose form has been dependent upon waging successful wars, is at least equally dependent upon the maintenance of good communications and transportation, which are a contribution of science.

History shows that the effects of scientific advance increase in importance without end, and much more rapidly than do the effects of war. Thus, if we were to evaluate the consequences of Watt's and Carnot's studies of steam, or of Faraday's study of electricity, which laid the foundation for the development of the electrical industry that is now so basic to our society, there is no question that our lives are now more affected by them than by the great war. Not yet felt is the full human effect of the more recent advances of science stimulated by the discovery of X rays. Even now we find them perhaps of comparable significance in practical life. Within another generation, when the world's scars from the war are almost healed, we shall be using more than ever the gifts that the new science is giving us. Balanced on the scales of the long view of history, Roentgen's work must vastly outweigh that of the generals.

There is another aspect that is harder to evaluate. How do these great events affect man's attitude toward life? In a great war all men are called upon to submerge their own interests for the advancement of the common cause. "Make the world safe for democracy!" was the cry that, mistakenly or not, thrilled us all, and for which many made the supreme sacrifice. On the other side of the ledger we find blasted hopes, disillusioned hearts, hatreds fanned by grievous wrongs. The heights of sacrifice and the depths of cruelty find expression in such a human cataclysm.

Contrast with this the accusation leveled at science that it is uninterested in human affairs: Human values are forgotten. By its emphasis on material things, art, philosophy, and religion appear of negligible importance. The scientist knows nothing but facts!

Yet what is of greater significance in forming our human attitudes than to learn what we can about our relation to the great powers that have brought us into being? In this regard, the rapid growth of the new science since the discovery of the X ray has greatly advanced our understanding. At almost every stage of these advances in physics, X rays have played an essential role. Atoms themselves were put in bold evidence by the paths of alpha particles (helium atoms) in C. T. R. Wilson's cloud chamber. We have seen how knowledge of the electron was clarified by study of ions produced by X rays. Either X rays or radioactive materials have been used in nearly all the studies showing the fundamental particles of matter.

They have played an important part in testing the relativity and quantum theories. From the significance of Moseley's atomic number to the observing of electron distributions and motions, X rays have been used in solving the electronic structure of atoms. Crystal lattices and the structures of molecules have thus been learned. With X rays, the dual wave and particle structure of the world was first revealed.* Each of these discoveries has been the starting point for other discoveries, so that practically the whole structure of the new physics is based at some point upon work with X rays. The new physics has itself illumined other sciences and stimulated their growth. Thus has our view of the world of nature been affected by a single discovery.

It is from our understanding of the world that we must form our attitudes toward life. May we not say that in learning our relation to our world and to each other, which is the task of science, we are developing the aspect of our being that makes us distinctively human? To many of us, at least, it is the possibility of adding something to this understanding that makes the task of science seem worthwhile.

If there is an undercurrent of hope in the world, a rejoicing of man as he finds himself gifted with new strength, if our young men see visions of a new world that they hope to create and our old men dream dreams of an ideal society, it is largely because the increasing knowledge of science is giving us new powers. We see deadly diseases becoming less deadly; we see new means of self-expression and enjoyment. If with these gains come also the troubles of hard times and unemployment, the evident successes of science persuade us of the effective power of reason diligently applied to their solution. If the war brought us grief, suffering, and discouragement, the advances of science have brought us new hope for the future. And of recent advances, the discovery of X rays has been the most inspiring.

Finally, you must have been feeling the great contrast between these two important events of the world war and the discovery of X rays. The values of one are largely destructive, whereas the values of the other are almost wholly constructive. It is for this reason that the contributions of science remain as permanent human assets, while the scars of war are eventually healed over and forgotten. Time was when warfare was considered a sport and the highest calling of noble men. Now, except as is necessary in national self-defense, we think of war as contrary to fundamental human interests. Our great men are those who advance our civilization, who give us those things that make life worthwhile. In our country, at least, where our life is built upon technology, it is thus not in the generals but in the shapers of science that we find real greatness.

# 4. Acceptance of Nobel Award

## 1927

In 1927 the Nobel prize in physics was shared by Charles Thomson Rees Wilson, for his invention of the cloud chamber, and by Arthur Holly Compton, for his discovery and interpretation of the change in wavelength of scattered X rays, a phenomenon known as the "Compton effect." * These remarks were made by Professor Compton in accepting the award, which was presented in Stockholm on December 10, 1927.

Several years ago I was reading Marco Polo's account of his experiences in the employ of the great Emperor of China, Kublai Khan. He was telling his incredulous Venetian friends of the daily life of the Chinese. "They take two baths daily," he wrote, "one in the morning and another in the evening. Not only this, but the baths are in warm water." The idea of daily baths was itself sufficiently difficult for the Venetians to believe, but that water could be warmed twice daily seemed to them to present an insurmountable difficulty.

Polo replied that it would indeed have been impossible to heat the water for millions of Chinese if they had relied on wood for fuel. They had, however, solved the difficulty by finding a kind of black rock that would burn. This rock had the advantage over wood that it would hold its fire overnight and have the water warm for the morning bath. Then Polo described in accurate detail how this black rock occurred in veins in the mountains, and the manner in which it was quarried. If the idea of baths twice daily was marvelous, the story of the burning rocks was beyond the realm of possibility.

Marco Polo's stories read like the tales of a man who after visiting a highly civilized country returns to his semibarbaric home to tell of the wonders he has seen. At that time, hardly seven centuries ago, China was far in advance of Italy, a land whose culture was the pride of our Western civilization.

Last year I had the privilege of visiting China, and I saw what, gauged by Western standards, was a primitive country. In seven short centuries the leadership has passed from the East to the West, until now we are as far ahead of the Orient as in Polo's day China was ahead of Italy.

Why this rapid change? Differences in native ability will not explain it. It was only a few centuries ago that a Mongolian ruler, Genghis Khan, held sway over the greatest empire, with regard to both area and population, that has ever been united under one government. Nor have the Chinese been lacking in feats of engineering. The Great Wall of China, a massive pile of masonry extending over mountainous country for fifteen hundred miles, takes a high place among the wonders of the world. It is doubtful whether either in individual ability or in aptitude for organization the European has any real advantage over the Mongolian.

Shortly after the days of Polo, however, there arose in various parts of Europe the scientific spirit—the eagerness to learn from nature her truths, and to put these truths to the use of mankind. The rapid change in our mode of living since that time can certainly be traced to the consequences of the development of this spirit of science. When we seek the reason for the present pre-eminence of the European peoples, we find that it lies in the great power given to us by the search for truth and its application to our daily lives.

I verily believe that in the advancement of science lies the hope of our civilization.

The benefits of science are not only material ones. The truths that science teaches are of common interest the world over. The language of science is universal and is a powerful force in bringing the peoples of the world closer together. We are all acquainted with the sharp divisions that religions draw between men. In science there are no such divisions; all peoples worship at the shrine of truth. The spirit of science knows no national or religious boundaries, and it is thus a powerful force for the peace of the world.

The prize you have given me today I consider the highest honor that a man can receive, for Nobel prizes have been a great stimulus to the advancement of science. In thanking you for the high honor you have conferred, I want also to congratulate the Swedish nation for having men of the far vision of Nobel, who could see clearly the importance to the world of encouraging the growth of science, and for having men with the enthusiasm and ability necessary to carry out Nobel's ideas and to extend them. Sweden has thus made good use of an unusual opportunity for stimulating science and for the promotion of international fellowship. Through her encouragement of science she has given us a greater hope for the future of our civilization.

# 5. The Responsibility
## of Free Science

### 1953

A Conference on Science and Freedom was held in Hamburg, Germany, in July 1953, under the joint auspices of the University of Hamburg and the Congress for Cultural Freedom. The conference was convened to discuss not only the necessity for freedom in scientific research but also the mental and material conditions required for the fruitful development of scientific ideas. Mr. Compton agreed to serve as one of eighteen members of an international Committee of Sponsors. At the conclusion of the conference, on July 26, he made the following remarks, in which he chose to stress the responsibility that is implied by freedom.*

On behalf of those who have come from over the sea to attend this Conference on Science and Freedom, I want to express our sincere appreciation of the many courtesies you in Hamburg have extended to us. We like your city. We admire the faith and courage and diligence with which you have rebuilt your homes and your harbor. We have enjoyed your hospitality.

The discussions of our conference have been notable for their freedom. If the ideas of scholars are suppressed elsewhere, they have been freely expressed here. To me this is a matter of great encouragement. Our freedom of discussion of controversial points demonstrates that if any of us feels that his thinking or expression is being limited, such limitations are not intentional. For those of us from the countries represented here, it is clear that political restrictions, however annoying, are of not more than secondary importance. The more serious limitations that we experience are those of lack of money and those imposed by the busy activity of modern life that robs us of leisure for thought.

We have, however, found reason for real concern about the freedom of science in the Soviet nations, according to firsthand reports that we have heard. We have hoped that science might be an area in which the people of these nations may experience freedom, and from this experience learn of its great advantages. This is still our hope, for in freedom of scientific thought we see a possible bridge of understanding between the two great areas of the world.

I want briefly this afternoon to consider an aspect of the freedom of science that has arisen several times in our discussions and that seems to me worthy of special emphasis. It is the responsibility of the scholar to whom society grants freedom of thought and expression.

Because the truths of science do not recognize national boundaries, knowledge wherever found can enrich the lives of men everywhere. For this reason the ultimate responsibility of the scientist is not to his profession, nor to his state, but to mankind. If he wishes to be most effective for the welfare of man, however, he works to best advantage when he cooperates with his fellow scientists, with his fellow citizens, or in smaller groups with his employer or with his students.

In any case, where freedom is important our prime concern is with individual men and women. For it is only to an individual that freedom has meaning. Only an individual can want and choose and aspire; only an individual can endeavor to achieve what he believes is good. Thus the free scientist, responsible to mankind, is really concerned with the growth of individual men and women. It is by promoting their growth that he would perform his duty to the society that supports him and gives him freedom.

In our discussions we have considered at length the distinctions between pure science and applied science. The fact is, of course, that all knowledge is useful. The only distinction is the purpose for which it is used. Science has its greatest human meaning and provides the greatest satisfaction to the investigator when he creates something significant and permanent through finding new knowledge. This is the prime practical value of research in pure science. Among the greatest satisfactions that a scholar can have is that of watching his students awaken to the joy of finding new knowledge. Not greatly different in kind is the satisfaction that comes from seeing the practical results of one's technological investigations, as for example in giving more adequate light to millions of men and women, or in bringing back safe from a war young men who probably would have died if one had not done his scientific task. It is the privilege of all scholars to share to some extent in such tasks. It is their responsibility to do what they can to insure that the conditions of their work shall be such as to make it fully productive of humanly significant knowledge.

Because of the immense power of knowledge, however, the scholar has much more than the usual responsibility expected of a citizen. He bears not only the responsibility implied by freedom; he bears also the responsibility that goes with power. Let me illustrate this by an example which involved several members of this congress.

In 1941 a small number of physicists and chemists in England and in the United States found that their knowledge of atomic nuclei had developed to a point where an atomic bomb of great military effectiveness could probably be made. Similar knowledge was available to their enemies. These scientists were lovers of peace, but they believed that the world's freedom was truly at stake. If they agreed not to make the atomic bomb, no one else on their side could do so, and the cause for which their nations were fighting would be imperiled. Their choice was to go ahead, accepting responsibility for whatever success or failure might follow, and thus to share fully in the effort to preserve freedom. You know the result.

This is only one dramatic example of what is repeated time after time. The man of learning shares with all his fellows the duties of citizenship. But the burden of his responsibility is heavier than that of most. For the knowledge he possesses is a mighty power. Whether his ideas are concerned with the rights of man, or with antibiotic chemicals, or with devices for the protection of peace and freedom, these ideas must be used with wisdom and with courage. The scholar must rely in the first instance on his own judgment in what he says and does, for no other person can know as well as he what his ideas will bring forth.

Thus the freedom of the scholar is possible only as he accepts the responsibility that freedom implies. He will do this if with all his heart he wants his fellows to grow to their full stature. It is in the endeavor to find knowledge that will be useful in building well the lives of men and women that the scholar finds his own full freedom.

# III

## Science and

## Man's Progress

"If I saw farther, 'twas because I stood
On giant shoulders," wrote the king of thought,
Too proud of his great line to slight the toils
Of his forebears. He turned to their dim past,
Their fading victories and their fond defeats,
And knelt as at an altar, drawing all
Their strengths into his own; and so went forth
With all their glory shining in his face,
To win new victories for the age to come.

ALFRED NOYES, "Newton," in
"Watchers of the Sky"

# 6. The Effect of Social Influences on the Development of Physical Science

## *1930–1931*

Arthur Compton's concern with the role of causality in human affairs grew out of his own scientific work. During the decade of the 1920's lively scientific controversy arose over the nature of light, as classical theory was found to be inadequate to explain the experimental results of Mr. Compton and other investigators. In an effort to explain the Compton effect (1922), a wave and particle dualism gradually supplanted the traditional wave theory of radiation. This, in turn, stimulated the formulation of the quantum mechanics (1925) and the uncertainty principle (1927), which have important implications both for philosophy and for politics. At Mr. Compton's invitation, Werner Heisenberg, the brilliant German physicist who took a leading part in the development of these theories, discussed them in a series of lectures * at the University of Chicago during the spring of 1929. The following year, on November 6, Mr. Compton presented before the Physics Club of Chicago some of his ideas on the role of causality in the development of science. This is one of his earliest talks on causality, a subject to which he subsequently returned many times.

As Mr. Compton has himself remarked: "It is rare indeed that the first formulations are found to be adequate." Yet it is felt that the reader may find interest in this early talk, which has been slightly condensed in transcription from one of Mr. Compton's scientific notebooks. Though not intended for publication in this form, it will be recognized as the seed-bed for ideas that were more carefully refined for subsequent occasions. This talk also illustrates Mr. Compton's continual effort to seek, and to try to understand, the implications that lay beyond the immediate details of his own field of specialization.

An explanation is perhaps in order to the members of the Physics Club for presenting a discussion on a subject other than Dirac's latest theory of absent electrons or the precise measurement of the grating space of calcite. At my last appearance before this group my subject was, as I remember it, "A New Method of Determining Electron Distributions in Atoms." Perhaps I may be permitted to take your thoughts this afternoon somewhat farther from the details of our science, and to call attention to some historical points that seem to me of importance to us, not only in guiding our work in the laboratory, but also in determining our attitude toward the place of science in modern life.

I have long been convinced that the hope of civilization lies in the advancement of science. I take it that most of you share with me this conviction. Otherwise we should not be here, but should have thrown our lives into some other field of activity that we considered of greater importance in human life.

When we emphasize the importance of science, one thing that we have in mind is the tremendous effect that the industrial applications of science are having in molding our manner of life. It would be too trite even to mention the many comforts and luxuries that science has thus brought us. It has freed us from much of the drudgery of labor and from many of the horrors of disease, and has indeed formed the basis on which it has been possible to make a civilization that excels in a material way those of Egypt and Greece and Rome.

Yet if these material advantages were all that science were prepared to supply, science would seem to me of doubtful value. The thing that makes science to me most worthwhile is its spirit of loyalty to truth and, by the severe service of truth, the more satisfactory adjustment to the world in which we find ourselves. This adjustment involves the exacting discipline of search for new truth, which inculcates the spirit of science. It requires the appreciation of the beauty of the world as revealed in its magnificence by the clear light of careful study. It makes possible the hopeful struggle to attain for ourselves and for our fellows the highest development of which man is capable.

May I present this as a vision that perhaps all of us see at times, but which is frequently obscured and sometimes lost in our studious attention to the details of our own special study.

In our university we have the dual function of advancing knowledge and of educating men. Our department's share of this education we usually consider to be careful instruction in the principles of physics and in the methods of physics research. None of us believes that in such instruction is a complete education. I must admit that things other than the study of the scattering of X rays seem worthwhile to me. We are actually leaving our students to their own devices in their efforts to secure a real education. Probably this is as it should be, for the only true education is what one acquires for oneself. Yet may it not be permissible to point out the directions in which some of us have found acquaintance with the spirit of science and an appreciation of its broader significance.

It is just because there seems to be no place in our university where these broader aspects of science are considered that I feel the need for calling attention to them here. In particular a study of the history of the development of scientific thought is important. Its social significance in molding civilization is evident to those who have eyes to see. But the profound effect of social conditions in molding the development of science is a point rarely considered.

> "If I saw farther, 'twas because I stood
> On giant shoulders," wrote the king of thought,
> Too proud of his great line to slight the toils
> Of his forebears.

Thus Alfred Noyes describes Newton's attitude toward the work of his predecessors in science.[1] Let us with Newton look down and see the giant shoulders on which we stand.

Science has not gained its present position of pre-eminence without a struggle. In many times and places scientific activity has begun, only to die out. Why is it that we now find ourselves in a world in which science plays a controlling part? Perhaps this query can best be answered by tracing the history of the attempts at scientific development by the world's various civilizations, seeking to find the power back of the movements and why these movements died.

## THE ROLE OF CAUSALITY
## IN THE DEVELOPMENT OF SCIENCE

"Man's greatest discovery of all time is that he can count on the world in which he lives." This, in effect, was a statement made by Robert A. Millikan only a few years ago. And rightly. For is not the reliability of nature the very bedrock on which the structure of science is built?

Yet Werner Heisenberg, co-author of the uncertainty principle, writes:

> The resolution of the paradoxes of atomic physics can be accomplished only by further renunciation of old and cherished ideas. Most important of these is the idea that natural phenomena obey exact laws—the principle of causality.[2]

[1] From "Newton" in "Watchers of the Sky" in *Collected Poems* by Alfred Noyes. Copyright 1906, 1934 by Alfred Noyes. Published by J. B. Lippincott Company.
[2] Werner Heisenberg: *The Physical Principles of the Quantum Theory* (Chicago, Ill.: University of Chicago Press; 1930), p. 62.

| 83 |

Does this mean that science, with its continual searching for fundamentals, has finally undermined its own foundations?

It so happens that my own experiments were partly responsible for this dramatic reversal of the physicist's point of view, so I have naturally been interested in tracing what the significance of this change may be to human life and thought. Does this new doctrine affect in any way the hoary problem of man's freedom and morality in a world of law?

But first let me explain why the paradox of causality and freedom is of truly vital importance to the man of science. This can best be done by describing how the development of science has been affected by the answer to this problem. It makes one pause when one finds that a flourishing science was once dealt a death blow by the philosophers because it seemed to remove the basis of morality. Does our present science rest on any firmer foundation than that of the ancient Greeks?

In what follows I cannot pretend to give a critical discussion of these questions, for my acquaintance with the history of science is only that of an amateur. Yet perhaps the presentation of the point of view even of an amateur will at least suggest what kind of thing can be found by delving into the history of science.[3]

## SCIENCE IN THE ANCIENT OCCIDENT

Let us turn to a consideration of the rise and fall of science in the ancient Mediterranean countries. Frequently this is thought to be merely a corollary of the rise and fall of the political civilization. This is not so. Science was at its peak when Rome was young and had practically died out when the Eternal City was at the zenith of its power.

It would seem that physical science got its start from the practical necessity in Babylonia and Egypt of making land surveys. For this pur-

[3] Such studies have recently been made much easier by the publication of Sarton's monumental *Introduction to the History of Science,* which deals chiefly with ancient and medieval science. I have myself found more useful Dampier-Whetham's *A History of Science* (1930) because he has related his science to the political conditions of the times with which he deals. Florian Cajori's *A History of Physics,* Henry Crew's *The Rise of Modern Physics,* and E. A. Burtt's *The Metaphysical Foundations of Modern Physical Science* all have much of value. One should also mention H. G. Wells's *The Outline of History.* Though he is criticized by historians on the ground that he has tried to read his own interpretation into his facts, he has at least treated more fairly than have most of his critics the place of the development of human thought. Finally, I must mention the epic poems of Alfred Noyes, who has shown in his "Watchers of the Sky" and *The Book of Earth* that the qualities of an appreciative scholar are not incompatible with poetic imagination of rare beauty.

pose in both countries there was developed very early a science of land measurement, or "geo-metry." There was also the need for standard weights and lengths, which were established in Babylon as early as twenty-five centuries B.C. Thus, as far as we can tell, science got its start in the coordination and standardization of common sense and industry. It would seem that this foundation, of application to practical problems, is the one sure basis that cannot fail to make science a permanent necessity of mankind.

Observations of the stars were also made at about the same time, and served as the basis for making a calendar—a year of 360 days in Egypt. It was found possible to predict eclipses. Starting doubtless with accidental coincidences, this led to the development of the attempt to predict from stellar motions the course of human affairs. This was astrology, developed highly by the Chaldeans who lived in the lower Euphrates valley. It was destined to play a role of great importance, both for good and evil, in human thought. The immediate effect of its popularity was to encourage priests to make permanent astronomical records literally over thousands of years, and to file them away in the temple archives. Whether the resulting superstition was responsibile for preventing development of any really scientific thought over this immense stretch of time one can only conjecture. In any case, when such scientific thought did arise in the Greek era, the records were available for making not only a highly precise calendar, but also for noting such comparatively obscure phenomena as the precession of the equinoxes.

As William Dampier points out:

> The idea that man's destiny was controlled by the stars, an idea which arose in early times in Babylon, led to the concept of an inexorable, inhuman Fate. Black magic and deadly nature indicated hostile gods, and in turn, doubtless the idea of hostile gods intensified the savage element in Babylonian magic and astrology. In a world dominated by such a gloomy religion, there was little opportunity for science or rational philosophy to develop.[4]

This Mesopotamian civilization was so highly cultured as to perform marvelous feats of building and irrigation engineering and to formulate the legal Code of Hammurabi, which has been the model not only for the Mosaic and the Roman law but also more distantly for British and American law. Yet this high civilization, running continuously over a period of two thousand years, failed to make any scientific advance beyond

[4] Sir William Cecil Dampier-Whetham: *A History of Science* (Cambridge, Eng.: The University Press; 1930), p. 5.

simple measurements and weighings. The idea of a reliable world whose laws might be learned and used to man's benefit had not yet dawned.

This example makes clear the necessity of appreciating something of the mental background—philosophy, if you please—of an age before we can understand its approach to nature.

## Mediterranean

It was in the sixth century before Christ that we find the dawn of the first era that was scientific in the modern sense. The Greeks were at this time dominant among the Mediterranean countries, and were just entering the classical age of Greek culture. The traditional polytheistic mythologies were gradually developing to the high monotheistic form with a supreme and righteous Zeus, which Plato later proclaimed.

The favored form of world view of the communities in which the first scientific activity developed was known as Orphism, which seems to have been imported from Egypt. According to this cult, in the beginning there was "a primordial night from which a world-egg appeared and divided into Heaven and Earth, representing the Father and Mother of Life. Between them flew the winged spirit of Light, sometimes called Eros, who joined the cosmic parents, from whose marriage sprang the Divine Son, Zeus. . . . In their higher forms Orphic ideas penetrated Greek idealistic philosophy and through it Christianity; in their lower forms, they passed into and reinforced every ignorant superstition for centuries." [5]

It was from a background of mysticism that Thales of Miletus came, the first Greek scientist of whom we have record. He and his colleagues proposed to themselves the definite question: "Of what, and in what way is the world made?" Though he could not get very far with his inquiry, its object is surprisingly close to that of much of present-day research in physical science. It marked at least the break away from belief in traditional authority.

Thales gained great reputation by predicting an eclipse, and is credited with the observation of both the electrical properties of rubbed amber and the magnetic properties of magnetite. Aristotle also credits him with originating the deductive geomery later developed by Euclid. The outstanding distinction of the school of Thales was its attempt to solve problems by rational deductions from the data of experience. He was thus the first of the great Greek philosophers, as well as the first scientist.

Pythagoras, the next important figure of Greek science, was on the other hand the first great exponent of experimental physics. According to Hera-

[5] Ibid., p. 13.

clitus, "he has practiced research and investigation more than all other men, and he has gathered his wisdom by doing things himself." He also came from an Orphic background, and though he saw the need of investigating nature he retained many of the mystical ideas of Orphism.

In physics perhaps his most important discoveries were in sound, where he discovered the simple numerical ratios of the lengths of vibrating strings under tension that give rise to the various musical intervals. Such a discovery could only have been made by experimental measurements. Not less striking was his astronomical work, in which he was the first to recognize that the earth is round, and that it is the earth's rotation that is responsible for day and night.

Philosophically, Pythagoras' teaching was very closely related to that of Buddha, who was teaching in India at the same time. Both taught the close relationship of men and animals, and observed for this reason strict vegetarianism. Both believed in the transmigration of souls, and both emphasized the virtues of self-discipline. Nevertheless, there was also a striking difference. Buddha's chief message was that man can free himself from all pain, trouble, and worry if he will only divest himself of all desire, for it is the failure to attain one's desires that causes the trouble. Though this to Buddha and his followers was a gospel of salvation, to us it is a counsel of death. It has certainly been a detriment to the ambition, scientific and otherwise, of the countries that have come under Buddha's influence.

Pythagoras, on the other hand, counseled a positive goodness, and became the center of a religious and political cult. The conflict between natural law and human freedom was not yet seen; but his efforts to spread the rule of reason and morality aroused the ire of the citizens of Crotona. In the words of Alfred Noyes, they cried, "Death to Pythagoras! Death to those who know!" Pythagoras himself was exiled, his school was scattered, and later many of his followers were killed.

In spite of this tragic end, the influence of Pythagorean thought on Greek philosophy was lasting. The spark of science had caught fire and could not easily be quenched. It should be remembered that it was not the objective of this early science to obtain knowledge with which to control nature. Rather, with increased knowledge of how things work, men hoped to learn whence they had come, and the purpose of life.

One answer to this problem was found by the atomists. Their early leader, Leucippus, stated the law of causality as clearly as any eighteenth-century mechanist: "Nothing happens without a cause, but everything with a cause and by necessity." The recognition of this principle, though it was soon to be lost sight of, is a landmark in human history.

In the words of Democritus, whose ideas were the most modern of any of the ancient scientists: "According to convention, there is a sweet and a bitter, a hot and a cold, and according to convention there is color. In truth there are atoms and a void." By this hypothesis he explained the difference between solids, liquids, and gases: "In stone or iron the atoms can only throb or oscillate, in air or fire they rebound to greater distances." According to Democritus also the motion of these particles persists unless opposed—Newton's first law of motion. This idea was so incredible to Aristotle that it was lost again until rediscovered by Galileo.

Democritus tried to account for too much by his atoms, however. Not only stones and air, but also life and thoughts, were thus supposed to be explained. Socrates and Plato found it easy to destroy the latter explanations and supposed that the whole idea must be wrong. Democritus had sound ideas, but his theories were too far ahead of his experiments and were therefore unconvincing to a skeptical philosopher. Though truths, they were not adequately tested truths and thus failed as true science. These atomic ideas, stopped for the time being by Plato, eventually passed on to Epicurus and Lucretius, thence over a span of centuries to Newton, and from him to Bernoulli and Clausius, who incorporated them into his kinetic theory of gases.

Then came that immortal trio, Socrates, Plato, and Aristotle. Though as philosophers they remain of the highest rank, from the standpoint of science Socrates and Plato, at least, must be considered as world calamities.* Except for them, it is not at all unlikely that science might have reached its present stage two thousand years ago. Let us see where the trouble lay.

Socrates was perhaps the first great skeptic. To him nothing should be accepted that could not be tested and proved. The test that it must pass, however, was the test of reason rather than that of experiment. To Socrates, who recognized that all knowledge comes to us through the mind, the mind was supreme and the world of nature must be interpreted in terms of logical mental processes. Thus it was natural for him to lead a reaction against the materialistic attitude of the atomists, who taught, following Leucippus, that all things follow definite law and, according to Democritus, that thought processes are a corollary of the movement of atoms. This led naturally to a thoroughly fatalistic attitude toward men's lives. Socrates saw that their mechanism left no room for that freedom of choice which is the basis of morality, whereas his reason told him that mind was the controlling factor in man's actions.

There can be no doubt that the logic of his position was sound. Because the atomists had tried to explain the whole world in terms of "atoms and a void," Socrates' destructive criticism caused an almost complete reaction against the materialistic attitude of the atomists, and made men lose sight of the fundamental truth back of Leucippus' doctrine of causality. Seeing that the mechanistic philosophy implied a world in which human effort could be of no avail, the Greek thinkers turned away from the science that led to such an impossible conclusion.

Plato, as Socrates' student, made effective use of his teacher's ideas. He developed an idealistic philosophy, based on the scientific data of Pythagoras and his successors, but with mind and reason as the ultimate authority. Thus while mathematics was highly prized, experiment was to him unworthy of a philosopher. He thus continued the antiscientific thought started by Socrates.

The great achievement of Plato was perhaps his insistence that *man is master of his own destiny*. This he develops at length in his *Republic*, in which he presents his vision of Utopia. It was a far cry from the attitude of two short centuries before, when men thought of their lives as being in the hands of the gods, whom they could control only by sacrifices, prayers, and mystic rites. Now a man stood out and said, with wide acceptance: "We can govern our lives as we will. In our own hands we have the forming of our destiny."

Such a change in world thought in so short a time can only be compared with the revolution in European thought at the time of the Renaissance. It had required first the vision of law in nature, glimpsed by Pythagoras and made the cornerstone of science by Leucippus, to break away from belief in a whimsical fate. Only then it became possible to see that man had some mastery over the world. This vision of course implied the effectiveness of human purpose, and thus led to the destruction of the scientific doctrine of causality that made possible its birth. With science thus undermined, man lost the tool by which he could carve out his destiny. Gradually, therefore, Plato's followers lost his great vision, and his own really excellent philosophy degenerated into a mystical form of idealism that sponsored every form of antiscientific magic and miracle.

It is doubtful whether the blow dealt by the philosophy of Plato and Socrates would itself have been sufficient to kill the scientific spirit. Their successor, Aristotle, though a poor physicist, was an excellent observer of animal life, and thus carried on in a diluted form something of the scientific tradition. But then came the military conquests of Alexander, in whose wake came easy intercourse between the East and the West. The immediate result was an influx of Chaldean magic, miracles, and astrology, and the mystic rites of Mythra. These mystical ideas fitted hand in glove with Plato's teachings, and led to a superrational idealism known as Neoplatonism. Gradually the new ideas spread as a cloud of poison gas over the Greek world, stifling scientific thought as it advanced.

For a brief period these Oriental ideas were held back by the revival of Democritus' atomic science in the form of Epicureanism and Stoicism. Both of these were essentially fatalistic in principle, basing their stand on a rigid law of causality. But the flood could not be held back for long.

Just before the deluge of antiscientific thought, in the more remote quarters of the Greek world, scientific activity was at its height. Towering among the physicists of all time was Archimedes, who lived in Sicily a century after Plato. To him we owe among other things the principle of hydrostatics that bears his name, and the laws of the lever and of pulleys. His method was strictly modern. The suggestion of the laws came from preliminary experiment. The laws were theoretically derived. Archimedes' principle was deduced from his conception of a fluid as being incapable of supporting any shearing stress. The law of the lever was derived from the principle of virtual work, which he considered axiomatic. Both derivations are identical in principle with the best derivations seen in today's textbooks. Finally, the predictions were tested by measurements designed for the purpose. No truer example of scientific establishment of a physical law is to be found anywhere. It was seventeen hundred years before Leonardo da Vinci, finding an old manuscript of Archimedes, revived the experimental method of approaching physical problems.

In the meantime, however, the physical science of astronomy was also making strides. To Aristarchus, an older contemporary of Archimedes who lived on the island of Samos, we owe the hypothesis "that the fixed stars and the sun remain unmoved, that the earth revolves around the sun on the circumference of a circle, the sun lying at the center of the orbit." He recognized that the sun was much larger than the earth. Eratosthenes measured the circumference of the earth with a result within four per cent of the now known value. Hipparchus, making use of old Babylonian records, measured the precession of the equinoxes, and measured to within 10 per cent the distance to the moon.

Ancient science had now passed its heyday. Men interested in learning the laws of nature became more and more rare as science was displaced by mysticism and credulity in all forms of miracles and magic. By the beginning of the Christian era the light of science had gone out. Science slept for a thousand years, anesthetized by philosophy, religion, and magic. Why had the light of science failed? It was a quest undertaken to help guide man on his way. Its apparent denial of the effectiveness of purpose showed its uselessness. Science had failed to illumine man's path of life.

## ORIENTAL SCIENCE

Having thus traced the rise and fall of science in ancient Europe, let us see if we can find at least a tentative explanation of the failure of the great Oriental civilizations to develop any systematic body of science.

## China

Of Chinese history we in the West are comparatively ignorant. According to tradition, however, a court minister of the first century after Christ, Ts'ai Lun by name, invented both paper and the art of block printing in order to disseminate the edicts of his emperor. Somewhere near the same time the mariner's compass was invented and, not long after, gunpowder. Such a series of important developments shows that the Chinese must have always had the same ingenuity and adaptability for practical knowledge that we see today among our Chinese students. Why then have they not developed a science?

Perhaps here again the philosophical background of Chinese thought supplies an answer. Nowhere in the world is the belief in spirits and devils, who exercise a controlling influence on men's thoughts, more prevalent than in China. Man's destiny is thus in the hands of a whimsical fate. Nor have leaders of Chinese thought done much to dispel these ideas. While Pythagoras was starting the Greeks on the road to science, Confucius was preaching a similar doctrine of self-control to the Chinese. But Confucius was not interested in the origin of the world, nor would he soil his hands in trying things for himself. Confucius' doctrine of self-control seems to have come from an idealistic background, somewhat like that of Plato. Man's mind was supreme, and man could make of his life what he would. In Greece this attitude was detrimental to the science that was struggling for a start. In China science had not got a foothold, and with Confucius' philosophy of life there was little incentive for scientific speculation.

In later days, in China, the slogan was always: "Back to the classic learning of the Golden Age." Knowledge consisted of acquainting oneself with what Confucius and the ancients taught. This again is undoubtedly connected with the very deep-seated belief in ancestor worship, which would tend to exalt ancient learning above anything that one might find for oneself.

## India

Hindu civilization was already old and traditionalized when Pythagoras was teaching in Europe. We have already noted how at the same time

Gautama Buddha was spreading his doctrine in India. His listeners had come as far away from belief in devils and magic as had those of Pythagoras. But the Hindu mind has always been of a too unworldly nature to bother itself seriously with hard facts. We have already called attention to Buddha's doctrine of avoiding desire, i.e., contentment with the present state. The whole import of his teaching is that the soul of a man is all-important and his body and all the material world should be kept in the background as much as possible.

Add to this teaching the age-old Hindu doctrine that the supreme good is to lose oneself in a contemplation of the Absolute, and you have people living in a world in which earthly things appear of negligible importance. Why then bother with developing a science that deals wholly with things of this world?

In spite of these handicaps some valuable work has come from India. Our so-called Arabic numerals are of Hindu origin. Medicine, the divine art of healing, was raised to a relatively high state. In chemistry, the discovery of oxygen long before the days of Lavoisier may perhaps have been a by-product of alchemy. In physics I am not acquainted with any notable achievements. Even in the sciences mentioned the work was sporadic. The atmosphere, like that of Greek philosophy, was such as to smother the spirit of scientific inquiry.

## ISLAMIC SCIENCE

It is of especial interest to consider the rise and fall of science in the Mohammedan countries, whose background of ancient learning is similar to our own. [*The remainder of this talk appears in Mr. Compton's notebook in the form of an outline, which is not repeated here. Within a few weeks Mr. Compton returned to the same theme of causality, writing out in detail the ideas represented in the outline. The appropriate sections of these notes are printed below to complete the contemporary statement of Mr. Compton's views. It is probable, however, that the following ideas were somewhat condensed when presented to the Physics Club.*]

About the year A.D. 800, Greek literature came into the possession of Arabic writers. The Sultan Harun al-Rashid, whom you will remember from the *Arabian Nights*, gathered around him a court of learned men who were stimulated to translate these Greek accounts into Arabic. These translations led the Arabians to revive the science of the Greeks and to develop it to a high stage. In their hands astronomy, alchemy, algebra, optics, and medicine developed and thrived. During this period Arabia was carrying the torch of culture.

Gradually, however, the religious leaders became worried. One of the primary tenets of the Mohammedan religion is the supremacy of Allah and the belief that, whatever may happen, in the end everything will come out according to the will of Allah. The religious leaders thus feared the study of science because it encouraged disbelief. The central argument was that the study of science leads to the view that all things happen because of a regular pattern of cause and effect, according to which God himself would be helpless to bring about the events he might desire.

Eventually, in the twelfth century, a decree was issued that science could not be taught "because it leads away from belief in God." Islam soon ceased to be a leader of civilization. The decline in Arabian civilization has frequently been attributed to the impact of warlike tribes on Islam. But as one reads the accounts of students of Mohammedanism, one sees clearly that it was rather a result of the religious, philosophical, and scientific thinking that the initiative of the country declined.

## MODERN SCIENCE

Only in the outskirts of the Mohammedan world did remnants of their culture continue. In Spain Aristotle's science was taken up and transmitted by Averroës and by the Jewish philosophers, especially Maimonides. Perhaps it was first through Spain that the torch of science was passed to Christian Europe, where it lit a flickering flame. The Western world during the first thousand years of the Christian era had been almost completely under the influence of Platonic philosophy. This served as a background not only for Neoplatonism, but also for the Christianity developed by the early fathers.

As it gradually filtered into Western civilization, science again became a stimulus to thought. It was Thomas Aquinas who, during the thirteenth century, set himself the heroic task of fitting this new knowledge into the religious teaching of the day. "*Scientia et religio ex uno fonte,*" was the motto, and with it came renewed interest in knowing the world of nature, for thus one might learn regarding the works of his Creator. Also prominent among those who early saw the need for firsthand inquiry into nature's secrets were Roger Bacon, Leonardo, Copernicus, Tycho Brahe, Kepler, and Galileo. The early scientific societies, such as the Royal Society of London, stimulated scientific discussion and experiment.

## Newtonian science and the philosopher's dilemma

Then came Isaac Newton, who found that his world fell in order as he

| 93 |

applied the simple laws of motion and gravitation that he had devised. Science had succeeded in explaining things that had puzzled the world for ages, and in this explanation everything obeyed exact laws. The effect of this achievement of Newton on men's view of their world was tremendous. Burtt describes graphically the attitude which came to be accepted as the "scientific viewpoint":

> The world that people had thought themselves living in—a world rich with colour and sound, redolent with fragrance, filled with gladness, love and beauty, speaking everywhere of purposive harmony and creative ideals—was crowded now into minute corners in the brains of scattered organic beings. The really important world outside was a world hard, cold, colourless, silent, and dead; a world of quantity, a world of mathematically computable motions in mechanical regularity.[6]

After two thousand years men had returned to the doctrine of Democritus: "According to convention there is a sweet and a bitter, a hot and a cold, and according to convention there is color. In truth there are atoms and a void."

If a given cause always produces the same effect—a fundamental assumption of Newtonian science—our every action is a necessary consequence of the conditions in which we find ourselves. Consciousness may keep us informed of what is going on, but our purposes must be ineffective; for if they altered the course of events it would imply that the physical result was not really determined by the initial cause. Thus logically we are forced to accept the position of a wheel geared to a great machine, over whose operation we have not the slightest control. The great school of French mathematicians that followed Newton—Laplace, Lagrange, D'Alembert, and others—accepted this mechanistic view completely.

And yet, did the force of this logic lead scientific men to a hopelessly fatalistic attitude? By no means. Though the logic was there, the exigencies of daily life made them adopt the working assumption that effort is after all worthwhile. As a result they have built up the foundation on which our present science and civilization rests.

History seems to show that men must pass through such a stage of mechanism, which reduces human effort to a meaningless concourse of atoms, and takes away all basis for morality, in order that they should see that such a philosophy cannot describe the really significant things of human life. As when Socrates pilloried the atomists, so again Leibnitz, Berkeley, and Kant reacted against the too easy materialism of Hobbes

[6] Edwin Arthur Burtt: *The Metaphysical Foundations of Modern Physical Science* (New York: Harcourt, Brace and Company, Inc.; 1925), pp. 236–7.

and Laplace and Voltaire. Their analysis of the problem made logically untenable the position that man is a machine; yet it was no longer possible to laugh science out of court. Men had too much common sense to abandon again the great truths that science had given. If nature was one unbroken chain of law, they would learn that law to master nature and let the philosophers worry about the fact that the strife for mastery is meaningless to a man who is merely a link in this unbroken chain.

For the past two centuries the man of science has thus of necessity blinded himself to the logical inconsistency of his position. He must have faith that his world is one of law, else it seemed his searching for truth must be in vain. He must not pause to consider that if his own actions are "with a cause and by necessity" he cannot in truth "make a search" at all.

## The laws of nature are not exact

Now, Heisenberg tells us, science must abandon its cherished law of causality. Nature does not obey exact laws.

This is a revolution of the first magnitude, overturning what we have considered the very foundation of science. But it is not the first revolution that science has undergone in recent years. There have been minor insurrections during the past generation. First there was the finding that our world of things is a world of discrete particles. Following Thomson, Rutherford, and Einstein, we replaced Democritus' atoms with electrons and protons and photons; but we must adjust our ideas to the concept that things are not what they seem: "In reality there are atoms and a void." Then came Einstein with his theories of relativity. Time and space, he told us, are much the same kind of thing. And space is itself curved. Could we receive any worse jolt?

Yet these were relatively minor revolutions. They had not affected the fundamentals of science itself. But if things do not obey exact laws, what basis is left for science?

At first we supposed that the excessively minute particles into which the world of nature has been resolved would obey the same laws as those that Newton and his followers had found to apply to planets and projectiles. These laws had never been tested on so minute a scale, and they were now found to fail the test. Photons and electrons and protons were found to move like waves; ordinary particles have nothing wavelike about them, however. Our efforts to understand the properties of these tiny bits of matter accordingly led to confusion.

Then came Heisenberg, while a student at Göttingen, with the key that unlocked the door. "Let us not read into these particles," he said, "the properties that we find in the ordinary things around us, but content our-selves with noting how they act, and with describing these actions in a systematic manner." At once the atmosphere cleared. We had supposed that the electrons must revolve in orbits within the atoms; now we found that these orbits were a gratuitous assumption. We really had no evidence that such orbits existed. But more startling was the fact that when an attempt was made to predict where any electron would be at any future moment, it was learned that however much we might know about its position and motion now, its position at a time in the future could not be accurately foretold. We might predict the average of many trials; but no conceivable physical experiment could tell us just where a particular elec-tron would be at a definite future time. That is, the laws of the new physics cannot predict an event; they tell only the chance of its occurrence.

## The uncertainty of ordinary events

Does this mean that within the atom the law of causality is no longer valid? It means rather that no physical experiment can test this principle on an atomic scale. One might still retain the principle as a postulate, supposing there are some qualities of photons and electrons which our experiments cannot reveal. If these qualities cannot be revealed by ex-periment, however, it makes no experimental (i.e., physical) difference whether they exist or not. Thus, it is as a *physical* principle that the law of causality must be abandoned. The philosopher may retain the ideas applied to things-in-themselves if he so desires; but he cannot refer to experiment for its verification.

Of course, every scientific principle is to be considered a *working* principle, in the sense that it is always subject to revision. Einstein, whose relativity theory is the spiritual ancestor of the new quantum mechanics, and who has himself helped in developing the principle of uncertainty, has recently expressed doubts regarding its ultimate validity. He frankly dislikes a world the laws of which are not exact. Yet the younger genera-tion of physicists considers this principle an inescapable consequence of existing data, and a powerful tool for unraveling the mysteries of atomic physics. Heisenberg's case has been made so convincing that I myself should consider it more likely that the principle of the conservation of energy or the second law of thermodynamics would be found faulty than that we should return to a system of strict causality.

We should not think of this lack of exactness as a loss to science. Heisenberg has shown that if the principle of causality is replaced by his principle of uncertainty, all those paradoxes of atomic physics that have been classed as "quantum phenomena" find a ready solution. This includes such things as the photoelectric effect and the emission of light. Nor has the classical dynamics of projectiles or planets been in any way affected. Science has indeed gained by introducing this flexibility into its most cherished law of cause and effect.

How then, if these elementary events are erratic in their outcome, can we account for the consistency of the world as we ordinarily observe it? The problem is very similar to that of the toss of a coin. Though we cannot predict the result of a single throw, if we throw the coin a million times, half the throws will probably come heads up to within a tenth of a percent.

One's shoes as one stands on the floor are supported by myriads of collisions with the molecules of the wood. Each of these molecules is in turn made of many electrons and protons. We have therefore to consider the average of a very large number of elementary events. Though any one of the individual processes may be unpredictable, the support resulting from the whole system of events becomes so nearly certain that the possibility of any alternative other than support by the floor is negligible. Thus a determinate effect may result from the average of many indeterminate events.

On the other hand, this indeterminacy of the elementary events makes certain types of large-scale physical phenomena unpredictable in terms of the initial conditions.

Professor Ralph Lillie [7] has pointed out that the deliberate actions of living organisms are events of just this kind. Such events are determined directly by certain nerve pulses, which are presumably electrochemical reactions on a minute scale. Our deliberative processes are probably associated with similar reactions, each involving a rather small number of molecules, and hence having an appreciable uncertainty. The sensation which starts the nerve pulse may itself be initiated by a small number of elementary events, such as a dozen photons of light entering the eye. The living organism thus acts as an amplifier of very great power, which may be set in operation by events on a scale comparable with the elementary events that we know to be indeterminate. Considering the complexity of the small-scale events associated with any of our deliberate acts, one may say with assurance that on a purely physical basis the end result must have a relatively great uncertainty.

As far as the physics of the question is concerned, however, though the action of an individual organism is not definitely determined, its behavior should obey certain laws of probability. There is not necessarily any suggestion here of an ability of the organism to choose a course of action.

[7] "Physical Indeterminism and Vital Action," *Science*, XLVI: 1702 (August 12, 1927), 139–44.

Such an indeterminateness may correspond merely to its lack of skill. There is nevertheless strong evidence that such nonphysical things as thoughts and motives are effective in determining the individual actions of men and animals.

Several years ago an Indian friend guided us along the streets of Agra, and through a noble archway, whence before us we saw the incomparable Taj Mahal, glistening like a Titan jewel in the noonday sun. We waited and watched as the evening glow painted its marble minarets a rosy hue, and came back later to see the moon's silver light reflected from its pearly dome. Never before had I appreciated that architecture could produce an emotional reaction like that from the music of a great organ skillfully played.

Physically speaking, a pile of stones in a quarry is infinitely more probable than the same stones built into a Taj Mahal, though both are possible. Humanly speaking, it is the wishes of a king, the creative enthusiasm of an architect, and the skillful work of the artisans, all working within the limits of physical law, which determine that the stones must assume the form of a beautiful building, a lasting monument to human love.

The behaviorist school of psychologists has learned much regarding our mental processes, using the assumption that every action of an intelligent organism is determined by its previous history and the conditions in which it finds itself. Yet the behaviorists would themselves be the last to claim that their studies have established the law of causality in those actions which involve deliberation. The architect of the Taj would certainly have insisted that he was free to design the building as he pleased, within the limits imposed by mechanics and the dictates of contemporaneous architectural practice.

If physics were all, we should now be tempted to favor the view that the world we live in is indeed a world of chance. This is not, however, demanded by the physical evidence, and is negated by the very effectiveness of human purpose. Most persons would agree that their ability to determine a course of action according to their motives is an experimental fact. Those who deny such freedom of choice do so primarily because of its conflict with the supposed uniformity of the physical world. We have just seen, however, that modern physics suggests instead nonuniformity of action as the rule for a complex physical organism such as man.

## Is freedom consistent with present-day physics?

Granting then that a man can choose his own course of action, is there any way in which his physically undetermined actions may be determined by nonphysical means, without violating the laws of the physical world?

In order to interpret men's actions, it appears desirable to assume that the substance of our brains may occur in conditions which though physically indistinguishable nevertheless correspond to distinguishable states of consciousness. Thus we may assume that we are directly conscious of certain thoughts, corresponding to a particular state of certain brain activity, whereas physical tests would at best be able to determine only the statistical probability of this state. It seems to me necessary to make some such assumption if consciousness is to be of any value to the organism.

It would be easy to outline a scheme whereby consciousness could select the desirable brain current, even though the undesirable one might be equally probable from statistical considerations, thus leading to the performance of the desirable act rather than its alternative. There is, however, no need to suppose that intervention of consciousness should modify the laws of conservation of energy and momentum as applied to the atoms of the brain. A favoring of one possible path instead of another so as to alter the statistical distribution of the motion of the particles in the brain current is all that would be necessary. We should thus find that where the physical conditions are not sufficient to demand a definite result, such nonphysical things as desire or purpose would give a greater definiteness to the organism's actions. In fact, it is possible from the physical standpoint that if all data of consciousness as well as of mechanics were known, our actions might again prove to be determined. We should again find ourselves machines, but with our thoughts and motives as essential parts of the mechanism.

Kant had an avenue of escape from the dilemma of freedom in a world of law. He postulated a nonphysical world of things-in-themselves, related to the phenomenal world with which we are familiar, but regarding which the phenomena of nature give no information. According to Kant, although the phenomenal world follows the laws of causality, which outlaw freedom, things-in-themselves are not bound by causality, and in this world the organism is free.

To the modern physicist the situation is reversed. He finds that the principle of causality does not apply in the physical (phenomenal) world. If we wish to retain any exact relation between cause and effect, we must postulate a world, related to the physical world but regarding which experiment gives us no information, in which the events may be determined. In such a nonphysical world motives and thoughts may play a determining part, while in the physical world, in which such things remain unnoticed, events appear to follow the laws of chance. The new physics does not suggest a solution of the old question of *how* mind acts on matter. It does definitely, however, admit the possibility of such an action, and suggests where the action may take effect. Perhaps this seems to be a small gain, since some modification of physical processes by consciousness is still necessary if consciousness is to be effective in controlling the action of an organism. Yet in making this supposition we are no longer violating any fundamental principle of science, as was the case when science declared that all things happen "with a cause and by necessity."

## MAN THE MASTER OF HIS OWN DESTINY

Nature is thus not altogether reliable. Does this mean that the foundations of science are being shaken? Not at all. If we mean by science the organized body of tested truth, such tested truths are eternally reliable. By gaining a more complete knowledge of her definite aspects and learning the statistical probability of her uncertain actions we can still use nature as our servant.

We hesitate even to suggest that the unreliability observed in the world of nature is a defect. For it seems that some degree of uncertainty, such as the physicist has recently found, is necessary if such nonphysical things as thoughts and motives are to have any relation to the physical world. Without this flexibility in physical law, it is very doubtful whether there could be an organic evolution, with its incessant struggle for life. It is, in short, only because the world in a physical sense is *not* wholly reliable that it can have any human meaning.

Plato viewed man as master of destiny, but an unfortunate twist of his philosophy took from man the tools of science by which that mastery might be attained. Newton found the tools again, but his followers interpreted his science so as to make us lose the vision. Now, if we will but raise our eyes, the vision of man as master of his destiny is once more opened to view. The way is at last clear for us to work with courage and faith toward such a goal.

# 7. The World of Science in the Late Eighteenth Century and Today

## 1956

In commemoration of the 250th anniversary of the birth of Benjamin Franklin, the American Philosophical Society, which he founded, devoted a portion of its 1956 general meeting to papers dealing with Franklin's various activities. As scientific writings and inventions were among Franklin's great achievements, Arthur Compton was invited to interpret the relation of the spirit of Franklin to the science of today. In his talk, presented on April 19, Mr. Compton first reviewed Franklin's study of electricity and then discussed the development of Newtonian mechanics and its implications for reshaping man's outlook on the world.

It is my privilege to speak about the world of science in the late eighteenth century and today. It is evident that those who arranged our program did not want a catalogue of scientific achievements. Rather, they have asked us to consider the setting in which science was studied when Benjamin Franklin was doing his important work.

I shall discuss this matter in two ways, first by telling something of the relation of Benjamin Franklin's studies of electricity to other similar investigations before and after his time. Then I want to draw attention to the development of mechanics, which during the eighteenth century was the main line of professional physics research. Galileo, Newton, and Laplace replaced Aristotle's view of the world as a God-impelled system with that of a world of material objects moving and acting according to simple mechanical laws. Our century has now replaced their deterministic world-machine with a new system where again physics permits us to suppose that events have human meaning.

It is this century's development of the understanding of the electricity that Franklin was studying which has been largely responsible for shaking the foundations of the mechanics that Franklin's contemporaries believed

| 101 |

they were establishing so firmly. Thus the studies of eager amateurs such as Franklin, carried on with a burning interest in finding new truth, have added greatly to our knowledge of nature.

We may think of Franklin as the prototype of the typical American scientist and engineer—the enthusiastic, resourceful, and ingenious searcher for new facts and relationships, who relies largely upon others for their systematic elucidation but is alert to put the new knowledge to useful work. Closely parallel would be the relation of Michelson and Morley's famous experiment to Einstein's relativity theory, or the discovery and application of thermoelectricity by Thomas Edison and Lee DeForest to its electron interpretation by J. J. Thomson and O. W. Richardson.

## BENJAMIN FRANKLIN AND THE UNDERSTANDING OF ELECTRICAL PHENOMENA

Let me then first indicate the relation of Franklin's study of electricity to that of others working in the same field. Franklin began his experiments in 1746 at the age of forty, and continued his most active investigation of electrical phenomena for about seven years. During this period he found his experiments of the most engrossing interest. "For my own part," he writes in his first letter to Peter Collinson, Fellow of the Royal Society at London, "I never was before engaged in any study that so totally engrossed my attention as this has lately done." He ceased his studies, as so many others have been forced to do, because of the demands of responsible citizenship, when he went to England to represent the American colonies.

Franklin stepped into a field of study that was of very live interest among amateurs in science but was for the most part thought of as a novel form of parlor entertainment. The professional physicists of the day were concentrating their attention on the elaboration of Newton's principles of mechanics and on the development of precision astronomical instruments or were exploring quantitatively the phenomena of heat. One reads of the Burgomaster of Danzig's lighting with an electric spark a candle that he had just blown out, and of igniting alcohol vapor by sparks drawn from an electrified jet of water. People lined up to receive the jolt of an electric discharge. It would seem that the appearance of improved machines for producing frictional electricity was a profitable business chiefly because of orders from those for whom these experiments were a fascinating hobby. One is reminded of the development of shortwave radio a generation ago by enthusiastic amateurs who were working in an area discarded by the professionals as of negligible importance.

It is, however, true that some of this amateur work was of strictly high scientific merit. Thus Stephen Gray in 1729 reported in the *Philosophical Transactions* of the Royal Society a series of systematic experiments on all kinds of materials to see which ones were insulators and which conductors. The effects of frictional electricity he found could be transmitted up to 765 feet over wires supported by silk thread. Also Charles François du Fay, of Paris, reported during the years 1733–7 a series of observations in which he established the existence of two kinds of electricity. The account of his results as reported in the *Philosophical Transactions* for 1734 is worth repeating:

> Chance has thrown in my way another Principle, more universal and remarkable . . . and which casts a new Light on the Subject of Electricity. This Principle is, that there are two distinct Electricities, very different from one another; one of which I call *vitreous Electricity* and the other *resinous Electricity*. The first is that of Glass, Rock-Crystal, Precious Stones, Hair of Animals, Wool, and many other Bodies. The second is that of Amber, Copal, Gum-Lack, Silk, Thread, Paper, and a vast Number of other Substances. The Characteristick of these two Electricities is, that a Body of the *vitreous Electricity*, for example, repels all such as are of the same Electricity; and on the contrary, attracts all those of the resinous Electricity.[1]

One of the developments that attracted Franklin's early interest was the Leyden jar. It was a clergyman of Pomerania, E. G. von Kleist, who seems first to have noticed by accident the properties of what we now call an electrical condenser. The phenomenon was, however, first reported to the French Academy of Sciences in 1746 as a letter from Musschenbroek of Leyden, communicated by the distinguished naturalist, Ferchault de Réaumur. As translated by Professor A. Wolf of London, a portion of this letter will give a sense of the level at which such experiments were being done:

> I wish to report to you a new but terrible experiment, which I advise you on no account to attempt yourself. . . . I was carrying out some researches on the force of electricity; for that purpose I had suspended by two cords of blue silk, an iron gun-barrel, *AB*, which was receiving electricity by conduction from a glass globe which was being rapidly rotated on its axis, and rubbed meantime by the application of the hands. From the other end, *B*, there hung freely a brass wire, the end of which was immersed in a round glass vessel *D*, partly filled with water, which I was holding in my right hand *F*, while, with the other hand *E*, I tried to draw sparks from the electrified gun-barrel. Suddenly my right

[1] *Philosophical Transactions*, XXXVIII, 258.

hand, *F*, was struck with such violence that my whole body was shaken as by a thunderbolt. The vessel, although made of thin glass, does not break as a rule, and the hand is not displaced by this disturbance, but the arm and the whole body are affected in a terrible manner which I cannot express; in a word, I thought it was all up with me.[2]

One Dutch physicist, writing shortly afterward, states that this effect was first noted by a man named Cunaeus, a wealthy amateur, living in Leyden. It was William Watson, a Fellow of the Royal Society, who in 1748 described a modification of the Leyden jar, with metal lining inside and out, essentially the form that is still used.

Franklin obtained from England one of the best frictional electrical machines that was then made, and began his experiments at Philadelphia. He described his results in letters to Peter Collinson, a London merchant through whom he had obtained the electrical equipment. One of his earlier letters (Letter III) gives his interpretation of the action of the Leyden jar in terms of his "one-fluid" theory of electricity. As he explains:

> At the same time that the wire and top of the bottle, &c. is electrised *positively* or *plus*, the bottom of the bottle is electrised *negatively* or *minus*, in exact proportion: *i.e.* whatever quantity of electrical fire is thrown in at the top, an equal quantity goes out of the bottom.[3]

By way of commentary he writes some years later to Collinson expressing some of his "Opinions and Conjectures concerning the Properties and Effects of the electrical Matter, arising from Experiments and Observations, made at Philadelphia, 1749." He writes:

> Thus common matter is a kind of spunge to the electrical fluid. . . . But in common matter there is (generally) as much of the electrical as it will contain within its substance. If more is added, it lies without upon the surface, and forms what we call an electrical atmosphere; and then the body is said to be electrified.[4]

Franklin's idea of a single electrical fluid stimulated other hypotheses, such as the two-fluid theory suggested by Robert Symmer in 1759. The result was further active experiments. It was not possible, however, to suggest any true difference that might be expected to appear according to the two alternative hypotheses.

Franklin's fame as a scientist arose chiefly from his identification of

---

[2] A. Wolf: *A History of Science, Technology, and Philosophy in the Eighteenth Century* (New York: The Macmillan Company; 1939), pp. 222–3.
[3] Cf. I. Bernard Cohen: *Benjamin Franklin's Experiments* (Cambridge, Mass.: Harvard University Press; 1941), p. 180.
[4] Ibid., pp. 213, 214.

lightning as an electrical phenomenon. This was not a new suggestion. Thus, among others, Isaac Newton, thirty-three years earlier, had described the audible sparks that can be drawn from a body electrified by friction, and compared them with lightning and thunder. What Franklin did was first to show one after another that the effects of electric sparks are identical in kind with those of lightning. He then gave convincing direct evidence by his kite experiment, as described in his Letter XI addressed to Peter Collinson in 1752:

> As soon as any of the thunder clouds come over the kite, the pointed wire will draw the electric fire from them, and the kite, with all the twine, will be electrified, and the loose filaments of the twine will stand out every way, and be attracted by an approaching finger. And when the rain has wet the kite and twine, so that it can conduct the electric fire freely, you will see it stream out plentifully from the key on the approach of your knuckle. At this key, the phial may be charged; and from electric fire thus obtained, spirits may be kindled, and all the other electric experiments be performed, which are usually done by the help of a rubbed glass globe or tube, and thereby the sameness of the electric matter with that of lightning completely demonstrated.[5]

Franklin's practical mind turned to the use of sharp-pointed conductors as lightning rods for protection of buildings. His writings show that he was well acquainted with the conditions needed to make these rods effective. Quite independently and at almost the same time the use of pointed conductors as lightning rods was being tried in Moravia by Father Procopius Diviš.

In passing it is worthy of note that the use of persons in these electrical experiments was not primarily for dramatic or entertainment effect. The fact was that the sensation of a shock was the most sensitive means then known for detecting the electrification of a charged condenser. The intensity of the shock was a rough measure of the degree of electrification. Similarly, a low-capacity spark was most readily detected by the ignition of alcohol vapor.

While Franklin was engaged upon these and other electrical experiments, a group of European experimenters (Wilcke, Canton, and Aepinus) discovered electrical induction. Qualitatively the chief phenomena of electrostatics were now known. The next stage was that of placing the knowledge of electricity on a quantitative basis. In this phase of the study the work of Joseph Priestley, Henry Cavendish, and Charles Augustin Coulomb was outstanding.

[5] Ibid., p. 266.

The use of balls of cork or pith suspended on thread had been long used as a means of observing electrification. Franklin, at this time living in England, told Priestley, who was twenty-seven years his junior, of an unpublished experiment that he had tried.[6] This was an attempt to electrify a pair of cork balls suspended *inside* a metal vessel. He had been unable to detect any effect on the balls when the vessel was charged. To Priestley, familiar with the consequences of the inverse-square law of force as developed in the theory of gravitational phenomena, this was a very suggestive result. He accordingly repeated Franklin's experiment, using a pair of pith balls hanging entirely within a tin quart cup. The very slight effects that were caused when the cup was electrified or discharged he explained as a result of using a vessel that was not completely closed. Thus Priestley asked the question, "May we not infer from this experiment, that the attraction of electricity is subject to the same laws with that of gravitation, and is therefore according to the squares of the distances?"

Such were the first suggestions of the famous experiment carried out in a more refined manner by Cavendish, which remains today as our chief reliance for accepting the inverse-square law of force between electrical charges. Cavendish enclosed an insulated metal ball, 12.1 inches in diameter, inside a pair of hinged conducting hemispheres. Having charged the hemispheres, he connected them momentarily to the sphere inside, and then removed the enclosing conductor. Using a pith-ball electroscope, he was unable to detect any charge on the inner metal sphere. If this result was exactly true, he reasoned that the repulsion between like electric charges must follow precisely an inverse-square law of force. From the precision of his experiments he concluded that the exponent must lie between 1.98 and 2.02. James Clerk Maxwell, who long afterward published this work of Cavendish, repeated the experiment with sufficient precision to reduce the uncertainty to one part in forty thousand.

Not knowing of this work of Cavendish, Coulomb in 1784 arrived at the same result by the more direct means of measuring the force between two pith balls similarly charged. Using his newly developed torsion balance, he compared directly the force between the balls when separated at different distances. Coulomb also performed an experiment similar to that of Cavendish, but with less refinement, from which he also correctly concluded that in an electrified conductor the charge does not penetrate the interior. It was these experiments of Coulomb that gave the basis for the subsequent mathematical development of electrostatic theory.

[6] Cf. A. Wolf: *A History of Science* . . . , p. 242.

To complete the story of electricity as known during the eighteenth century we must refer to the well-known work of Luigi Galvani at Bologna and of Alessandro Volta at Pavia. It is noteworthy that Galvani was engaged in a systematic study of the effect of electrical impulses in causing contraction of animal muscle. It was accidental that he had a frog leg in contact with both iron and brass when about 1780 he made his famous discovery, but it was because he was alert to the convulsive effects of electric discharges that the contractions of his frog legs appeared significant. Nor was it thus surprising that he should have recognized the contractions as an electrical phenomenon. The fact that Galvani ascribed the effect mistakenly to electricity in the animal organism did not prevent the very fruitful development of his observation.

It was Volta who correctly identified the galvanic current as a flow of electricity arising from the contact of the two dissimilar metals. The electrical nature of the current he demonstrated by use of a condenser of widely variable capacity and an electrometer of greatly improved sensitivity that he had invented. Then in 1800, at the close of the century, by means of his voltaic pile the potential differences became large enough that all kinds of electrical phenomena could be readily produced. Animal electricity had no part in such experiments. Electricity could now be made to flow in a continuous current. The way was open for the study of electrodynamics, which was carried on so effectively during the nineteenth century and was to affect so greatly our whole picture of the physical world.

I have spent this time on the development of our understanding of electricity during the eighteenth century because it was in this field that Benjamin Franklin made his most important contributions to science. He also added to our understanding of radiant heat, meteorology, hydrodynamics, and many other aspects of science. But time will not permit me to discuss this work if I am to tell in a balanced way what the world of science in the late eighteenth century was like. In concentrating on the subject of electricity we have seen how one man contributed to an important new field of knowledge and stimulated its rapid development. As noted before, however, this was not the field where most of the great scientists of Franklin's day were devoting their efforts.

## DEVELOPMENT OF NEWTONIAN MECHANICS

Isaac Newton died when Benjamin Franklin was twenty-one years old. It was Newton's great generalizations regarding mechanics and gravitation, formulated in his *Philosophiae Naturalis Principia Mathematica* of

1687, that continued during the eighteenth century as the focus of attention for the professors of natural philosophy. D'Alembert's Principle, Maupertuis' formulation of the principle of least action, Lagrange's use of generalized coordinates in his elegant statement of the laws of mechanics, and Laplace's application of these principles to the stability of the solar system in his *Mécanique Céleste:* studies such as these occupied the chief scholarly scientific thought of the period, especially on the continent of Europe.

At this distance it is difficult to appreciate the importance attached to the development of mechanics in reshaping man's outlook on the world. The change that was going on was from a Ptolemaic description of the universe to a Copernican system, which was in turn simply interpreted according to the laws of mechanics. It was Laplace's work, published from 1796 to 1805, that put the finishing touches on this development with a completeness that carried full conviction as to its truth. Why did this seem so important?

The answer lies in the world view accepted by Europe in the Middle Ages. In its essence this view was not so much Christian as it was Aristotelian, but it had become basic to the thinking of scholars in both the Christian and the Islamic lands. As far as my reading goes, it appears that until the time of Galileo, this Aristotelian interpretation of order in the world was universally accepted by Western scholars. The new mechanics completely undermined this view. According to the older system, order in the universe was maintained by the continual free action of a God on whose wisdom and generally beneficent attitude one could rely. Now order in the universe was seen to follow as a necessary result of simple and immutable properties of matter. The world was thus indifferent to the needs that man might feel. It was the firm establishment of this revised point of view that was the great accomplishment of the natural philosophers of the eighteenth century. Because Aristotle's physics had been incorporated so implicitly in Christian and Islamic thought, this revolution in mechanics meant that the whole idea of God had to be thought through again from the beginning. Those of little faith dropped religion as being inconsistent with science. Those who knew the basic realities of religion from their own experience sought a framework for religion that was consistent with science.

The central difficulty was simple but fundamental. According to Aristotle the normal state of undisturbed matter is that of rest. When motion was observed it implied a cause. For animals and man the cause of their own motion was their volition. Similarly the stars were kept moving in their courses by the God of the universe. The reliability of God's will was demonstrated by the great regularity of these motions.

Even in Copernicus' writings and those of Kepler there is nothing to disturb this point of view. Only now it is the earth instead of the sun that moves with regularity. God is still the Prime Mover.

The revolution against this view was started by Galileo when he postulated that a body would continue in uniform motion unless acted upon by some force. No longer was a Mover needed to keep the body in motion. The next big step was taken when Newton showed that if gravitation between bodies followed an inverse-square law of force, the motion of the planets was just what was to be expected from the laws of mechanics as observed in the laboratory. There was nothing here that required special attention from the Master Hand. Such orbital motion followed from the simple properties of matter.

There remained, however, certain perturbations in the motions of the planets, irregular departures from the elliptic orbits that Newton's calculations predicted. These might be disturbances caused by the attraction of other planets. What was to prevent the whole solar system from thus flying apart? Did not the heavens still need God's guiding hand? It was this lingering question that was answered so completely by the work of Laplace, when he showed that the orbits were stable under gravitational forces. Here was the point of his oft-quoted reply to Napoleon's remark, "M. Laplace, they tell me you have written this large book on the system of the universe, and have never even mentioned its Creator." As the story is told by Professor Rouse Ball of Cambridge,[7] Laplace answered bluntly, "I had no need for that hypothesis."

It was the fact that he could now truly make this reply that gave the epochal significance to Laplace's work. Now it could be said with confidence that the regular motion of the planets follows in detail the predictions based solely on the assumption that matter has certain simple mechanical properties. Perhaps the original creation of matter with such properties was a divine act; but there is no indication whatever of continued divine intervention in the physics of mechanical or celestial affairs. The Aristotelian argument for an all-powerful Creator continuously at work was gone. It was easy to infer, as stated for example by G. S. Brett in his book Sir Isaac Newton,[8] that: "In this way a severe rationalism was put forward in opposition to all the romantic forms of religion that went by the name of 'enthusiasm.' The seat of religious belief was thus moved from the heart to the head; mysticism was excommunicted by mathematics . . . the way was opened for a liberal Christianity which might ultimately supersede traditional beliefs," and for the "religion within the limits of reason" sought by Kant.

[7] In Dampier: A History of Science, p. 193.
[8] (Baltimore; 1928), p. 269.

It should be noted in passing that the common interpretation here given by Brett is precisely the reverse of the facts. It was the professors of systematic theology who believed they were establishing religion on a rational foundation who were caught off base by the mechanical revolution. It was those whose religion was based rather on intuition and experiences of the heart, which they knew firsthand as reliable facts, who found themselves undisturbed by the mechanists' arguments. These were those whose guide was not Aristotle's philosophy but the Hebraic writings, which had little to do with cosmology. Immanuel Kant, though a member of a theological faculty, counted himself in this latter group when he noted that the true evidence for God is to be found in the majesty of the heavens above and of the moral law within. Such evidence was not to be sought, that is, in intellectual arguments; though as a true philosopher Kant recognized that the idea one holds of God must be consistent with the limits of reason.

To make his point completely clear Laplace explained that if there were a mind of such infinite capacity that it could know at any time the positions and motions of all the particles in the universe and the forces between them both the past and the future would be present to his eyes. In other words, the world is a completely determined mechanical system. Note that this statement not only rules out the effectiveness of an assumed *Divine Agent,* but it rules out also the effectiveness of the *human* will in determining the course of physical events. That is, man's feeling of responsibility for what happens is an illusion. This is an accurate statement of the implications of Newton's mechanics.

As of the mid-twentieth century no physicist would now subscribe to such a statement, if for no other reason than that the precise knowledge of the position and motion of a particle is meaningless or impossible according to the quantum concepts that replace Newtonian mechanics when dealing with small-scale phenomena. Thus determinism is no longer considered a valid interpretation of the physical world.

An accurate statement would be that while, on the one hand, observation of physical events reveals nothing that requires for their interpretation the operation of intelligence, on the other hand what we can observe, and the physical laws as they are now known, are not inconsistent with the effectiveness of purpose in shaping the course of the events in nature. This balanced statement applies equally to one's own actions with reference to his responsibility for what he does, and to events occurring in the external world as related to other intelligences, either of men or of God. That is to say, we recognize now that we cannot call on physics and astronomy to give evidence for the effective action of free minds, either human or divine. But at the same time we recognize also that we cannot, on the basis of any kind of physical observation, deny that either human or divine minds may be effective in determining the course of certain types of events, in particular the actions of living organisms. Whether mind may participate in determining the course of events simply cannot be answered by physical observations.

Perhaps we of the post-Laplacian period have not taken seriously enough the moral implications of a strict belief in Newton's laws. Immanuel Kant, by juggling an unknowable world of things-in-themselves about which observed phenomena give us no information, wrested to his own satisfaction a ghostly kind of freedom. But it could not mean real responsibility for what happens. Actual physical events, according to Newton's laws, have been determined from the beginning of time. In practice men have resorted to the common-sense assurance that they are responsible for their acts, and have shaped their lives accordingly.

At other times and places people have not been so complacent. Dampier in *A History of Science* points out that the decline of Greek science began when Socrates urged that it is one's will, not the laws of physics, that determines action.[9] Waiting in prison to drink the hemlock, with the door left open by a friendly jailer, Socrates asks his students why they suppose he is sitting there in a cramped position on his bed when the door has been left open for him to escape. Is it, as Anaxagoras would have him believe, because of the tension of tendons over his joints? Not so, says Socrates. It is because I have been condemned by the people of Athens, and as a man of honor I will not run stealthily away.

Fifteen hundred years later the religious authorities of Islam, under the leadership of al-Ghazali, became concerned over the influence of science. Tolerance gave way to persecution. Science must no longer be studied because it leads "to loss of belief in the origin of the world and in the Creator."

A few years ago I had the opportunity to ask Professor Habib of the department of history at Aligarh University * whether it was in fact this religious antagonism to science in the early twelfth century that was responsible for the decline of science, or whether we should look for other factors. He answered that he had just been lecturing on this point to his classes, and he told me the counts that the religious leaders of that period had against science. In brief, science reduced the course of events in the world to natural law. If events are thus determined, what becomes of the effectiveness of God's will? Is not God all powerful? How can this be if He is bound by the laws that science proclaims? Here was indeed the chief reason that science was abandoned in Islam.

Shortly afterward, at Lahore, I was talking with a young Muslim Oxford

[9] *A History of Science*, pp. 27–8.

graduate who was working ardently to establish Pakistan as a Muslim state. I asked him, "How, in a nation that is committed to the concept of God, are you going to develop the scientific technology that you see so necessary?" He understood at once what I meant. This was to him and his associates a live problem. But he had his answer ready: "You Christians have shown that science can be consistent with belief in God. If you can solve this problem so also can we."

It is worth noting that the great leaders of eighteenth-century thought who were reshaping the outlook on the universe did not themselves see in what they were doing any reason for abandoning the idea of God. Their ideas were merely moving from the traditional pattern to a new view that was to them more satisfactory. It was the lesser minds, or those reacting against a dominating religious authority, who shied away from religion when the new science showed that old interpretations were inadequate. Copernicus, Galileo, Newton, Kant, and even Laplace himself counted themselves firmly as theists. In placing Laplace in this group I am using as authority our late associate George Sarton, who called my attention to letters that Laplace wrote to his son. In these letters Laplace urges the young man to maintain his belief in God, for this, he says, is the best basis for a stable attitude toward life.

So likewise the scientists of our century who have sought to orient our thinking regarding man's place in his world. Representative among these are such persons as the mathematician-philosopher A. N. Whitehead; the astronomer Arthur Eddington; the physicists Albert Einstein, Erwin Schrödinger, and Werner Heisenberg; and the physiologist Charles Sherrington. These men, like their eighteenth-century counterparts, have no need for introducing the concept of purpose, either human or divine, in accounting for the events that they see happening in the physical world. They are, however, unanimous in recognizing the importance of ideas, ideals, and purpose in understanding the meaning of what happens, and most of them introduce the concept of God into their world picture.

The idea of God used by today's men of science is far different from that of the followers of Aristotle; but, in a form fitted to science as now known, the idea remains alive among them. We of the present day are, however, far from agreement about the form that the idea of God should take.

## EIGHTEENTH-CENTURY PHILOSOPHY
## AND THE GROWTH OF SCIENCE

Time will not permit us to consider adequately certain other important aspects of eightenth-century scientific thought. Published summaries of the science of this period are available which treat these matters in detail. A more adequate picture would include the marked development of precision instruments, especially for use in astronomy and navigation. It would show how advances were made in the measurement of temperature and of quantity of heat, and how meteorology became a subject of systematic study. The great advances of chemistry in which Lavoisier played so important a part, the extension of our geographic knowledge to include most of the earth, the classification of plants and animals by Linnaeus, Buffon, and many others, the introduction of inoculation against smallpox, a concern with psychological phenomena, and a beginning of the science of demography, with Wallace and Malthus calling sharp attention to the threat of overpopulation—these would all be included.

But perhaps more significant, because it reflects the spirit of the age, was the strong development of philosophy. It is perhaps correct to describe the eighteenth century as the modern philosopher's great period. The basic reason for this growth was the impact of scientific thought on the traditional ideas that had been incorporated into religion. Thus philosophy affected people where they lived.

A mere mention of names will indicate what I mean. Thomas Aquinas, in the mid-thirteenth century, had performed the remarkable feat of synthesizing the heritage of classical scientific and philosophical thought with Christian doctrine. Descartes, Spinoza, Leibnitz, and Locke, during the seventeenth century, had begun to wrestle with the new problems posed by science. Chief among these problems was that of understanding how we can know anything.

It was at this point that early in the eighteenth century Bishop George Berkeley entered, calling sharp attention to the fact that one can know only what is in his own mind, and that in one's ideas, of which he is directly aware, is the essence of reality. David Hume was skeptical even of the reality of ideas. By general consent, however, Immanuel Kant is considered the person who, toward the close of the century, went as far as one could then go toward understanding how knowledge is reached.

Kant was himself a physicist of considerable stature. He anticipated Laplace in formulating a nebular hypothesis. He was the first to point out that tidal friction must retard the earth's rotation. He explained the trade winds as an effect of the earth's rotation on the atmosphere. He was thoroughly conversant with Newtonian mechanics, and accepted its complete validity. Coming before the establishment of the principle of biological evolution and the physicist's proof of the limitation of precision to our knowledge of physical events, his views of the place of ultimate ends in the interpretation of what happens in the world show remarkable balance.

In the view of J. B. S. Haldane and many others, as described by Dampier, "of all the older philosophies, Kant's metaphysics best represents the position to which physical and biological science [now] point. . . . Relativity and the quantum theory; biophysics, biochemistry and the idea of purposeful adaptation; all the latest developments of science . . . have brought scientific philosophy back to Kant." [1] Bertrand Russell and certain others have expressed themselves strongly in opposition to this high rating of Kant. But until the twentieth-century philosophers, notably A. N. Whitehead, brought into the total world picture such concepts as that of organism, it is perhaps fair to say that Kant supplied us with the most suitable systematic working philosophy that men of science had available. In fact, one may question whether without Kant's analysis of our concepts of space and time such a development as Einstein's theory of relativity could have occurred. It is equally doubtful whether our ideas of physical causality would have been revised without Kant's criticism of the basic meaning of this concept.

In sum, we see the eighteenth century as a period of completion of the classical analytical mechanics, establishing on a firm basis our understanding of the motion of matter under force. This achievement carried with it a revolutionary change in attitude toward the place of God and men in the world of nature, arriving at a position which has again been fundamentally altered during the twentieth century. During the eighteenth century nearly all of the main fields of science showed marked advance. Only biological science, following Harvey and waiting for Darwin, was relatively stagnant. The great new field of science that was opening was electricity, in the investigation of which Benjamin Franklin and other amateurs took a leading part. It was these studies that led directly to modern electrical technology and the electron theory of matter, and played an important part in making possible our new view of the universe.

The dominant spirit of the eighteenth century was shown in the release of scientific thought from authoritarian theology and in the strong growth of a type of philosophic thought that was fitted to the new world of science. It was these developments that cleared the field and laid the foundation on which later generations of science, including our own, could build substantial structures.

[10] A *History of Science*, p. 211.

# 8. Science and Man's Freedom

## 1957

Beginning in 1954, Mr. Compton organized a unique series of private conferences on "Science and Human Responsibility." The conferences, which were held at Washington University, brought together small groups of influential persons who shared Mr. Compton's determination that man shall meet successfully the dangers and opportunities developing so rapidly under the stimulus of rapid scientific advance. As the discussions were conceived primarily as an opportunity for thought needed to guide constructive action by those who attended, no formal account of the proceedings was published, although some of the conclusions were summarized by individual participants.* The conference members also took part in several public discussions, which were arranged in conjunction with the more numerous private meetings.

Basic to a discussion of man's human responsibility is the question of whether man is in fact free to choose his course. Mr. Compton directs attention to this fundamental question in the following remarks. They were originally presented as the opening paper on September 24, 1956, for the series of conferences held during the fall semester of that year. Later, they were expanded for publication in *The Atlantic Monthly* as the lead article in a special supplement entitled "A Forward Look at Science and Industry," which was published in October 1957.

What is the best in life that we can hope for? What shall we do to attain this best? These are the great questions always before us.

The very asking of these questions implies that we can do something to change our lot. Can we by trying really in any way affect what happens to us? Is it consistent with the laws of science that man shall have such freedom? On this essential point theologians, philosophers, and scientists have had sharp differences among themselves. Yet here is the very basis of man's responsibility. Responsibility has no meaning except as one is free to set his own course of action. If he is not thus free, both the sense of achievement and the feeling of failure are illusions. Indeed it is only as man is free that his aspirations make any difference, that his life has meaning and worth.

It is accordingly toward this basic presupposition of man's freedom in light of science that I wish to draw attention. Practical men have already reached a working answer to the question of their freedom. If they are aware that such a question exists, they are content to leave it in the hands of the philosophers. They are going ahead with life's jobs. They try to avoid what may hurt them and try to win what they want. They accept the consequences of their acts. They are proud of their achievements. They regret their failures. Here is the common-sense answer, by which most men live. Yet the course of civilizations has been altered by those who have concerned themselves with whether man is in fact able to shape his own destiny. The question remains of vital concern today. If we are to discuss science and human responsibility we must ask first of all, does science admit that man is a free and responsible being?

## THE HISTORICAL ROLE OF THE QUESTION OF MAN'S FREEDOM

One of the crucial episodes in Greek history was Socrates' decision to accept the verdict of death as given by the people of Athens. Socrates was waiting in prison for the appointed day. A friendly jailer had left the door unlocked. His disciples were urging him to flee. Socrates' reply has had an impact on the thinking of nearly a hundred generations. In effect this is what he said:

> When I was a young man, I studied Anaxagoras' book on physics. He would have me believe that I am sitting in this crouched position on my cot because of the tension of the tendons over my joints. What Anaxagoras doesn't seem to know is that I sit here because I will not break the law of Athens. The people have condemned me to drink the hemlock. As a man of honor I will not creep stealthily way.

It was not the laws of physics that determined that Socrates should remain in prison; it was the code of honor to which he committed himself. Even in death Socrates was free.

Here was one of the great moral acts of all time. Yet one of its most significant consequences was that of discouraging the growth of Greek science. The Greeks were searching for a better way of life, hoping that this better way might become evident in finding how nature works, i.e., is discovering the laws of science. Now Socrates gave an effective demonstration that it was not the principles of physics but what was in one's heart that in time of crisis shaped a man's course of action. The result was a decline in the Greeks' interest in science and a growth in their attention to the philosophical principles of morality. Perhaps it was a good thing that the development of man's powers through advance in science was thus delayed for two thousand years. The delay gave mankind time to grow in the moral understanding that we now see is so urgently required to control the powers of science for the common good.

In another notable case the conflict between science and faith in the power of will altered the course of history. In the tenth and eleventh centuries in the Arab world, science was growing vigorously, but in the twelfth century this growth suddenly ceased. In the Islamic world science is only now beginning to recover. I was told by Islamic historians that the reason for the sharp decline was the antiscientific attitude of their religious teachers from the twelfth century onward. These teachers, in particular the famous al-Ghazali, feared the study of science because it tended toward disbelief in God. The center of the difficulty was that according to science the world obeys laws that cannot be changed. How can this be reconciled with the doctrine that everything happens according to the will of God? Is not God—and man, too—thus reduced to an automaton? Again, it took several centuries for the growth of science to recover from this new setback.

Both of these incidents grew out of the conflict between physical law and man's belief in freedom. The present generation concerns itself little with the limitations imposed by physics. We think rather of the new possibilities that physics and chemistry are continually opening to us. We are, however, alert to the limitations imposed by biological and psychological factors. We see ourselves acting as demanded by our heredity, our psychological conditioning, and the forces of social pressure. But even such factors are irrelevant if in the mechanics of life things happen as they do because of predetermined physical cause and effect.

## THE MECHANICAL DETERMINISM
## OF NEWTONIAN SCIENCE

The accepted view among Western scholars until the sixteenth century was that things move because agents make them move. Such was the view of the great Greek teacher, Aristotle. To Greeks and Christians alike, the Unmoved Mover, who makes things go, was one description of God. The remarkably uniform motion of the planets, for example, was seen as evidence both of God's power and of his reliability.

Then came Galileo. His experiments showed that no force is needed to keep objects in uniform motion. The effect of a force is rather to change the motion, to slow it down or speed it up or change its direction. Newton found further that the force of gravity, a universal property of matter, was all that was needed to hold the planets in their orbits. When the significance of these discoveries was fully realized it seemed that all that happens in the world was to be accounted for as a result of the mechanical forces between the particles of matter. A classical statement of this conclusion was made in 1812 by Pierre Simon de Laplace:

> We ought to regard the present state of the universe as an effect of its antecedent state, and as the cause of the state which is to follow. An intelligent being who at a given instant knew all the forces animating Nature and the relative positions of the beings within it would, if his intelligence were sufficiently capacious to analyse these data, include in a single formula the movements of the largest bodies of the universe and those of the lightest atom. Nothing would be uncertain for him: the future as well as the past would be present to his eyes.

Laplace meant that everything that happens is the mechanically necessary result of what has gone before and requires of necessity what will come to pass in the future. Such is indeed the implication of Newton's laws of motion.

This scientific view of mechanical determinism did precisely what had been feared by the Moslem fathers of the twelfth century. The hypothesis of a God that governed the motions of the worlds was no longer needed. He was replaced in people's thinking by mechanical forces inherent in the nature of matter. But the scientists had not only taken away the idea of a God that was free to act as he chose. They had also taken from man his most essential character. Man's idea that his efforts had meaning was an illusion. According to this science that was so successful in explaining the motion of the planets, man's actions had been fixed from the beginning of time. Neither blame nor praise for what a person did was justified. There was no such thing as freedom. All events occurred simply as a result of particles moving under mechanical forces, following their inevitable course.

It is these ideas of mechanical determinism that have shaped much of the philosophical thinking with which we still live.

## TODAY'S PHYSICS HAS ROOM FOR FREEDOM

The fault in this theory of mechanical determinism was not discovered until about thirty years ago. It was then found that the laws of Newton do not describe what happens to the atoms of which matter is composed. It was found instead that the properties of these atoms are such that prediction of what happens to them can only be made within certain limits. The amount of this uncertainty is fixed in the very nature of matter itself.

On my laboratory desk I have two simple devices. The first is a freely swinging pendulum. Its beats are regular, repeating themselves uniformly at equally timed intervals. This pendulum is typical of the objects with which the physicists of Laplace's time were familiar.

The second device is a Geiger counter, responding with a click to each ray that enters it from a nearby capsule of radium. The clicks occur at irregular intervals. It may be that about 100,000 clicks will occur each day. But several seconds may pass without any clicks, while during the next second two or three will occur. Whether in the following second a ray will be counted cannot be foretold. This device responds to the action of individual atoms. Nothing of this kind was known until near the end of the nineteenth century.

The pendulum swings back and forth according to a precise law. The clicks of the counter occur at random.

If such a pair of experiments had been known in Newton's time, it is doubtful whether the idea that events must happen according to precise laws would ever have been formulated. It would have been evident that only under special conditions can one predict definitely what will occur. These conditions are that what we observe shall be the average of a very large number of individual events.

Consider what happens when an atom of radium disintegrates. This event can be recorded by such an instrument as a Geiger counter. The average life of a radium atom is about two thousand years. That is, in any one year from the time the radium atom is first formed, the chance is about one in two thousand that it will disintegrate. It may disintegrate during the present year, but there is roughly one chance in eight that it will remain unchanged six thousand years from now. What the physicists of the twentieth century have shown is that there is no kind of observation that can be made which will tell in what particular year the radium atom will disintegrate. If the atom was in existence six thousand years ago, it was then identical with what it is today. The possibility of disintegration has always been there. Whether it will in fact disintegrate in this particular year is, as far as physics is concerned, a matter of chance—a likelihood of one in two thousand.

There is something comparable with this example in the case of every atomic or molecular event. Thus when light falls on a photographic emulsion, under its stimulus there is a certain chance that any particular grain of silver bromide will be changed so that it can be developed to silver. With a given light exposure, this chance may be one in ten, so that on the average about one-tenth of the grains will be transformed. But which particular grain will thus be changed is by the very nature of the process unpredictable.

These examples illustrate a point of critical importance in today's interpretation of the physical world. Nature provides nothing whose precise measurement would make possible the exact prediction of an atomic event. On this limitation that nature sets on our knowledge both experiment and theory are agreed. The average of large numbers of atomic events does indeed follow exact laws. In a large lump of radium in one year almost precisely one part in two thousand will have disintegrated. In a square inch of the photographic emulsion, almost exactly one tenth of the silver bromide, after the light exposure, will be reduced to silver. The number of atoms in my laboratory pendulum is huge, roughly a million billion billion. The statistics of the action of such numbers of particles are very precise—even more so when one observes the moon's regular revolution around the earth.

Not all large-scale events, however, are thus precisely predictable. If at any stage the big event depends on some atomic process, the end result shares in the uncertainty of this small event.

A typical large-scale event of this kind is the explosion of an atomic bomb. Such an explosion is triggered by the appearance of a neutron during the particular fraction of a microsecond when the chain reaction must be started. But this neutron comes from a radioactive process, which cannot be precisely foretold. If the chances were only even that during the critical time interval a neutron would appear, there would likewise be only even chances that the bomb would explode. In order that the bomb shall be sure to fire, it is arranged that during the critical time interval some thousands of neutrons will probably be present. Thus the chance of failure becomes practically zero.

Now most of life's processes are like such an atomic chain reaction. They begin with some very small event and grow. They are in fact chemical chain reactions. What starts these reactions in living organisms is not known in detail, but we do know that the beginning is on a molecular, or in certain cases on a submolecular, scale. Thus when I touch something hot and quickly withdraw my finger, the nerve currents that stimulate the muscular contractions are themselves small-scale reactions. The events that are involved when choices and decisions are made have so far defied physical identification; but in all probability they are reactions involving such small numbers of particles that definite prediction on a physical basis is by the nature of things impossible.

| 120 |

As far as physics is concerned, a person's actions which we think of as free would thus appear to occur simply according to the rules of chance. We find nevertheless that in practical life such actions can be predicted when we know the person's intentions. This implies that something additional to the physical phenomena is involved. What we actually note is that in such a case the person has a kind of firsthand knowledge of his own situation that is not gained from any physical observation. This additional knowledge is the awareness of his own intentions. When he acts he feels that he is acting freely. That is, his action corresponds with what he intends.

Thus, for example, I told the editor that I would have this article prepared in time for the present issue of the *Atlantic*. How could I confidently give him this assurance? Was it on the basis of physical data? Only to the extent that it appeared physically possible that the article could be prepared in time. As a physical event an immense number of other possibilities were equally likely to occur. Was not the primary basis of my prediction rather that I knew my own intention? And this I knew, not through any kind of observation, but by an inner awareness; not through a deduction from data, but because of a choice that I was making from among the various possibilities before me.

After thousands of years of discussion among scientists and philosophers, the place of free acts in a world that follows physical law has thus become clarified. There is nothing known to physics that is inconsistent with a person's exercising freedom.

A set of known physical conditions is not adequate to specify precisely what a forthcoming event will be. These conditions, insofar as they can be known, define instead a range of possible events from among which some particular event will occur. When one exercises freedom, by his act of choice he is himself adding a factor not supplied by the physical conditions and is thus himself determining what will occur. That he does so is known only to the person himself. From the outside one can see in his act only the working of physical law. It is the inner knowledge that he is in fact doing what he intends to do that tells the actor himself that he is free.

## THE RELATION OF BIOLOGY AND PSYCHOLOGY
## TO FREEDOM

Knowledge of the physical conditions and of the physical laws that apply to our situation thus opens to us a limited range of possibilities for action. Within this range the biological and psychological factors become of ruling importance. That life shall continue and thrive makes certain types of choice self-defeating and other choices so successful that they become dominant. Hereditary and psychological conditioning make certain types of response difficult and others easy. Much of such conditioning is beyond the control of either the individual or society.

There are physiologists and psychologists who look upon such conditioning factors as compelling. They would say that the choices a man makes are required of him by his nature and his circumstances. Whether this type of determinism in fact exists, the physicist can neither affirm nor deny. Conditions not specified by physical observation are here taken into account. There is nothing that physics knows which would deny the possibility that these conditions determine precisely the action of an individual in a particular situation.

I believe most physicists would, however, agree with me in making this suggestion: Physical laws, which at one stage seemed so exact and compelling, are now found to leave open a wide range of possibilities. May not the physiological and psychological restrictions likewise serve merely to limit further the range and likelihood of the possibilities left open by the physical conditions? If this is true, a choice may still be made from within this more limited range. One may give personal preference to certain relevant psychological factors that affect the course of action. True freedom and responsibility would thus remain.

To this possibility it is evident that the physiologist and the psychologist are unable to give a firm no. The final test for freedom must be one's own sense of doing what he intends. Beyond this test, science has no means of going.

It is within the wide range of possibilities opened by physical science that the biological, social, and psychological sciences do their great work. How can life be made to thrive, the social order be made healthy and strong, and persons be enabled to grow to their best? These are the humanly important questions. These questions begin where the physical sciences leave off. Our faith is that the principles learned by these sciences of life will help us see the choices we must make in order that we may attain our greatest freedom.

## SCIENCE HAS CLEARED THE WAY FOR CONFIDENCE IN FREEDOM OF ACTION

A few years ago in Geneva, Switzerland, I met with an international group of some thirty scientists and philosophers, brought together to discuss how man sees himself in the light of science.* Is man morally responsible for doing what seems to him good? Can man in fact choose his course? To such questions the response of these men was almost unanimous: Man is free and responsible.

There was one possible exception. He was an Italian student of genetics who was strongly impressed by the effectiveness of inherited tendencies in influencing a person's choices. To myself as a physicist such inherited tendencies correspond simply to a shift in what one scientist calls "the spectrum of action probability." The shift still leaves open the choice of any action that lies within that spectrum.

However, the significant fact was this: whereas in a similar gathering of scientists and philosophers a century or two earlier, freedom would undoubtedly have been denied by a large number in favor of physical determinism, in 1952 with this possible exception not one of the internationally respresentative group would deny on the basis of scientific law the responsibility that is implied by freedom.

I am not sure that this degree of unanimity would have been present if scientists bound by Communist ideas had attended the meeting. I am told, I believe reliably, that for a considerable period after the Second World War the teaching of the scientific principle of indeterminacy, which we have been discussing, was under a ban in Russia. Marx, who was a younger contemporary of Laplace, had taught that man is a machine that obeys exact mechanical laws. The scientific idea of physical indeterminacy was dangerous. Who knew? It might open the way to belief that man has some special kind of value, or even to belief in God!

Let me then summarize how a physicist now views man's freedom. It is not from scientific observation that we know man is free. Science is incapable of telling whether a person's acts are free or not. Freedom is not something that one can touch or measure. We know it through our own innermost feelings. The first essential of freedom is the desire to attain something that one considers good. But desire lies outside the realm of science—at least outside of physics. You can't locate desire as somewhere in space. Similarly our recognition that within limits we can do what we try to do is not a matter of measurement or of external observation. It is a matter of immediate awareness. There is nothing in such awareness of freedom that is inconsistent with science. Freedom does, however, involve the additional determining factor of choice, about which science tells us nothing.

For myself, at least, this answer satisfies. Yes, I am free. I say this because I have found in my inner experience that the world does in fact respond to my efforts. And the findings of science, in particular the findings of physics, which at one stage so sharply denied that freedom had any meaning, are completely consistent with this experience.

Thus the way is cleared for our great task. We are free to shape our destiny. Science opens vast new opportunities, greatly enlarging man's freedom. Let us look to see what kind of world we want for ourselves and our fellows. Let us learn what we must do to create such a world. Let us put our hearts, our minds, and our combined strength—everything we've got—into making that better world a reality. In this undertaking we will find our greatest freedom.

# 9. The Human Mind and Physical Law

*1958*

Werner Heisenberg, the eminent German physicist, is in large measure responsible for the interpretation of physical phenomena that have brought revolutionary changes in the theories of atomic physics. In this review of Heisenberg's book, *Physics and Philosophy* (Harper; 1958), the author calls attention to some of the philosophical and political implications of these theories.

Here is a book the world of thought has been waiting for since 1930, when Heisenberg published his *Physical Principles of the Quantum Theory*. This will not be a popular book: not many will read it with understanding. But those who do read it understandingly will be the shapers of thought, not only scientific and philosophical thought, but shapers also of the thinking that goes into politics and statesmanship and world peace.

Thus Marx drew his social ideas from a background of materialism where matter was fixed in its course of action and in turn was itself the final determinator of all that happens. This was the world of physics of a century ago, within which such men as Hume and Kant and Hegel and Nietzsche had to develop their thinking. Today's world of physics is vastly different, and to a considerable extent because of the work of Werner Heisenberg. That is why we have been waiting so eagerly to hear how he interprets what is happening. Modestly he calls his thesis the "Copenhagen" interpretation, referring to discussions led by Niels Bohr * but with Heisenberg, Max Born,* and others as active participants. Their conclusions are stated in muffled tones, but with deep undertones of meaning: "Modern physics has perhaps opened the door to a wider outlook on the relation between the human mind and reality."

Today, as Heisenberg sees it:

| 125 |

Modern science penetrates into those large areas of our present world in which new doctrines were established only a few decades ago as foundations for new and powerful societies. There modern science is confronted both with the content of the doctrines, which go back to European philosophical ideas of the nineteenth century (Hegel and Marx), and with the phenomenon of uncompromising belief. Since modern physics must play a great role in these [Marxist] countries because of its practical applicability, it can scarcely be avoided that the narrowness of the doctrines is felt by those who have really understood modern physics and its philosophical meaning. Therefore, at this point an interaction between science and the general trend of thought may take place. Of course, the influence of science should not be overrated; but it might be that the openness of modern science could make it easier even for larger groups of people to see that the doctrines are possibly not so important for society as had been assumed before. In this way the influence of modern science may favor an attitude of tolerance and thereby may prove valuable.

One of the most delightful portions of the book is Heisenberg's account of the history of the development of the quantum theory. His story of Max Planck's almost unwilling recognition in Berlin in 1900 that his hypothesis of quanta of energy could be the answer to a theoretical problem that was insoluble according to classical physics reflects the warm freshness of these events in German university circles when Heisenberg was a student. His picture of Max Planck as the conservative expert of the old school and Albert Einstein as the venturesome and imaginative newcomer, both faced with the novel possibilities presented by the concept of quanta, has the ring of human truth and understanding. Only lightly does he refer to the thrills that must have been his own when as a student at Göttingen he tried introducing probability into the quantum concepts and found the phenomena of experimental physics falling neatly into order.

The author's prime concern is with the revolution that has had to occur in the thinking of physicists in order to understand how seeming paradoxes posed by experiments can be comprehended in their own field of science. Much of what had come to be taken for granted has had to be re-examined and in some cases replaced by new concepts. Thus the law of causality must be replaced by a law of probability when it is found that the alpha disintegration of a radium atom is not occasioned by anything that is done to the atom but follows a probability pattern that was built into the structure of the nucleus when it was first formed. Particles and waves, once thought of as the fundamental realities that comprise matter, are found to be recognizable only through events that happen occasionally in particular places. What the form or condition of a particle or wave pattern may be in between these occasional events, we have no means of knowing. To suppose even that they have continuous existence is not demanded by what we know, and serves only to confuse our thinking.

Having followed the effect on physics of replacing the Newtonian laws of motion by different but related quantum principles, the author proceeds to discuss the effects of quantum mechanics on other fields of science. He notes that the classical physics had only failure to report from its exhaustive efforts to account for the chemical properties of atoms. When the idea of electron orbits was replaced by the conception of "probability functions" that told where electrons were apt to occur in atoms, these difficulties were replaced by interpretations that carried in principle a full solution of the problems of chemical combination. Thus, adding a new dimension to the thinking of physics made possible the successful interpretation of chemistry in terms of physics.

In an analogous manner, Heisenberg suggests that just as in order to account for the stability of chemical atoms physics had to introduce a new concept, so before biological phenomena can be completely understood something new must be added to the laws of physics and chemistry:

> If we go beyond biology and include psychology in the discussion, then there can scarcely be any doubt but that the concepts of physics, chemistry, and evolution together will not be sufficient to describe the facts. . . . We would never doubt that the brain acts as a physico-chemical mechanism if treated as such; but for an understanding of psychic phenomena we would start from the fact that the human mind enters as object and subject into the scientific process of psychology.
> . . . In biology it may be important for a complete understanding that the questions are asked by the species man which itself belongs to the genus of living organisms, in other words, that we already know what life is even before we have defined it scientifically.

One should note that not all competent students agree with this "Copenhagen" interpretation of quantum mechanics. This view, as the author correctly states, has become recognized in physics circles as the "orthodox" interpretation of quantum ideas. Among those who share the author's outlook are such notables as Niels Bohr, Max Born, and most American theoretical physicists. In other camps, however, stood the late greats, Max Planck and Albert Einstein, and still remain such notable contemporaries as Erwin Schrödinger and Louis de Broglie. A valuable chapter is used by the author in summarizing these alternative views and outlining his own replies. This reviewer finds the author's line of thinking the most acceptable, for the simple reason that any other proposed interpretation seems to him forced and unnecessarily complex.

We have here a firsthand account of what is probably the most significant development in thought since the time of Galileo and Darwin. It is a development for which the theories of Einstein to some extent prepared us, but it has gone much farther in that it has given a new flexibility and comprehensiveness to the meaning of physical law itself. The world of physical law is becoming more closely related to life as we know it by experience.

# IV

## On the Nature

## of Things

Rather would I find the true cause of one fact than
become king of the Persians.

DEMOCRITUS

# 10. Aeronautics

## *1909*

〰〰 In 1908, in an airplane constructed under his supervision, Glenn Curtiss won the *Scientific American* trophy for the first public flight in the United States of at least a kilometer. This achievement followed by only a few years the Wright brothers' first successful flight in their new motor-driven airplane, which was tested at Kitty Hawk, North Carolina, in 1903.

While confined to his room by illness, young Arthur Compton chanced to read an article about the flying machines that Glenn Curtiss and the Wright brothers were making. He became much interested in these machines and not only read everything about flying that he could find but made some thousands of airplane models with which to study the conditions required for stable flight. He soon set out to plan a glider in which he could fly. As his father was then in England, it was necessary to write for permission to build the glider, which he eventually flew successfully. In later years he often contrasted these early experiments in aeronautics, which were his first scientific experiments and which were performed virtually alone, with his last major scientific task, the atomic reactor, which engaged the skills of many thousands of persons.

Mr. Compton retained an interest in airplanes throughout his life. During the First World War he worked on the development of airplane instruments as a civilian associate of the United States Signal Corps. For several years (1956–9) he served as a member of the Board of Visitors of the newly established Air Force Academy. He also served as a member of the Advisory Board of the McDonnell Aircraft Corporation.

Wooster, Ohio
March 24, 1909 *

Dear Papa,

I have mentioned several times in my letters the achievements of my little aeroplane models: how I would take one of them out to the golf links when there was a breeze blowing up the east hill, and how my little white winged gull would soar through the air, sometimes rising several yards over my head, but finally come to a stop on the level lawn at the foot of the hill. I have also sent you copies of the articles which I have written, giving my ideas concerning aeroplanes. You know from my letters that I am highly interested in aeronautics, and know that you wish me to follow this science as far as is for my benefit. I know that if you think it for my benefit and pleasure, you will want me to make a man carrying motorless aeroplane, or glider, in which I can fly.

Last year I heard you speak of "circus performers and aeronauts," speaking of them as people who risked their lives without cause, and so I suppose that you would think it too dangerous for me to ride in an aeroplane. It is true that some people have been killed and others injured in attempts to fly, but in most cases, the injured were men who tried to fly without any means of balancing themselves in the air. How then, you ask, did the accident occur last summer to Mr. Orville Wright, one of the foremost aviators of the world? I answer by stating that this accident was caused by a defect in the propeller, which tore loose and broke one of the guiding wires, and so *could not* have happened in a motorless aeroplane. As a practical proof of this statement I will quote what the Wright brothers themselves have said: "In all our experiments with flying- and gliding-machines, we have not even sprained a limb, we have scarcely scratched our flesh." This was written a little before their public flights last summer. In all my reading, and I have read almost everything about aeronautics that I have been able to find, I have not heard of a single serious accident with an aeroplane, which has occurred during the past year, except the one of the Wright machine at Fort Myer last September.

Mr. Wright says that the only danger with their machine is that of tipping over. In mine it is the same way, only this danger also is practically eliminated. As I stated in my article in *Fly*, a properly constructed glider can*not* stop while in the air, but must continue moving rapidly forward almost horizontally. Santos-Dumont has proved that small models act just like full-sized machines of the same design, and I have developed by actual experiment, a model which will hold itself perfectly steady while flying through the air, with almost no possibility of diving into the ground. The flights of my model at the golf links, about which I have told you, were of course among the best ones, but my latest machine would be able to repeat them any number of times under the same weather conditions. In upwards of a hundred flights (roughly guessing) on calm days and in windy weather, my last machine has never once tipped over, nor dived into the ground, nor even slanted to a dangerous degree.

The Wright brothers say: "It has been a common aim among experimenters with the aeroplane to solve the problem of equilibrium by some automatic system of balancing. We believe that the control should be left in possession of the operator. The management of our machine, like that of the bicycle, is based upon the sense of equilibrium of the operator." In my glider there are both advantages. The equilibrium is automatic enough so that when even a model is started, it will go forward smoothly on an even keel, and strike the ground at a very small angle, and also in my man carrying glider, the control would be absolutely in the hands of the aeronaut. Moreover, as I have a simpler steering gear to operate the balancing planes than have the Wrights, it will be more simple to learn to guide the machine. It would be impossible for my glider to break in the air, as it would purposely be made many times as strong as necessary.

I have cut out an editorial from *Fly* which gives that person's opinion of the danger of flying machines.

I do not mean to say that there is absolutely no danger in flying in a glider, but I do mean that the danger is very little. There was great danger to the first riders in automobiles, but would you, if it had been possible, have kept any one for that reason from developing that machine? It was much more dangerous for Karl to play football on the college team than for me to fly in a glider, but did you for that reason keep him from the fine training and quick judgement and skill which the game would give him? Why then should you keep me from the better training in quick judgement, steady nerves, and scientific thought which flying in a glider would give me?

But perhaps you think I do not know how to make one which would be safe. I have made four different models since last September, all of which were able to fly. Did you not say yourself, Papa, that by my articles I showed a knowledge of technical terms which could come only from much and thoughtful reading? I have written articles which contain my own ideas, which the publishers of both *Fly* and the *Scientific American* thought were authoritative enough to publish; * and although the *Scientific American* refused my last article, I hardly thought that they would accept it, as it was written about something proposed instead of something actually done as all their publications are. I have just this afternoon finished figuring out the dimensions, shape, strength and weight of each stick to be used in the construction of the model, and find the total weight to be almost exactly that of the Wright brothers' glider, that is, a hundred pounds.

But then as most of my "bugs" are about as long lived as a mosquito, perhaps although I could make an aeroplane if I could keep at it, my

| 133 |

interest might die away before the machine was finished, and nothing would come out of the attempt. But it seems as though this hobby were not like the others, as I have been trotting it since last summer without slackening interest, as this letter proves. Moreover, if I would start to make a glider, I would not dare to stop because of the way in which people would tease me. On the other hand, perhaps it might take up too much of my thought and time. I wrote you last vacation about this, how my "Aeronuts" would keep me from study, but since that time it has not done so, and if I exercise a little will power, I am pretty sure that such a thing will not happen again; even if it should, I would still have enough sense left to quit work and reading upon the subject. As to taking too much of my time, I have unlimited time to build it in, and although I would be working at it during the school year I would do most on Saturdays when I would not have to study. Last fall when my thoughts were all taken up with the subject, I still had enough will power left not to let it interfere with my studies in regard to *time*.

Supposing that all these objections are answered, you will wish to know how much it will cost to make a glider. It would cost approximately twenty dollars for everything; Prof. Montgomery in California made one for ten dollars several years ago. Everything except the lumber; muslin, screws, hinges, piano wire etc., will cost within 50¢ of ten dollars, and I estimate the lumber at the same, but of course that is not exact. I feel as though I could easily spare twenty dollars for the experience, the sport and the education which the machine would give me.

But if I have a glider, I must have some place to ride it, and there is no better place imaginable than the rolled, sodded hills of the golf links. Of course I would have to gain special permission from the Country Club to use these hills, but I am pretty sure that could be done. At the golf links one could fly over six hundred feet if so wished, or when learning to fly, could make little short jumps of any length.

But then it would be pretty hard, you say, to shelter a big frame with wings twenty-five feet long, with a height of nine feet, and from the back to the front rudders a distance of eighteen feet. On this account I have planned my glider so that it can be folded up and taken apart without losing any strength, so that it can be easily kept in the carriage room of our barn.

With all these objections answered, I see no reason why I should be *kept* from making a glider; but there must also be a cause why I *should* make one. Why was it that you went to Europe and are studying there now? Was it not because you wished a fuller and broader education, some recreation and sport? Or why is it that Karl likes to play football? Is it not because it gives him steady nerves, a level head, quick thought and action, and lots of fun? It is for all these reasons that I wish to make and ride in a glider. It would greatly increase my scientific knowledge, it would be recreation and great sport with just enough excitement to make it interesting, it would give me steady nerves, a level head, quick thought and action, and above all, I would be striving with some of the best thinkers of the times to solve the problem of mechanical flight.

Nevertheless if you do not think I ought to do this, I do not wish to, but at present I see no reason why I should not.

Your loving son,
*Arthur*

P.S. Please answer soon.
P.P.S. After Mamma read the letter and made her remarks upon it, it seems advisable that I should tell you that I do not intend to fly in the machine myself until I have found that it will fly safely. I would first put a sand bag or something of that kind in the operator's seat and see whether the machine would fly by itself. If it would do this I could easily fly in it myself. You may think possibly that the machine wouldn't stay in the air. If it wouldn't I would be the happiest boy that ever happened, because I would have disproved all the existing laws of aerodynamics, and could earn many moneys by writing articles on the result. If the glider were not going to stay up, it would drop as soon as started, but at that time I would only be a couple of feet above the ground, and would not be hurt in falling. The Wright brothers' glider works on the same principles as mine, and they have a greater weight to be supported than I would have, but their machine stayed up in the air all right. As said above, Santos-Dumont has proved that models act just like a large machine, and my model stays in the air all right. As I have said above, if the machine came down suddenly, it would break the laws of aerodynamics. I am sending you a paragraph from *McClure's* which shows what the Wrights think of staying in the air. After the motor has been stopped, their machine becomes a glider. Also, if you will read over the second and third paragraphs of my article in *Fly* you will find my thoughts on the subject.

Lovingly,
*Arthur*

# 11. What the Atom Looks Like

*1931*

As a leading investigator of atomic structure, Professor Compton discussed the nature of the atom in a Science Service radio talk presented over the Columbia Broadcasting System. Knowledge of the atom has grown increasingly sophisticated since these remarks were prepared. They are reprinted here simply to show a typical effort by the author to make a somewhat abstruse subject understandable to a youthful audience.

To those of us who work in physical and chemical laboratories atoms become familiar acquaintances. I gave as my subject for this afternoon "What the Atom Looks Like," because I wanted to introduce you to these little friends of ours. First let me show you something that an atom can do. I have here in front of me a little electroscope, connected through an amplifier to a loudspeaker. My watch has a luminous dial, which has in it a weak preparation of radium. I shall take off the crystal from the face and hold the watch close to the electroscope. Do you hear the "plops" coming from the loudspeaker? Remove my watch and the plops cease. Repeating the experiment, I find that the face of my watch must be within about two inches of the electroscope before more sounds are heard. What causes the sounds? Evidently something shot from the radium in the watch face. But what are these somethings? Let us call them "alpha particles" for want of a better name.

Lord Rutherford once caught a lot of these alpha particles to see what they made when there were enough of them. He compressed some radioactive gas into a glass tube with walls so thin that the alpha particles would pass right through. After a few days he noticed gas collecting in the space surrounding this tube. On passing an electric discharge through this accumulated gas, and looking at it through a spectroscope, he saw the brilliant colors characteristic of the gas helium. Thus he showed that the things that make these plops, when a speck of radium is brought close to the electroscope, are bits of helium shot from the radium.

Many of you know the romance of helium. Observed many years ago by Lockyer in the spectrum of the sun, it remained unknown on the earth for a generation until Rayleigh and Ramsay, making a precise measurement of the density of the nitrogen in the air, found it different from the nitrogen prepared in the laboratory. Search for the cause of the discrepancy revealed a whole series of new gases—argon with which our incandescent lamps are filled, neon with which we advertise our wares in blazing red, helium with which we now fill our dirigibles, and two others, krypton and xenon, which are now of great value in certain laboratory experiments. Thus was helium found, and now we hear it being formed—the birth of helium atoms. For these alpha particles are none other than atoms of helium gas.

Imagine that by means of such an electroscope as this we have thus counted all the atoms of helium that came through the walls of Rutherford's glass tube, and made the gas that he observed in his spectroscope. How many atoms would we have? In a small thimble filled with helium at atmospheric pressure, the number of atoms is about one with nineteen ciphers after it. Perhaps that doesn't mean much to you. Let me put it this way. Two thousand years ago Julius Caesar gave a dying gasp, *"Et tu, Brute?"* In the intervening millenniums the molecules of air that he breathed out with that cry have been blown around the world in ocean storms, washed with rains, warmed by the sunshine, and dispersed to the ends of the earth. Of course, only a very small fraction of these molecules are now in this room; but at your next breath each of you will probably inhale half a dozen or so of the molecules of Caesar's last breath.*

Molecules and atoms are very tiny things; but there are so many of them that they make up the world in which we live. I wish there were time to tell you about the remarkable experiments that have shown the parts of atoms. There are some hundreds of different kinds of atoms that make up this wonderful world of ours; but all of these atoms are made of two more fundamental elements, known as protons and electrons. Hydrogen, the simplest atom of all, has one proton and four electrons. The proton and two of the electrons are concentrated in a tiny nucleus at the center of the atom, and the other two electrons buzz around the nucleus, forming a kind of atmosphere. And so on for the heavier atoms, until we get to uranium, the heaviest of all, which has ninety-two electrons in its atmosphere.

## HOW THE ATOM IS BUILT

Old Ptolemy, the ancient Greek astronomer, knew that there is a sun and a moon, the earth, and the planets; but he did not know what the solar system is. When Copernicus and Galileo showed, however, that there is a sun, around which planets revolve in definite orbits, then men felt that they had become acquainted with their world. So, though we have found the parts of which the atom is made, we really do not know the atom until we know how these parts are put together.

Perhaps the best way to find out how something is made is to look at it. If it is like a watch, which we can hold in our hands, this is comparatively easy. If it is the cell structure of a muscle that we wish to examine, we put it under a microscope. But some things are too small to see even in a microscope. By using ultraviolet light of wavelength shorter than ordinary light, we can photograph such things as typhoid bacilli with increased sharpness. But atoms are too small even for this. Now X rays have a wavelength only a ten-thousandth that of light, and if we could use them in a microscope it should be possible for us to observe even the tiny atoms. Unfortunately, we cannot make lenses that will refract X rays, and even if we could our eyes are not sensitive to X rays. So it would seem that we shall never be able to see an atom directly. It is, nevertheless, possible in the laboratory to get by more roundabout methods precisely the same information about an atom that we should get if we could look at it with an X-ray microscope. I have spent a large part of the last sixteen years trying to find what the atom looks like, and it has become something of a game with me.

Last summer, while spending a brief vacation in northern Michigan, I noticed a diffuse ring, not very large, around the moon. Half an hour later the ring was perceptibly smaller, and within an hour we came in out of the rain. This ring was due to the diffraction of the moonlight by tiny water droplets that were beginning to form a cloud. The size of the ring depends upon the size of the water drops—if the drops are small, the ring is big, and vice versa. So when the ring grew smaller, it meant that the drops were growing larger. Soon they would fall as rain.

Our method of studying atoms is very similar to this method of finding the size of the droplets in a cloud. Instead of the moon we use an X-ray tube, and in place of the cloud of water droplets we use the atoms in air or helium. For the wavelength of the X rays bears about the same ratio to the size of a helium atom that a light wave bears to a droplet of water in a fog. The helium atoms spread the X rays into a halo in just the same way that the water droplets diffract the moonlight. Likewise now, from the diameter of this halo, we can estimate the size of the helium atom. We can in fact tell almost as much about its appearance as if the atom were under an X-ray microscope. When looked at by such an X-ray microscope the atom looks like a fuzzy ball. If this ball is to appear the size of a baseball, we shall, however, have to use such a magnification that a marble would appear as big as the earth.

In the middle of this fuzzy ball somewhere is the nucleus of the helium atom, which has in it the protons. This cloudlike atmosphere is due to the electrons. We commented a few minutes ago that the atmosphere of the helium atom has only two electrons in it. You may wonder how with only two electrons the atom can seem so diffuse. Did you ever see the boys on the Fourth of July waving the sparklers to make circles or figure eights? Of course the sparklers were not in the form of circles; they appeared that way because they moved so fast. So here, the electrons give this continuous, diffuse appearance to the atom because they are now here and now there, and we have caught a "time exposure" of their average positions. This is of course what we would see if we could really look at the atom.

There have been fifty-seven varieties of atomic theories proposed. Lord Kelvin thought the atom was something like a smoke ring; J. J. Thomson said it was a sphere of jelly. Rutherford called it a miniature solar system, while Bohr and Sommerfeld calculated precisely the orbits of the planetary electrons revolving about the central nucleus. Lewis and Langmuir objected, and said the atom is a cube. "Not so, it's a tetrahedron," claimed Landé. "Quite a mistake, it's a diffuse atmosphere of electricity around a central core," says Schrödinger. "Only it isn't diffuse electricity," complains Heisenberg, "it's electrons moving now here, now there, which make up this atmosphere." Thus the debate was waged. Now that we see how it looks we find that they were all wrong except Heisenberg. He seems at last to have predicted correctly what we should find.

# 12. The Paradox of Light

## *1929*

The nature of light was the subject that provoked the liveliest scientific controversy during the decade of the 1920's as the concept of the duality of waves and particles replaced the traditional wave theory of radiation. The author, whose own researches provided an important foundation for the new theory, here discusses the problem in nontechnical terms. *

Thanks to the light about us, we guide our steps, escape from remote danger, enjoy a beautiful scene, learn the nature of a distant star, see the smile on a friend's face. Light is vital to the growth of both plants and animals. Our work, our pleasures, our very life are continually dependent upon its presence. Yet of its own nature we know very little.

Newton thought of a beam of sunlight as a stream of little particles shot from the sun toward the earth. The rival conception of light as trains of waves, analogous to the waves in air that give us the sensation of sound, though familiar to Newton, was not generally held until the beginning of the nineteenth century. At this time Young and Fresnel discovered the surprising fact that by adding one beam of light to another under proper conditions it is possible to produce darkness. If light consists of streams of particles, no one could find an explanation of this remarkable phenomenon; but if it is a wave motion, a satisfactory interpretation is easily found. Everyone has watched the ripples forming when pebbles are thrown into a pool. If the crests of one set of ripples fall upon the crests of another, the ripples are high; but where the crests of one group fall on the troughs of a second, the ripples are small or disappear. It was only necessary to imagine that light comes in trains of waves like these ripples to see how it might be possible for the crests of one train of waves to be neutralized by the troughs of another. Thus experiments that showed that one beam of light could interfere with a second to produce darkness convinced its students that light is not like a stream of bullets, but is to be compared rather with the ripples on a pond.

## THE CONCEPT OF THE "ETHER"

Sound waves are propagated through the air; but light waves may come to us from the filament in an electric light bulb, within which is the best vacuum we know how to produce. In order that there might be some medium to transmit these waves, an "ether" was invented, which should pervade all space. This ether was supposed to have the properties of an elastic solid, something like the Jell-o served for dessert, through which the vibrations could be transmitted. Fresnel found that if the ether waves are to act as light does the ether must be immensely more rigid than steel. Yet through this rigid medium the earth and sun and we ourselves must freely move. A truly difficult conception!

Such a mechanical view of light waves was abandoned by Maxwell some sixty years ago when he showed that there should exist a kind of electrical wave that travels through space at the same speed that light had been found to travel. It was some years later when Hertz produced such electrical waves in his laboratory, by passing a spark between metal balls, and found that these waves had many of the characteristics of light. The development of the idea from there on is familiar: how the electric waves of Hertz suggested to Marconi the wireless telegraph, and how this further developed into the wireless telephone and the radio. We have now become so familiar with the idea of wavelengths of radio waves and of frequencies of vibration that the possibility that such rays may be anything other than waves rarely enters our minds.

In speaking of radio waves and light rays we still frequently use the term "ether." According to Maxwell's picture, however, there is nothing material about the medium through which the waves pass. We merely ascribe to space certain electric and magnetic properties, those indeed which the space must have in order to account for the pushes and pulls between magnets and electric charges. On the other hand, though there is no material medium, the electric waves are themselves a form of matter, that is, they have mass and weight, the essential characteristics of matter in the physical sense. It has been shown that when a beam of light strikes a surface it exerts a pressure, just as if the light beam were a stream of water from a hose. This means that the light waves have momentum, and hence also mass—that they are themselves a form of matter. Nor is the amount of matter in light rays insignificant, as is emphasized by the example of the sun, which radiates away as light four million tons of its material each second.

The motion of the nozzle of a hose back and forth does not of itself produce any wave; but when the water is turned on it is thrown in a wavy stream. The existence of these waves does not depend upon any medium through which the stream of water moves. The stream is its own medium. In a somewhat similar way it is possible to imagine an atom at the sun oscillating back and forth and emitting a stream of radiation toward the earth. The stream of waves is its own medium, and when the radiation ceases the space is again empty.

My friend Professor Nazir Ahmad once told me the following story, ascribed to one of the wise men of ancient Persia, as we were whiling away together the evening hours in a dak bungalow in the mountains of Kashmir:

A certain Arab at his death bequeathed all of his property to his three sons, one-half to the eldest, one-third to the second, and one-ninth to the youngest son. Now it so happened that the most valuable part of his estate consisted of seventeen camels, and the sons fell to quarreling regarding how they should be divided. At last they brought their camels to the sheik that he might apportion them justly. After listening patiently as they presented their problem, the old sheik spoke:

"Allah has granted his servant an only camel. I pray you, my children, to accept this camel at my hands, and add it to your father's estate. You now have eighteen camels."

To the eldest son he said: "Take thou now the half of the camels, nine, which is more than thy share. Go thou and be content."

To the second son, likewise: "Thy share was one-third. Take thou six camels, which is more than thy share. Go thou and be content."

And to the youngest son in the same manner he spoke: "Take thou now the ninth, two camels, which is more than thy share. Go thou also and be content."

And so they departed joyfully, taking with them nine camels and six and two. Then the old sheik lifted his eyes and saw standing before him his own camel.

"Behold the reward of the faithful! I have given my camel away, and Allah has restored my camel to me. Blessed be Allah!"

It is perhaps fair to say that the concept of the material ether played the same part in the development of the wave theory of light as did the eighteenth camel in the division of the Arab's estate. Both made the solving of the problem easier, but neither was really essential to the solution.

Some five years ago, Nichols and Tear, at Cleveland, showed that it was possible to detect electric waves of the same type as those used in radio transmission, though of shorter wavelength, by the same method that is used to detect heat rays. The spectrum of these heat rays in turn can be followed continuously through the infrared region and the region of visible light to the region of ultraviolet light, those rays with which we are now becoming familiar because of their value in curing rickets and tuberculosis. A young Scotsman by the name of Osgood, working at Chicago, showed last summer that the spectrum of ultraviolet light could be followed right through to the region of X rays, so that these are also known to be of the same nature. Beyond the X rays are in turn the gamma rays from radium and the penetrating cosmic rays that are found at high altitudes. Whatever we say regarding the nature of one of these types of rays must therefore hold equally well for the others. If then radio rays and light rays are waves, so also are X rays and gamma rays.

## EINSTEIN AND THE PHOTOELECTRIC EFFECT

The first serious challenge to the view that light consists of waves, since the time of Fresnel and Young, was made by Einstein in 1905. When a beam of light falls upon the surface of certain metals, such as sodium or zinc, electricity in the form of electrons is found to be emitted from the surface. The number of these electrons is proportional to the intensity of the light, but the speed at which they move does not depend upon its intensity. It depends only upon the color, or frequency, of the light that strikes the metal. Thus the feeble light from a star will eject an electron from a surface with just as great speed as will the intense light from the sun.

This "photoelectric effect" is especially prominent with X rays, for these rays eject electrons from all sorts of substances. X rays are produced when a stream of electrons hits a block of metal inside an X-ray tube. It is as if one were shooting at a steel plate with a rapid-fire gun. The stream of bullets represents the electrons shot at the metal target of the X-ray tube. The racket produced when the bullets strike the steel plate corresponds to the X rays emitted from the target of the tube. Let us suppose that an electron strikes the target of an X-ray tube at a speed of a hundred miles a second—these electrons certainly move tremendously fast. The X ray produced by this electron may pass through a block of wood and strike a piece of metal on the other side. If when it strikes it ejects an electron from the metal the speed of the ejected electron will be almost as great as that of the original electron which gave rise to the X ray.

The surprising nature of this phenomenon may be illustrated by an experience that I had in my early boyhood. During the summer vacations my father would take our family to a lake in northern Michigan. My older brother, with several of the older boys, built a diving pier around the "point" a half mile away from the camp, where the water was deep. We younger boys built a diving pier in the shallower water in front of the camp. It so happened, one hot, calm, July day, that my brother dove from his diving board into the deep water. By the time the resulting ripples had spread around the "point" to where I was swimming a half mile away, they were of course much too small to notice. You can imagine my surprise, therefore, when these insignificant ripples, striking me as I was swimming under our diving pier, suddenly lifted me bodily from the water and set me on the diving board!

Is this impossible? It is no more so than for an ether ripple, sent out when an electron dives into the target of an X-ray tube, to jerk an electron out of a second piece of metal with a speed equal to that of the first electron.

It was considerations of this kind that showed to Einstein the futility of trying to account for the photoelectric effect on the basis of waves. He suggested, however, that this effect might be explained if light and X rays consist of particles. These particles we now call "photons." The picture of the X-ray experiment on this view would be that when the electron strikes the target of an X-ray tube its energy of motion is transformed into a photon, that is, a particle of X rays, which goes with the speed of light to the second piece of metal. Here the photon gives up its energy to one of the electrons of which the metal is composed, and throws it out with an energy of motion equal to that of the first electron. Such a picture accounts at once for the fact that the number of photoelectrons is proportional to the intensity of the radiation; for if one beam is twice as intense as another it has twice as many photons, which will eject twice as many electrons. In order to explain why the electrons move faster when thrown out of a metal by light of higher frequency, Einstein borrowed a suggestion made originally by Planck, that the energy of a photon is greater for light of high frequency; that is, photons of blue light carry more energy than photons of red light.

In this way Einstein was able to account in a very satisfactory way for the phenomenon of the ejection of electrons by light and X rays. But his theory had been devised for just this purpose. It was not surprising that it should work well for this one phenomenon. It would naturally carry much greater weight if it could be shown that the theory accounted for other facts for which it had not been originally intended. This is what it has recently done in connection with certain properties of scattered X rays.

## PECULIAR X-RAY ECHOES

If you hold a piece of paper in the light of a lamp, the paper scatters light from the lamp into your eyes. This is the way in which the paper is made visible. In the same way, if the lamp were an X-ray tube, the paper would scatter X rays to your eyes. If you had a blue light in your lamp, the paper would appear blue. If the light were yellow, the paper would appear yellow, and so on. But some five years ago we noticed that when a sheet of paper or anything else scatters X rays the "color" or frequency of the rays is changed. The corresponding effect with light would be for the paper to appear green when illuminated with blue light, yellow when illuminated with green light, red when lighted by a yellow lamp, and so on.

If light and X rays are waves, the scattered X rays are like an echo. When one whistles in front of a barn, the echo comes back with the same pitch as the original tone. This must be so, because each wave of the sound is reflected from the barn, as many waves return as strike, and the frequency or pitch of the echoed wave is the same as that of the original wave. In the case of the scattered X rays the echo should similarly be thrown back by the electrons in the scattering material, and should likewise have the same pitch or frequency as the incident rays. Thus the wave theory does not account for the lowered frequency of the scattered X rays.

The corpuscular idea revived by Einstein suggests, however, a simple explanation of the effect. In this view we may suppose that each photon of the scattered X rays is deflected by a single electron, just as a golf ball might bounce from a football. Since a part of the golf ball's energy is spent in setting the football in motion, it bounces off with less energy than when it struck. In the same way, the electron from which the X-ray photon bounces will recoil, taking part of the photon's energy, and the deflected photon will have less energy than before it struck the electron. This reduction in energy of the deflected photon corresponds in Einstein's view to a decrease in frequency of the scattered X rays, just as the experiments show. In fact, the theory is so definite that it is possible to calculate just how great a change in frequency should occur, and the calculation is found to correspond accurately with the experiments.

## PLAYING BILLIARDS WITH PHOTONS
## AND ELECTRONS

If this explanation is the correct one, it should, however, be possible to find the electrons that recoil from the deflected X-ray particles. Before this theory was suggested no such recoiling electrons had ever been noticed. Professor C. T. R. Wilson of Cambridge University had, however, invented a beautiful method for making visible the tracks left by electrons when they go at high speed through air. Within a few months after this new theory of the scattering of X rays had been proposed he photographed the trails left when electrons in air recoiled from the X rays that they scattered. Thus we have observed not only the loss in energy of the deflected golf balls, but have also found the footballs, or electrons, from which they have bounced.

Finally, it was found possible to follow not only the electron that recoiled from the impact of the X ray, but also the path of the deflected X-ray particle as it bounced from the electron. Wilson's method was used for photographing the trails left by the electrons that had been struck by the X-ray particles. A faint beam of X rays was shot through air of such intensity that in each photograph would appear the trails of one or two recoiling electrons. Now if the recoiling electron moves to the left, the X-ray particle must have glanced to the right, just as when the golf ball bounces to one side the football recoils to the other. If the scattered X ray goes as a wave, like a ripple spreading in all directions, there is no reason to expect it to affect a second electron on one side rather than on the other. But if the X ray is a particle glancing to the right, the second electron that it strikes must be on the right side of the particle's original path. A large number of photographs showed that this was indeed the case.

Such experiments show very directly that an X ray is scattered from an electron in a definite direction, as it should be if it is a particle.

## THE PARADOX OF PARTICLES AND WAVES

But if X rays consist of particles, so also must light rays and heat rays and radio rays. We are thus confronted with the problem either of accounting on the corpuscular theory for the properties of light that have been explained in terms of waves, or of reconciling the view that light consists of waves with the view that light consists of corpuscles. For centuries it has been thought that these two conceptions of the nature of light are contradictory; but when we are confronted with apparently convincing evidence that light consists of waves, and equally convincing evidence that it consists of particles, the two conceptions must in some way be reconcilable.

The theoretical physicists are hard at work on a reconciliation of the two conceptions. One suggestion is that the energy of radiation is carried by the particles, and that the waves serve merely to guide the particles. According to a second view the particles of radiation exist in any true sense only when the radiation is acting on atoms or electrons, and that in between such events the radiation moves as waves. It is as yet difficult, however, to state these ideas in any satisfactory form. Perhaps the best picture that one can give of the relation between waves and particles is the analogy of the sheets of rain that one sometimes sees in a thunderstorm. We may liken the waves to the sheets of rain that one sees sweeping down the street or across the fields. The radiation particles, or photons, would correspond to the raindrops of which the sheet is composed. This picture is probably a fairly accurate one when we are thinking of radio rays. For in the case of radio rays even a feeble signal, such as one broadcast from Los Angeles and heard in New York, would have waves consisting of thousands of photons per cubic inch. But in the case of X rays one can perform experiments with a single photon, and it is difficult to imagine one particle arranged in sheets.

The fact remains that the evidence before us seems to demand that light and other forms of radiation consist both of waves and particles.

## OUR NEW ACQUAINTANCE, THE "PHOTON"

During the last generation we have familiarized ourselves with electrons, the elementary units of negative electricity, and protons, the smallest units of positive electricity. It is of these two types of particles, arranged in different manners, that the various kinds of atoms are built. Now we recognize in nature a third type of elementary particle, the photon.*

The photon is a concentrated bundle of energy that moves through space at the speed of light, fast enough to circle the earth seven times in a single second. We have gradually been accustoming ourselves to the idea of disembodied energy, or rather of energy which is its own body. Thus it has long been recognized that the most reasonable explanation of the mass of the electron is to suppose that it is due to the electric energy that it possesses. The same is presumably true of the proton. But we have never observed an electron or a proton giving up its electrical charge and all of its energy, though such an event very possibly occurs in the interior of the stars. The photon on the other hand is created, apparently out of nothing, when an atom or an electron loses energy; and when the photon gives up its energy to another atom we can find nothing left. The photon has momentum just as does any form of radiation, and hence has mass,

| 147 |

and is thus truly a bit of matter—a material particle. But it is a particle that is created from the energy spent by an atom, and when it releases its energy it vanishes.

The work that a mosquito does when it walks an inch up the side of a wall takes the energy of a hundred million X-ray photons, and an X-ray photon has some ten thousand times as much energy as a photon of visible light. It is true that these energies are excessively small. Yet they are sufficient for each individual photon to produce a detectable effect.

The mass of these photons makes itself evident by knocking the electrons around, as we have described above. For ordinary frequencies of light or X rays the mass of a photon is much less than that of an electron, but a photon of hard gamma rays from radium weighs about the same as does an electron at rest. In a piece of matter at ordinary temperatures, the photons do not add appreciably to the mass. But inside the stars, where temperatures are measured by millions of degrees, the photons weigh about one per cent as much as the electrons present. This means that it would take several earths to weigh as much as the photons in the sun.

Of the fundamental things in the world there thus remain these three: protons, electrons, and photons.*

### ELECTRON WAVES

If then light, which has long been known as waves, is now found to consist of particles, may it not be that such things as atoms and electrons, which have long been known as particles, may have the characteristics of waves? Thus reasoned the French physicist Louis de Broglie. His suggestion was put to experimental test during the last year by two American physicists, Davisson * and Germer. They found that a stream of electrons could be made to show interference effects in just the same way as can a beam of light or X rays. It was, however, this interference property of light that was the chief argument in the proof of its wave character. We now have precisely the same kind of evidence for believing in the wave characteristics of electrons.

Our paradox of waves and particles is thus not confined to the nature of light, but applies to electrons as well. Light, which we have long thought of as waves, has the properties of particles; and electrons, which have long been thought of as particles, have the properties of waves. There seems to be a dualistic aspect to these fundamental entities. The distinction between the conceptions of waves and particles may not be as sharp as we have thought.

# 13. What We Have Learned from Scattered X Rays

## *1940*

&#x2767; The Franklin Institute awarded Arthur Holly Compton its Franklin medal in 1940 "in recognition of his brilliant experiments on various properties of X rays." In accepting the award Mr. Compton reviewed his work with X rays from his graduate days through the period of his most active interest in this field of research.* His remarks were read by his brother, Karl T. Compton, at the Medal Day ceremony in Philadelphia on May 15, 1940.

Just as sunlight is scattered by sky and clouds, so X rays are scattered by any object that they strike. Most of our information about the world has come through light scattered by objects into our eyes. It is thus not surprising that important additions to our knowledge should come from the scattering of the light of superfrequency that we call X rays. The new information thus gained has concerned the nature of X rays and light, and the nature of the objects that scatter the X rays.

Only a few months after Roentgen's announcement of the discovery of X rays, Michael Pupin, working with an X-ray tube of unusual power and using Edison's fluoroscope as a sensitive detector, discovered scattered X rays. He noted that when any object, such as a book or a man's hand, was placed in the X-ray beam, the object itself became a source of radiation that would light up a fluoroscope placed in the neighborhood. It was like brightening a room by placing a sheet of white paper in the path of a sunbeam that comes through a window.

An interpretation of this phenomenon of scattering was given some years later by J. J. Thomson in terms of electromagnetic waves acting on electrons. He had already calculated the energy that should be radiated when an electric charge is moving with changing velocity. When X rays are scattered, he supposed that the electric field of the impinging wave changes the velocity of the electrons in the scattering material. Thus Thomson was able to calculate how intense the scattered rays should be in terms of the number of electrons present.

The calculation was a bold one with far-reaching consequences. Up to this time no satisfactory quantitative test of the theory of radiation from an accelerated charge had been possible. Though the charge and mass of the electron were roughly known, no one knew how many electrons were to be found in each atom. It was, however, correctly assumed that most of the electrons had natural frequencies comparable with those of light, and hence that with regard to X-ray waves of a thousandfold greater frequency they would act almost as if free from constraining forces. A favorable test of Thomson's calculations would thus at once establish the theory that X rays were electromagnetic waves, that an accelerated charge emits radiation, and, assuming the validity of the theory, serve to estimate the number of electrons in the scattering material.

In 1905 Charles Barkla, stimulated by Thomson's calculations, found a slight polarization of the X rays coming directly from an X-ray tube, which strongly suggested the electromagnetic character of the rays. Within a year he had performed the then very delicate experiment of measuring X rays scattered twice at right angles. The first scattering should theoretically polarize the rays completely, and the second scattering of these already polarized rays should serve to analyze their polarization. His experiments showed 50 per cent polarization as compared with a theoretical 100 per cent, which was adequate to show the strong probability of the correctness of the electromagnetic wave theory of X rays.

Seventeen years later Charles F. Hagenow and I repeated Barkla's work with the more refined equipment then available, and found that the lack of complete polarization that he had observed was due chiefly to multiple scattering in his large polarizing and analyzing blocks, and that when smaller blocks are used the polarization does indeed approach 100 per cent as the theory demands.

It is interesting to note that this first verification of Thomson's theory indicates a motion of the electrons in the scattering material along the direction of the electric vector of the X-ray wave. This shows that the electrons carry electric charges. A few years ago Eric Rodgers, working in our laboratory, extended the polarization experiments to show that the electron has likewise a magnetic moment. Assuming that an electron is spinning, it should act as a gyroscopic magnet. The magnetic field of an incident X-ray wave should set the resulting magnet in motion in such a way as to produce a scattered ray which has no polarization. This magnetically scattered ray should, however, be appreciable only for X rays produced at potentials greater than 200 kilovolts. Using X rays up to 800 kilovolts potential, where the theoretical value of the scattering by the magnetic doublet of the electron should be comparable with that by its electric charge, Rodgers observed just the expected amount of unpolarized X rays. Thus scattered X rays have shown also that the electron is magnetic.

Following his polarization experiments, Barkla measured the intensity of the scattered X rays. This was found to follow a much more complicated rule than was indicated by Thomson's simple theory. Part of the difference was traced to the fact that in the heavier atoms the electrons are grouped so closely that the scattered X rays are nearly in phase with each other. This leads to an intensity of scattering greater than Thomson's normal value. On the other hand, for very short X-ray waves the scattering was found to be less than Thomson predicted, a departure whose origin was not revealed until later.

By carefully selecting the experimental conditions, however, and assuming the essential validity of Thomson's calculations, Barkla was able to make a reliable estimate of the number of electrons in the scattering material. This he found to be a number in each atom equal approximately to half of its atomic weight.

It was one of those striking coincidences of physics that this first reliable determination of the number of electrons in an atom should have appeared in the same 1911 issue of the *Philosophical Magazine* as that in which Rutherford published his first measurement of the charge on the nucleus of the atom based on the scattering of alpha particles. This charge was likewise estimated as equal to half the atomic weight. At once it became evident that the atom consists of a positively charged nucleus, surrounded by a number of electrons sufficient to neutralize the charge. With Moseley's remarkable X-ray spectra two years later, we found how the number of these electrons changes merely by one as we go from element to element, the basis of our concept of atomic number, a result which might indeed have been inferred from the earlier experiments of Barkla and Rutherford.

A complete account of what scattered X rays have taught us would include at this point a consideration of the diffraction of X rays by crystals and of X-ray spectra, for these are merely special aspects of scattering. With the work of Laue, the Braggs, Moseley, Siegbahn, and many others, however, this work has become so well known that in spite of its outstanding importance we may properly leave it with this passing mention.

My own active interest in scattered X rays came first when I realized that here was a method of determining the arrangement of electrons in atoms. You are familiar with the ring around the moon caused by the diffraction of moonlight by droplets of fog. In this phenomenon the size of the ring depends upon the ratio of the length of the light wave to the size of the drop. When the size of the corona becomes smaller, we know that the droplets are growing and that very probably they will fall as rain. In a similar manner X rays are diffracted by the atoms in a gas, and it should be possible by studying the diffraction halos to estimate the size of the atoms. Since it is the electrons in an atom that scatter X rays, this would mean finding the distances of the electrons from each other.

It was in 1914 that I began by this direct method to investigate the electronic structure of atoms. The Braggs had been using X-ray diffraction as an effective method of learning the arrangement of atoms in crystals. Why should not a more refined study lead to a knowledge of the electron distributions in the atoms themselves? The most promising approach seemed at first to study the intensity of the various orders of X-ray diffraction from crystals. C. G. Darwin had made some calculations of intensity of this diffraction in terms of the electron distribution, and I was able to show how it should be possible to calculate backward from observed intensity measurements to arrive at the electron arrangements. The necessary experiments were delicate, and involved many corrections; but they were at last completed, only to find that the resulting electron distribution contained an important unknown factor. This factor was the magnitude of the heat motions of the atoms in the crystal that was diffracting the X rays. Until more was known about the heat motions of atoms, we could not reliably use experiments with crystals to determine the electronic structure of their component atoms.

The obvious alternative to studying atoms arranged in the regular order of a crystal lattice was to use atoms distributed entirely at random. Whereas for the crystal it is necessary to take account of the diffraction pattern of the regularly arranged atoms themselves, for an amorphous substance the diffraction by each molecule should be independent of that of every other, and no such correction for their mutual effects need be considered.

It was from such considerations that in 1917 Debye and Scherrer, working in Switzerland, began to study the diffraction of X rays by such supposedly amorphous materials as sheets of metal. The result was diffraction patterns showing that these materials were really masses of tiny crystals. Instead of developing a method of determining electronic distributions, therefore, they discovered the powerful and convenient powdered-crystal method of studying atomic arrangements in metals.

My own objective was turned toward the scattering of X rays by monatomic gases, where, if under any conditions, one might rely on the random arrangement of the scattering atoms. The first major problem was the experimental one of obtaining enough scattered X rays to measure. By certain improvements in technique, Barkla had succeeded in measuring reliably the scattering of the total X-ray beam from a large block of solid material. We needed to measure the scattering of a single wavelength of X rays from a volume of gas small enough to determine precisely the angle at which the rays were scattered. As compared with Barkla's experiments, a factor of roughly a millionfold had to be gained.

The problem was precisely similar to that of striving to photograph spiral nebulae at greater and greater distances. The telescope is made larger, the plates more sensitive, the time of exposure increased, and the aim of the telescope toward the star is improved. So we introduced water-cooled X-ray tubes, ionization chambers with more strongly absorbing gas, an electrometer of greatly increased sensitivity (which my brother who reads this paper helped to develop), and finally reached the required factor of a million by using P. A. Ross's difference-absorption method of obtaining the effects of a homogeneous X-ray beam a hundred times more intense than that reflected from a crystal.

Before this technical difficulty had been overcome, however, we were faced by an unforeseen theoretical problem. When a spectroscope is turned toward the sky, the same Fraunhofer spectral lines are observed as are to be seen when the spectroscope is pointed directly at the sun. This must be so. For every light wave that strikes an air molecule is scattered, and the number of scattered waves will thus be the same as the number of incident ones. This means that the frequency and wavelength of the scattered light must be the same as that of the light that comes from the sun. It had gradually become evident, however, that the diffused X rays and gamma rays coming from a scattering block were more readily absorbed than the incident rays. Various attempts to explain this phenomenon were put forward, most of them based on the idea that an important part of the diffused rays was of fluorescent origin. When, however, we turned the X-ray spectrometer on the diffused rays we found that almost all of the X rays were increased in wavelength. Fluorescent rays should not be polarized, but these rays of increased wavelength were. If we were to consider those rays to be scattered whose intensity was given by Thomson's classical theory, certainly we had found a change in wavelength of scattered X rays. Here was a fundamental difficulty that needed to be resolved before any diffraction theory could reliably be applied that would assume that the diffracted ray and the primary ray were of the same wavelength.

We soon found that the observed change of wavelength could be quantitatively explained by assuming that the X-ray beam consists of a stream of photons, particles carrying a quantum of energy each, as had been suggested previously by Einstein in his theory of the photoelectric effect. We supposed that each photon is deflected by a single electron, which recoils from the impact, taking away some of the photon's energy. This theory involved thus both the energy and the momentum of the photon, whereas to explain the photoelectric effect only its energy was important.

The theory thus used to account for the change in wavelength implied that scattered X rays should be accompanied by electrons recoiling with an energy only a few per cent that of photoelectrons. Such electrons had not yet been identified, but were now immediately observed by C. T. R. Wilson, using his cloud chamber; and our studies showed that their number and energy corresponded accurately with the values predicted from the photon theory.

In a desperate effort to save the wave theory of radiation, it was then pointed out that these phenomena were consistent with the view that X rays are waves if we would consider that the conservation of energy and momentum is only statistically conserved in the scattering process, but not in the motion of the individual electrons. This proposal to abandon the exact validity of the conservation principle stimulated tests by Bothe and Geiger in Germany and by ourselves of the individual process of electron-photon interaction. It was found that whenever a recoil electron appears, a photon is scattered in just the direction and with just the energy required for the exact conservation of their energy and the momentum. Thus not only did the conservation principle receive an important new confirmation, but we had actually traced the path of an X ray from place to place, showing that it travels as a compact bundle of energy. In other words, X rays were particles.

As these studies were in progress, Louis de Broglie brought forward his now famous theory that the motions of waves and particles are really indistinguishable, if we suppose that associated with each particle is a wave whose length is inversely proportional to its momentum. His results were immediately applicable to our experiments on the wavelength change of scattered X rays. A year or two later they were shown by Davisson and Germer and by G. P. Thomson to predict accurately the wave properties of electrons. Soon it was found that moving hydrogen and helium atoms and hydrogen molecules can be diffracted by crystal gratings, and that their wavelengths are also given by de Broglie's theory.

So here was the duality of particles and waves, introduced first in the case of X rays when our scattering experiments revealed the particle properties of rays long known to be waves, and then extended by de Broglie's theory to moving particles of every type.

It would take us too far afield to describe how this duality became the basis of the uncertainty principle, philosophically one of the most significant developments of modern physics. Nor can we stop to describe the development of the new quantum mechanics, which, as Heisenberg showed, could be derived from this principle as a starting point. For our present purpose the significant fact is that within a half dozen years from the first measurement of the change in wavelength of scattered X rays a new quantum theory of X-ray scattering had been developed in which electrons had only probable, not actual, positions within the atom. Now it was evident that when X rays are scattered with changed wavelength they act independently of each other. It is only the scattered rays whose wavelength remains unchanged that are affected by the arrangement of the scattering electrons. The theory was now in shape for reliable application to the data on X-ray scattering.

New work on the scattering of X rays by helium, neon, and argon was now undertaken by Charles Barrett and E. O. Wollan in our laboratory, and by G. Herzog in Zürich. In helium the electrons were found to be distributed diffusely in a region whose average size is about that specified by Bohr's old orbital theory. In neon, two groups of electrons are identified, and in argon three groups, though the resolving power of the X-ray waves was not sufficient to distinguish clearly between the two inner groups. The results are indeed as definite as if we were looking directly at the atoms with an X-ray microscope. Though perhaps not so exciting, it was however very satisfying that the electron distributions thus observed are in complete agreement with modern quantum theories of atomic structure, at least if we interpret the wave function in terms of the probability of electron occurrence rather than as an actual volume density of electricity.

Comparing the new electron distributions from gases with the older ones from crystals, it was now possible to estimate the thermal motions of the crystal atoms. We were thus able directly to show that even at the zero point of temperature a motion of the atoms occurs equal to half a quantum of energy in each mode of vibration. This served to distinguish between two forms of quantum theory of heat, which had been a vexing question since the early theories of Planck.

So finally, after some twenty years of study by experimenters in this country and in Europe, the problem that I had set myself for my doctor's thesis has received an answer. I am happy to have had a part in its solution. Fortunately, my professors did not demand the completion of the problem before they released me from the university halls. It gives me great pleasure that the Franklin medal committee has seen in my share of this work a worthy contribution to science.

# 14. A World Survey of Cosmic Rays

## *1933*

A pioneer in the detection and analysis of cosmic rays,* Mr. Compton described some aspects of this work * during one of a series of science programs prepared by the General Electric Company to acquaint the public with the most recent developments in the field of scientific endeavor. The program originated in Schenectady, New York, on March 24, 1933, and was broadcast over the NBC radio network.

Karl Darrow has recently described the study of cosmic rays as "unique in modern physics for the minuteness of the phenomena, the delicacy of the observations, the adventurous excursions of the observers, the subtlety of the analysis, and the grandeur of the inferences." * These adjectives were aptly chosen. The cosmic rays are bringing us an important message. Perhaps they are telling us how our world has evolved, or perhaps they are bringing news of the innermost structure of the atomic nucleus. We are now engaged in trying to decode this message.

Let me explain how cosmic rays can be detected and measured. One way is to measure the electrical conductivity of air. We use a steel bomb, about four inches in diameter, filled with air or argon gas under high pressure. The cosmic rays make this gas slightly conducting, and the tiny electric current that flows through it is measured with a sensitive electrometer. The rays from radium and other radioactive materials also affect the gas inside this bomb. So we surround the bomb with a heavy shell of lead to keep out these undesired rays.

If we carry such a bomb, protected by lead, into a deep tunnel, we find that the compressed gas inside is almost a perfect nonconductor of electricity. On the ground outside the tunnel there is, however, a measurable current through the gas, due to the cosmic rays. If the apparatus is carried to the top of a mountain, or high up in a balloon, the current flowing through the gas rapidly increases, showing that the rays are much stronger at these high altitudes.

Last July we performed this experiment under very favorable conditions on the Central Railway of Peru, which has at its highest point a deep tunnel through a mountain, three miles above sea level, a thousand feet higher than Pikes Peak. Inside the tunnel we could not detect the rays at all. Just outside the tunnel they came in strongly and caused a relatively large current to flow through the instrument.

The cloud expansion chamber, invented by C. T. R. Wilson, makes visible the paths of the ionizing particles associated with the cosmic rays as they break into ions some of the air molecules through which they pass. Some of these particles seem to be the cosmic rays themselves, whereas others are secondary particles produced by the cosmic rays. Highly sensitive ion chambers, connected through amplifying tubes to electrical recorders, serve to count the cosmic rays as they pass through the chambers. These are known as "counting tubes." By arranging these tubes in pairs, so connected that they will record only when both are excited simultaneously, it is possible to study the direction from which the cosmic rays are coming.

Cosmic rays come from outside the earth, no one knows how many thousands or millions of light-years away. They speak to us in a language that we are only beginning to understand, telling us of the conditions where they were born. Whether this birth occurred within the heart of the atom, or in the vast regions of interstellar space, we have not yet learned.

One of the most distinctive characteristics of these rays is their remarkable penetrating power. We think of X rays as very penetrating. Will they not pass through a man's hand, or even through his body? Yet while it takes about one inch of water to absorb half a beam of X rays, or a foot of water to absorb half the gamma rays from radium, it requires some twenty feet of water to absorb half a cosmic-ray beam. That is how it happens that these rays will pass right through the heavy blanket of air that forms our atmosphere, through the roof and upper floors of a building, and affect our instruments that are surrounded by heavy shields of lead in the laboratory.

Attention both of scientific men and of the public was called forcibly to the importance of studies of cosmic rays by Robert A. Millikan's suggestive theory of their origin. He developed the idea that the cosmic rays are produced during the formation of atoms in interstellar space, and presented evidence that this is one stage of a cyclic process through which the universe is continually passing. It will be worthwhile to dwell for a moment upon this theory and to describe other hypotheses that have been proposed regarding the nature and significance of cosmic rays.

Millikan based his theory on the assumption that the cosmic rays are electromagnetic radiations, or photons, similar in type to X rays and gamma rays, but of shorter wavelength. This was a natural assumption, in view of the surprisingly great penetrating power which the cosmic rays were found to possess. Considered as photons, it was possible to calculate the energy which each individual cosmic ray must have to give it the penetrating power observed in the experiments. On the other hand, he could also calculate the energy liberated by certain types of atomic processes. Thus, if an atom of helium is formed by the sudden combination of four protons and four electrons, the energy liberated is just that necessary to give a photon of penetrating power equal to the least penetrating cosmic rays. The protons and electrons would presumably occur in interstellar space in the form of hydrogen gas. Thus Millikan pictured helium as being formed by aggregations of hydrogen atoms in the intense cold of the space between the stars, and he spoke of each cosmic ray as being "the birth cry of an atom."

You will recall how Millikan made this process of the formation of helium out of hydrogen one stage in a great cycle. In a similar process it was supposed that heavier atoms, such as oxygen and iron, were formed, giving rise to the more penetrating components of the cosmic rays. The resulting atoms were supposed to come together under gravitational force to produce nebulae and stars. These, in turn, would radiate their energy away as light and heat. While coursing through the vast regions of space, this light and heat energy was in some unknown manner transformed again into protons and electrons, from which the simplest atoms (hydrogen) are formed. From here the great cycle of the universe starts over again in a world continuing forever.

Immediately following this hypothesis of Millikan, Sir James Jeans suggested the alternate view that these rays result from the annihilation, rather than from the transformation, of matter. Jeans noted that if they are photons, like light or X rays, the most penetrating part of the cosmic rays should have just the energy that would be liberated by the sudden coalescence of the electron and proton in a hydrogen atom. That is, whereas Millikan pointed out that the least penetrating cosmic rays have the energy to be expected from the formation of helium atoms out of hydrogen, Jeans found that the most penetrating cosmic rays correspond to the annihilation of hydrogen atoms themselves. This appeared to Jeans as one more way in which the universe was running down.

Recently an interesting theory regarding the nature of cosmic rays has been proposed by a young French physicist Dauvillier. This is not based on the idea of cosmic rays as photons, but rather on the conception that they are electrons shot toward the earth from the sun. This theory is thus somewhat similar to that of Störmer, in which he accounts for the aurora borealis as due to electrons thus shot toward the earth. Dauvillier finds evidence for strong electric fields existing in flocculi on the surface of the sun, estimated at thousands of millions of volts. These powerful electric fields, he supposes, serve to eject the electrons in all directions, some of which would approach the earth. Near the earth they would be affected by the earth's magnetic field and cause at the same time the auroral displays, which are known to be concentrated near the earth's magnetic poles.

But by far the most romantic and by no means the least plausible theory is one just proposed by the Belgian physicist Lemaître. The powerful telescopes and spectroscopes of Mount Wilson Observatory have revealed the fact that the very remote heavenly bodies seem to be moving rapidly away from us. Lemaître has woven this observation into a theory of the universe according to which some thousands of millions of years ago the universe was much more concentrated than it now is and started to expand with explosive violence, so that the distant nebulae continue to fly away with ever increasing speed. At the time of this primeval explosion, he conjectures, not only nebulae and stars were thrown out, but also atoms and electrons and photons—the tiniest pieces of matter. According to his theory, it is these elemental pieces of the original world-stuff, still flying around in space after thousands of millions of years, which constitute the cosmic rays.

Before it is possible to select which if any of these theories is correct, it is necessary for us to learn whether these cosmic rays are electrically neutral photons as Millikan and Jeans assume, negatively charged electrons as Dauvillier supposes, or a mixture of different kinds of rays as Lemaître concludes.

About five years ago, two German physicists, Bothe and Kolhörster, did an experiment with counting tubes that convinced them that the cosmic rays are electrically charged particles. If this conclusion is correct, it means however that there should be a difference in intensity of the rays over different parts of the earth. For the earth acts as a huge magnet, and this huge magnet should deflect the electrified particles as they shoot toward the earth. The effect should be least near the magnetic poles, and greatest near the equator, resulting in an increasing intensity as we go from the equator to the poles.

Accordingly, Millikan took his cosmic-ray electroscope from Pasadena to Churchill on Hudson Bay, near the north magnetic pole. Bothe and Kolhörster took their counting chamber from Hamburg up to Spitzbergen and back. Kerr Grant sent Kennedy from Australia to the Antarctic with a cosmic-ray counting chamber. Corlin traveled in different parts of Scandinavia, where the earth's magnetic field changed in intensity. Only one of this first group of investigators studied the rays near the equator. This was Clay of Amsterdam, who thought he could detect a difference between Holland and Java. On bringing together their results, it was found that although Clay and Corlin had both seemed to detect effects which they considered greater than experimental error, the other investigators failed to find any detectable differences that could be ascribed to the earth's magnetic field.

It was highly important to find out definitely whether any such variation of cosmic-ray intensity with magnetic latitude occurs. If not, it would mean that Bothe and Kolhörster's conclusion was wrong, and that there is no appreciable part of the cosmic rays that consists of electrically charged particles. If, on the other hand, a variation of the predicted kind occurs, it would mean that a part at least of the cosmic rays is electrical in character.

Accordingly, with financial help from the Carnegie Institution, a group of us at the University of Chicago have sent nine different expeditions into as many different portions of the globe to measure cosmic rays during the past eighteen months. These parties have worked on all the continents except Antarctica, and that is included in our plans for the current year. The tropics of the Eastern and Western hemispheres, the Arctic seas, and the southern parts of Africa, America, and New Zealand have been visited. The observers have gone from sea level to the tops of mountains nearly four miles high in the Andes and the Himalayas. Two capable mountaineers, Carpé and Koven, lost their lives on a glacier on the side of mighty Mount McKinley; but their data stand as the highest-altitude data yet obtained for latitudes so close to the pole.

It was, of course, necessary in a program of this kind to get the extensive cooperation of a large number of physicists. Our invitations to join this work met with an enthusiastic response. In order to make a reasonably complete survey within a brief period, the globe was portioned into nine regions, each of which was assigned to a different investigator. In charge of these various expeditions were the following men, each of whom has been responsible for the results obtained by his own party:

(a) Professor Ralph D. Bennett, of the Massachusetts Institute of Technology, whose party has studied Alaska, California, and Colorado.

(b) Dr. E. O. Wollan, of the University of Chicago, who has made measurements in Chicago, Spitzbergen, and Switzerland.

(c) Dr. D. la Cour, director of the Danish Meteorological Survey, whose expedition is now working in northern Greenland at the north pole of the earth's uniform magnetization.

(d) Mr. Allen Carpé, research engineer of the American Telephone and Telegraph Company, whose ill-fated expedition made measurements on Mount McKinley, Alaska.

(e) Professor J. M. Benade, of Punjab University, who has worked in India, Ceylon, Java, and Tibet.

(f) Professor S. M. Naudé, of the University of Cape Town, in South Africa.

(g) Mr. P. G. Ledig, in charge of the Carnegie Magnetic Observatory at Huancayo, Peru, who is now traveling from Peru around Cape Horn and back by way of Brazil to the United States.

(h) Admiral Richard E. Byrd and his associated physicist, Professor Poulter of Iowa Wesleyan University, who plan to continue these studies in Antarctica.

(i) My own branch of the expedition, which has worked in Switzerland, Colorado, Hawaii, New Zealand, Australia, Peru, Panama, Mexico, northern Canada, and northern United States.

Accompanying these leaders there have been some fifty other cooperating physicists, who have worked intensively for periods of from a few days to several months to help in completing the survey. A glance at a world map will indicate how these expeditions have attempted to cover representative portions of the earth's surface.

On bringing together the results of these expeditions, it was found that the cosmic-ray intensity near the poles is about fifteen per cent greater than near the equator. Furthermore, the intensity varies with latitude just as predicted due to the effect of the earth's magnetism on incoming electrified particles. At high altitudes the effect of the earth's magnetism is several times as great.

At first, when this result of the earth's magnetic field was announced, Professor Millikan thought it was contrary to certain data that he and his collaborators had taken. Further examination of his measurements seems to have satisfied him, however, that his data are in accord with ours.

These results show that a considerable part, at least, of the cosmic rays consists of electrified particles. Some of the cosmic rays, however, are not appreciably affected by the earth's magnetic field. Other types of measurement, such as those of Piccard and Regener in their high-altitude balloon flights and Bothe and Kolhörster's counter experiments, lead to the conclusion that very little of these rays is in the form of photons, like light, but that there is probably a considerable quantity of radiation in the form of atoms or atomic nuclei of low atomic weight.

This conclusion is exactly that which is assumed in Lemaître's explosion theory of the origin of cosmic rays. It is not necessary for us, however, to suppose that these atoms and pieces of atoms have been flying through space since the beginning of time. Swann, Gunn, and others have suggested ways in which the stars may act as huge high-potential generators which would serve as continuous sources pouring such high-speed particles into space. It is thus too early to draw positive conclusions regarding the significance of these particles.

I should finally say a word, however, regarding the tremendous energy represented by an individual cosmic ray. Let us take as our unit of energy the electron volt. About two such units are liberated by burning a hydrogen atom. Two million units appear when radium shoots out an alpha particle. But it requires ten thousand million of these units to make a cosmic ray.

Where does this tremendous energy come from?

In the answer to this question lies perhaps the solution of the riddle as to how our universe came to be. Perhaps its answer will tell us how nature liberates power of which we now have no knowledge. Shall we be able to tap and use that power? We know not. But the physicist has been entrusted with the job of finding if he can the answer to this mighty riddle.

# 15. Time and the Growth of Physics

## *1939*

The will of James Arthur, New York manufacturer and noted horologist, established an endowment at New York University to provide an annual lecture on "Time and Its Mysteries." In this paper, the eighth James Arthur Lecture, delivered on April 26, 1939, the author discusses the importance of precise measurement of time to modern scientific thought and research.

We were on a scientific expedition in Peru. Having completed our work near Lima, we found that measurements should also be made at Arequipa, several hundred miles farther south. If we followed the old method of travel by rail and steamship, it would have required five weeks to collect the desired data, and the season would have been so far gone that other work essential to our program would have had to be omitted. By flying to Arequipa and back with our apparatus, we completed several days' observations and were again in Lima within a week, ready to take the ship for Panama and to go north of Hudson Bay before the summer was over.

Our Peruvian friends appreciated our desire to see the country from the air. But once we had arrived at the beautiful garden spot of Arequipa, at the foot of majestic El Misti, they could not understand why we should wish to hasten back. The name of the city reflected the call of the peaceful valley, "Remain here." As we explained the urgency of our work they exclaimed, "To you time is golden; to us it is lead."

For in simple, unorganized life, why should one be concerned with time? Consider the Punjabi's remark when the train left him on the station platform as he was going through the traditional Mohammedan prayers at sunset: "What matter? If I have missed the train today, I shall take it tomorrow."

We can thus see that people's concern with time runs closely parallel with the degree of organization of society. If we are eager to complete

some undertaking, every moment is precious; if life is routine and monotonous, time hangs heavy on our hands. Where the activities of many
persons have to be coordinated, precise knowledge of the time is needed.
The forces which make our society grow more complex are the very ones
which require us to number the hours.

## MAN'S PLACE IN TIME

As man attains humanity, he concerns himself with such questions as:
How am I related to the world about me? Whence did I come? Whither
is life leading me? We want to know how long things have been as they
are, and how rapidly they are changing.

It is noteworthy that the problem of when things began does not seem
to concern primitive peoples very much. Myths of origins, such as Venus
rising full grown from the wave, do not require dating. It is sufficient that
they happened before the memory of anyone who could have told it to a
living person.

When written history appears, a few generations before the time of the
earliest record is enough for the origin of man. Thus we find the story of
Adam and Eve dated by a few definitely counted generations before the
time of writing. It is only within our own memory that the scientific
world, let alone the public, has freed itself from this tradition sufficiently
to make an unprejudiced estimate of the age of man.

If we regard physics as the study of the world of matter, the study of
time is one of its most essential aspects. Time, space, and mass are indeed
the concepts in terms of which the physicist tries to describe everything
he sees. The measurement of the time intervals with which man is concerned is thus as true a function of physical science as is the surveying
of land, the gauging of a steel bearing, or the weighing of an atom.

It was because of their concern with the mystery of the passage of time
that the early Babylonians and Egyptians and Mayans placed the observers of the stars in their sacred position. The physicist owes to the historian,
the archaeologist, and the geologist a major debt for acquainting him with
the time required for such cycles as the rise and fall of family dynasties,
the growth and decay of cities and empires, the rise of man to power
over nature, and the evolution of life on our planet. It is notable, however,
that without the physicist's contributions those events which have occurred on a prolonged time scale could not have been dated with any
precision. The geologist had divided the history of the earth into great
ages, based upon the nature of the strata of rock that were formed at the
time. Thus from the ancient archaic to the most recent Pleistocene

there was found a continual development of life. But when asked how many years ago these things happened, geology could give only the vaguest replies.

Then came the discovery of radioactivity. Certain of the atoms occurring in rocks are of only temporary existence. Chief among these from their geological interest are the chemical elements uranium and thorium. Efforts to change their rate of disintegration by applying high and low temperature, by electrical bombardment, and by other methods have proved unavailing.[1] Here then is a natural clock whose rate can be relied upon to remain constant through the ages.

The method of telling time from this uranium clock consists in finding how much of the products of disintegration are present in the rock that is being studied. Suppose, for example, one per cent of the uranium atoms disintegrates in each hundred million years, eventually forming atoms of lead. If then a rock under examination contains ten per cent as many atoms of lead as of the parent uranium, we can safely say that the rock was formed about a thousand million years ago. Following this method the oldest rocks that are known are found to be about two billion years old. For the very recent rocks, the amount of disintegration of the uranium, or thorium, is so small that the age determinations are not very precise. But a time scale is established whose reliability goes far beyond that imagined possible a generation ago.

Old Pythagoras, six centuries before Christ, is credited with having known that where hills now stand there was once sea, and to have correctly inferred that the world has been continuously changing through long ages. Here was perhaps the origin of the geologist's vision of the vast extent of the history of life. Now that the physicist has joined his distinctive methods to those of the geologist, the dating of earth history has become reliable and exact.

We must, however, go still farther into the question of world origins if we would complete our knowledge of the time scale. When was the earth formed? The sun, the Milky Way, the universe itself: when did these come into being? Until within a century the answers to such questions seemed to be hopelessly remote. We do not now know the answers. But it is fair to say that we are making progress in solving the problem. We may now justifiably hope for an answer to the question, When was the world made?

---

[1] The very recent discovery of uranium "fission" caused by neutron bombardment can hardly correspond to a process that would have occurred to an appreciable extent in the earth's history, and in any case does not result in the production of lead. This effect does not therefore alter the uranium time scale.

With regard to the earth itself, the phenomenon of radioactivity sets other definite limits. Our planet is at least as old as the two-billion-year age of the archaic rocks. On the other hand, if it were more than ten billion years old the radioactive materials initially present in the planet should have given rise to more lead than is actually found. Between these rather wide but reliable limits we can be confident that our earth was born. Most authorities favor the lower limit as approaching more closely its actual age.

If the earth was born of the sun, the sun must of course be the older body, but not necessarily much older.

When we ask about our galaxy, and the system of galaxies that forms the known universe, we can find theories that will assign ages varying all the way from an infinite life to a life but little longer than the shortest permissible age of the earth. On the basis of observations of the apparently rapid recession of the remote galaxies, as shown by the spectroscopes of our great telescopes, many astronomers are favoring this shorter time scale. Whether or not this will eventually be found to be correct, the significant fact is that hypotheses regarding the origin of the universe are leading to significant tests. The great two-hundred-inch telescope of Mount Palomar was intended primarily for carrying through tests of certain of these hypotheses. This procedure of hypothesis and test has time and again solved our scientific problems. When did things begin? We hope to find out.

The future of the earth is more dim than its past. Definite knowledge of what is to come is of course impossible, because unforeseen events will inevitably arise. The best that can be expected of a prophet is a statement of the probabilities for the future. What lies ahead, however, is suggested by what has gone before. Having traced man's record in the rocks for more than a million years it would be surprising if this organism which is now so dominant on the earth should not continue for at least an equal period. By comparison with the cycle of growth and decline of other organisms whose history the paleontologist has traced, we might well expect him to continue for a hundred million years or so without losing his essential physical characteristics. Considering only geological and astronomical conditions, Sir James Jeans once gave a million million years as mankind's reasonable life expectancy.

It thus becomes evident that, through the cooperation of many fields of knowledge, the physicist's majestic problem of finding the limits of time as it is of interest to man is working toward a solution. The growth of man's time perspective during the life of those now living is typified by the contrast of the age of 5943 years assigned to the earth by Bishop

Ussher [who stated that Creation took place in 4004 B.C.] and the several billion years reliably recognized by present geology, astronomy, and physics.

## PHYSICAL AND PSYCHOLOGICAL
## MEASURES OF TIME

One of the first requirements of a science that is based on measurement is the establishment of suitable units in terms of which the results of the measurement can be expressed. In the measurement of time certain natural units have been obvious. These include the heartbeat, the solar day, the lunar month, the year, the generation, and the life span. The day has been artificially divided into hours, minutes, and seconds. It is to be noted that all of these units are arbitrary. Obviously the generation and the life span when measured in years will vary from one race of men to another, from one period of history to another, and from one geographical region to another. But so likewise are the day and year themselves arbitrary. We have been speaking of the age of the sun. If we describe it in years, what do these years mean before there was an earth to revolve? Or if we say that the earth's rotation is slowing down, how can we determine the fact if the day itself is the standard of measurement? Clearly we think of some more ultimate standard. Perhaps it is the period of vibration of a cadmium atom that emits a sharp spectral line. But we know that even such a standard will vary with the position of the atom in the gravitational field or with its rate of motion relative to the observer. Thus great care is necessary if a reliable standard of time measurement is to be found.

An extreme example of this problem arises in assigning an age to the universe. Presumably most of the world's history occurred before there was an earth, so that a counting of days and years is impossible. On the theory of the expanding universe it is supposed that the parent of our present system of galaxies was a dense concentration of all the material which is now scattered throughout the universe. In this dense mass not even atoms would have existed, and intense gravitational forces would have been present. Thus atomic clocks could not have existed, and even the rate of radioactive processes would have been greatly altered. Thus, as Milne has pointed out, it may be possible to choose two alternative methods of measuring time, according to one of which the age of the universe will be infinite and according to the other perhaps only some ten billion years. In such a case the answer to the question of when the world began depends upon our definition of the unit of time.

There is, however, an even more fundamental sense in which these physical measures of time are arbitrary. Fundamentally time is a psychological concept, based upon the feeling of duration and the intuitive distinction between past and future. To this sense of the passage of time the physical time as measured by a clock is only a rough analogue. The fact that some hours or days seem much longer than others, depending upon how we are occupied, is a familiar one.

If then psychological time is the fundamental concept, why do we not use it as a basis for measurement? The answer is evident; there is no precise psychological standard that will mean the same to all people. Nevertheless, we must remember that in a human sense time as measured by the clock or the calendar is not a true measure of the duration of life. Humanly speaking, the person to whom much has happened within a few years may have experienced a greater expanse of life than the one of many years whose simple unvaried routine has made all days alike.

For the purpose of organizing our collective life, as well as for the precise concepts of physics, however, we need some basis of time measurement upon which all men can agree. We may assume that all days are of equal length and devise mechanical methods of dividing the day into equal portions. It must have seemed contrary to common experience when this procedure indicated that the sleeping period from sunset to sunrise was as long as the waking day from sunrise to sunset. Yet, having accepted the postulate that all hours as measured by the clock are equal, we have become so accustomed to rely on the mechanical clock that we merely protest that the hours of sleep seem all too short.

It is in the field of mechanics that science is most directly concerned with the concept of time. Our senses give us an awareness of the motion of bodies that is quite distinct from the impressions made by those at rest. We can, moreover, distinguish readily between rapid and slow motion. But if we wish to express these concepts in precise form, we find it most convenient to determine the position according to some length scale corresponding to the time as measured by a clock. Then we can determine the time rate of change of the position, and this is our quantitative measure of the velocity.

We should note, however, that this procedure assumes that we already have a clock with which to measure time. Actually, I suppose the physicist's fundamental definition of the time interval is implied in Newton's first law of motion: "If a body is not acted upon by any force, it proceeds with uniform motion in a straight line." This implies that, if a body moves without friction or other forces acting upon it, we can assume that the time intervals required to move equal distances are equal. As an example, consider the rotation of the earth, for which the friction is negligible. If we divide a complete revolution into 360 degrees, each twenty-fourth of the rotation will be fifteen degrees, and the hour is the time required for the earth to turn through this angle. Thus the hours, and similarly the minutes and seconds, are defined to be equal by the postulate of Newton's first law.

Here then is a starting point from which dynamics can develop. Velocity now has a definite meaning, and the time rate of the change of velocity, or as we call it "acceleration," becomes equally definite. Not until this stage was it possible to give the quantitative statement of force, as equal to mass times acceleration. Likewise energy, which involves force and distance, and power, which is the time rate of the use of energy, can now be given exact meaning. Thus it is evident how the development of precise ideas in dynamics had to wait until the idea of the time interval was clearly defined.

I should add the historical note that although the statement of uniform motion is given as the first of Newton's laws, this law had already been formulated by Galileo and was taken by Newton as a part of the accepted body of the contemporary science of dynamics. The complete absence of such notions at the time of Aristotle may help us to understand his failure to grasp the idea of moving bodies as they came to be understood by Galileo.

## THE DISTINCTION BETWEEN PAST AND FUTURE

Eddington has called attention to a striking difference between the mechanical time as measured by such a clock as the rotating earth and the psychological time of which we are immediately aware. We may write an equation representing the angular position of the earth at any instant. This might have the simple form,

$$A = Rt,$$

where $A$ represents the angular position of the earth, measured perhaps in degrees from the original position, $R$ is the rate of rotation in degrees per hour and $t$ is the time in hours from the initial moment. If we want to determine the time, this may be written,

$$t = A/R.$$

This equation holds equally for past and future time. For past time we usually reckon $A$ as a negative angle, and $t$ then becomes negative time. A graphical plot of the hours would be given by a series of equally spaced points, thus:

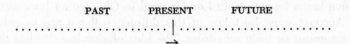

The "present," indicated by the vertical line, would be moving in the direction of the arrow from one point to the next each hour. Here, Eddington notes, there is no distinction in kind between past and future. We can describe the future position of the earth at a time $t$ just as precisely as we describe its past position at the time $-t$.

Psychologically, however, the past and the future are qualitatively distinct. Past events have left a definite record in our memory, compared with which the many contradictory pictures of the future presented by our imagination stand in striking contrast. There is nothing comparable with this in the dynamical case that would tell us in which direction "time's arrow" is to be drawn.

We are, however, provided with natural clocks which seem to be much more closely similar to our direct time sense than is the earth's rotation. One of these, which has already been mentioned, is the radioactive atom. Consider a group of two thousand atoms of radium, of which on the average one will disintegrate each year. We can measure the lapse of time by the number of atoms that have disintegrated. There is the distinction between past and future, however, in that those atoms which have changed to lead can be definitely identified, whereas there is no way of specifying which of the remaining atoms will be next to go. Here is an example of an irreversible reaction, in which radium atoms can be destroyed but cannot be re-created. There is thus in such a physical process an essential distinction between the past and the future.

The definiteness of our intuitive contrast between the past and the future would seem to imply that our sense of the passage of time is based upon physiological processes that are similarly irreversible. It is true that heartbeats and breathing are cyclic events, somewhat comparable with the rotation of the earth. But the performing of a voluntary act is essentially a one-way event. So also are the eating and digestion of food, and the growth and aging of the body. In fact none of the life processes is truly reversible. Thus it is but natural that the closest physical parallel to our immediate perception of the passage of time is to be found in such one-way events as radioactive disintegration.

## RELATIVE CLOCKS

A familiar example of the need for adjustment of clocks to varying conditions is the presence of different time zones. Noon occurs in New

York five hours later than in London, and in Chicago an hour after New York. Account must be taken of this difference if we are to coordinate radio programs or train schedules. The idea of simultaneity has thus lost some of its simplicity.

More than three centuries ago Galileo suggested the use of Jupiter's moons as a clock which would tell a time that would be the same all over the earth. By comparing this universal time with the local sun time it would be possible then to locate the longitude of ships at sea. This suggestion marked an important stage in the development of precise chronometry.

Galileo initiated a careful study of the rate of revolution of Jupiter's moons. Slightly but definitely divergent results from different series of observations caused confusion until Roemer [1644–1710] noted that the rate of revolution appeared to be faster when Jupiter was approaching the earth than when the two planets were moving away from each other. This could be explained, he found, if the light required time to come to us from Jupiter. He estimated that the relative motion of Jupiter and the earth must sometimes reach a ten-thousandth the speed of the light. Knowing the orbital motions, Roemer thus calculated that the light was traveling about 186,000 miles per second. It was a long time before this conclusion was verified in the laboratory.

Many years afterward Doppler called attention to a similar apparent change in the rate of vibration of atomic clocks, as observed in the spectrum lines from moving stars.* If the star is approaching us, more vibrations should reach us per second than should come if the star were at rest or moving away. The idea was precisely the same as Roemer's change in the apparent rate of Jupiter's moons, only Doppler used a different clock, vibrating atoms instead of moons. Doppler saw that the same effect should be observable with sound if the source were moving fast enough. He secured the use of a newly invented steam locomotive for the experiment, and verified his calculations with a dramatic test.

It is a striking commentary on the recentness of rapid transportation to note that the Doppler effect on the change of frequency of radiation was thus recognized for light before it was for sound. It means that optical instruments were improved to the degree required to show the hundredth of a per cent change in wavelength of a spectral line caused by the earth's motion before man traveled at speeds high enough to make evident the changes in the pitch of a sound with which we are now so familiar.

It was Einstein who made the next important advance with regard to clocks in motion. Even after we take account of the time required for light to travel from the clock to the observer, there remains a question. Einstein showed that if observer $A$ is moving relative to observer $B$, two events which seem to $B$ to occur at the same instant will not appear simultaneous to $A$. Also, even after the effect of approach or recession has been taken into account, each observer will find that the other's clock is running slightly slower than normal. This latter effect, frequently called the "transverse Doppler effect," is expressed by the formula,

$$t = t_0/\sqrt{1 - v^2/c^2}.$$

Here $t$ is the time that observer $A$ measures as the duration of an event on $B$, as compared with the time $t_0$ that would be required if $B$ were at rest. Such an event might be the swing of a pendulum, the revolution of a satellite, or the vibration of an atom. $v$ is the speed of the motion of $B$ relative to $A$, and $c$ is the speed of light.

The first successful attempt to make a direct test of this prediction was reported only two years ago by Ives. He used a stream of hydrogen atoms shot at high speed by an electric discharge in a vacuum tube. The wavelength of the hydrogen lines observed in his spectrograph was affected by the motion. Along the line of motion the Doppler effect showed the speed $v$. Even at right angles to the motion, however, the wavelength was altered by about 0.001 per cent, a definitely measurable amount.

Within a year after Ives's announcement of this important verification of Einstein's prediction came the striking discovery of a clock which travels so fast that its rate is slowed down manyfold. This clock is the "mesotron," * announced independently by [Carl] Anderson and Neddermeyer and by Street in 1937 as present in cosmic rays. The mesotron was soon found to be radioactive. Thus Rossi observed that about ten per cent of the mesotrons disintegrated as they traveled through a kilometer of thin air, down the side of Mount Evans; that is, the average lifetime of a mesotron is that required to move about ten kilometers, which means about 0.00003 of a second.

From measurements of their mass and energy, however, it is known that the speeds of the mesotrons in Rossi's experiments average about 0.998 of the speed of light. At this tremendous velocity, by Einstein's equation, its rate of disintegration should be reduced by fifteenfold. This would mean that if the mesotrons were at rest their average span of life would be only two millionths of a second.

If the observer were riding on the mesotron, he would measure its life as two microseconds. Watching the rapidly moving mesotron as he does from the earth, he finds its life to be thirty microseconds. For those immensely energetic mesotrons that penetrate a thousand feet into the earth, the apparent life is calculated to be a hundred times greater. Here indeed is a clock whose timing is worthless unless we know accurately the speed of its motion.

One is reminded of the young lady named Dwight, who could travel faster than light. She went walking one day, in a relative way, and returned the previous night.

True, our mesotrons do not travel faster than light, but the distortions of their time measures caused by their fast motions is almost as surprising as that of the remarkable Miss Dwight.

## SCIENCE EXPANDS OUR PSYCHOLOGICAL LIFETIME

We frequently comment that rapid transportation has greatly shortened distance. It would be equally true to say that our days have been lengthened because so much more happens to us. This is no new idea. Did not the Israelites declare that Joshua had stopped the sun and moon as they were chasing the Philistines? So much happened that day that only thus could its increased length be described. I felt the same way when recently, having spent the morning at my office in Chicago, I flew to New York for dinner and a lecture, and returned home to Chicago the same evening.

A visit to the more primitive society of the Orient shows the basis for the old conception that the world has always been essentially as it now is. During a lifetime no important changes have occurred. In such a community, life is stagnant.

We, on the contrary, have come to expect change as a matter of course. Fundamental are the technological changes which alter both our individual habits and our social organization. It is a kind of social evolution of increasing rapidity. When new knowledge came by accident, changes were slow. With the growth of writing, the use of metals, and the scientific method, the search for new knowledge has become profitable, and the many changes in our way of living have resulted.

The increasing rate of this change can perhaps best be appreciated by using the device of compressing the time scale, shall we say, by a millionfold. Then the first men, a year or two ago, found that certain sounds had meaning, and speech appeared. By a month ago they found that sticks and stones could be accurately shaped to serve their needs as tools and weapons. Last week man became an artist, drawing and carving pictures of animals on the walls of his cave. By the day before yesterday his drawings had become formalized to picture writing, and by yesterday a phonetic alphabet was in use. Speaking as at noon today, on our millionfold scale, it was yesterday afternoon that Greece developed her brilliant art and science. At dinnertime last evening was the dawn of the Roman Empire and of Christianity. Last midnight Rome fell, hiding for several hours the values of civilized life. At eight fifteen this morning Galileo dropped the large and small balls from the tower of Pisa, starting the period of modern science. By ten thirty we had the steam engine. At eleven the classical laws of electrodynamics were completed, which by eleven thirty had given us the telegraph, the telephone, and the incandescent light. By twenty minutes to twelve X rays were discovered, and automobiles were on the scene. Ten minutes ago, airmail was started. Within the last few minutes have come color photography, new artificial fabrics, and the unification of the world by shortwave radio.

This quick survey shows the graph of man's science, technology, and social organization rising with an upward curve. If we are to measure time by the changes that occur, we thus must conclude that modern man lives many times as long as his ancestors. It is clear that man is being rapidly transformed from the primitive stage of an individualistic animal to a later stage as a social animal. Someday science may bring to some completeness the task set by Francis Bacon, of "effecting all things possible." If so, he will have reached a higher plateau of achievement where there will presumably again be stable conditions. Meanwhile man's life is full and his time is greatly extended by the richness of his new experiences.

# V

## The Search
## for Truth

The search for truth is in one way hard and in another way easy. For it is evident that no one can master it fully nor miss it wholly. But each adds a little to our knowledge of nature; and from all the facts assembled there arises a certain grandeur.

ARISTOTLE

# 16. Creativity in Science

## 1952

&#9758; In 1952 the Industrial Research Institute devoted its spring meeting to a discussion of "The Nature of Creative Thinking." Inventive men in various fields of the arts and sciences assembled at Skytop, Pennsylvania, on May 5 for a three-day symposium on creativity and the conditions under which it can be stimulated. Mr. Compton was invited to discuss creative thinking in science, which he did by means of illustrations drawn from several scientific developments with which he had been personally associated. Mr. Compton's remarks are taken from a transcript of his talk. Though delivered informally, they were based on a carefully prepared outline.

### CHARACTERISTICS OF OUTSTANDING PHYSICISTS

When I was asked to discuss some case histories of creativity in research, I thought first of taking some individual scientists I have known and considering the particular aspects of creativity that they illustrated in their own lives. To consider them individually would become tiresome. There were, nevertheless, certain general features that I found as I reviewed a list of Nobel prize men that I have known. One of these is with regard to age. The physicists did their most important creative work between the ages of about twenty-three to fifty-one. These specific ages are the bottom and the top age limits at which these physicists produced their masterpieces. The average age turned out to be thirty-six, which is pretty close to that for other fields of science.

Another characteristic that seems to be universal among these men is their exceptional self-starting ability. When they are irritated by something, they get at solving the difficulty; they don't wait for somebody to tell them to do it.

Also, these men were working under conditions of substantial freedom

| 179 |

and leisure. They were not in a position where there was some boss telling them what they should do next. They were free. They had some time to themselves. I noted also that in every case they had at least reasonably good equipment for doing the tasks that they wanted to do. We have heard frequently of people doing important experiments with a piece of string and some sealing wax. If this really happens, it is only when the task they need to do can be done with that kind of simple equipment. The great creative tasks, the really important ones, are done by people who can get hold of the equipment they need to do the task.

One more generalization that seems to be universal is that at some stage or other these men have worked in an atmosphere where the kind of work in which they are creative is recognized as important. To do this creative task has thus become something inherently valuable in their minds. They do not necessarily do their task in a stimulating atmosphere, but at some stage they have been in such a stimulating atmosphere.[1]

It is essential that we consider the incentives for research. I was interested in F. S. C. Northrop's comment that the creative scientific man first of all is a philosopher. Speaking literally, a philosopher would be one who loves knowledge. Actually, it is not the love of knowledge; it is rather the love of *adding* to the knowledge that is important to the man of science. As a matter of fact, I think that to the typical research man the learning of new knowledge is of itself a rather boresome occupation, unless he sees that by this learning he can more effectively add to the body of knowledge. It is the adding of knowledge that is the stimulating adventure to which the research man looks.

The characteristic motivation of the creative scientist is that of Chaucer's Oxford scholar: "And gladly wolde he lerne, and gladly teche." He wants to learn new knowledge that he may impart it to someone else. There are also, however, the kinds of motivation that are common to everyone, such as, for example, the desire to win prestige in some respected enterprise. For many persons who follow science, research is one of the most highly respected enterprises to which they are eligible. It is noteworthy that many research men come from rather simple homes from which it is difficult to get into enterprises that bring large material rewards. They become aware at some stage of the human value of knowledge, and that here is a direction in which they themselves can contribute and perhaps acquire prestige.

[1] Professor W. I. B. Beveridge of the University of Cambridge has written a very interesting book on *The Art of Scientific Investigation* (New York: W. W. Norton; 1950). This book includes an excellent discussion of some of the factors that are necessary in order that research shall be effective. It contains valuable information not only for the young research man, for whom it is intended, but likewise for the person who has to direct and plan the conditions under which research can be done.

There is also the desire to win in competition. I was talking with someone this afternoon about Robert A. Millikan, one of the great figures in American science. I commented that he was always in some kind of controversy. He was an athlete when he was young. I think it was the same kind of spirit that brought him into competition with the British when he began measuring the charge on the electron. When challenged by an Austrian scientist, he came out very well. When he started his study of the photoelectric effect, others were ahead of him and he must beat them to the final result. In his study of cosmic rays Millikan took on the whole world and everybody was fighting with him. In some of his claims he won and in others he didn't; but it was always a stimulating adventure to be in a field of research with which Millikan was associated, because one could count on keen competition. The desire to win was important to him.

Then, of course, there is the ever present desire to keep one's family alive. The desire for security is common to all men, and applies to research men just as to everyone else. But I would note a conspicuous absence among research men of any desire for great wealth or for political power. I think of an individual exception with regard to political power, and that was the German physicist Philipp Lenard. Almost universally the scientist is one to whom power over his fellows is completely irrelevant.

Thus you get the picture of the scientist as having the usual pattern of human desires for an adequate living, for prestige, for success in competition. You have the absence of the desire for power. You do not help yourself at all by trying to put the scientist in your organization in a position where he is the boss. He would prefer to be in some other position if he is a scientist. He may take an administrative position, but if he does it will be because it is necessary for the company's welfare. On the other hand, your scientist will be keen to add to the known facts, to have a free hand, in some new creative achievement.

## X RAYS

Having given some generalizations, I want now to describe some examples. I have chosen cases with which at one stage or another I have been personally associated. As the first of these, consider the discovery and the scientific use of X rays. The key man was Wilhelm Conrad Roentgen. He discovered X rays in 1895 when he was forty-nine years old. He was a professor in a little German university at Würzburg. He had an assistant, a laboratory, and a few students. Thus he was almost a lone worker. His background was one that you might expect of an imaginative scientist. He had not done too well in school; in fact, he flunked out of one school because he had his own ideas about what he should study and they did not fit with those of the teacher. So his family put him in another. He was finally graduated and later won his doctor's degree. He was one of those careful, meticulous investigators whose work was in the forefront at the close of the last century. The best information on the density of crystals that I could find in the literature some years ago was the product of Roentgen's work. He was familiar with the fluorescence of crystals. It was thus that he happened to have at hand at the critical time some crystals of a fluorescent material when he was engaged in experiments with evacuated tubes. Roentgen was irritated by the fact that Lenard had reported the existence of a new kind of ray when the evidence did not seem to Roentgen good enough. He thought that Lenard's rays might be something quite different. So at considerable pains he set up in his own laboratory similar equipment to that used by Lenard but differing in certain essentials. He covered his tube with black paper. Yet when the electric discharge went through the tube he noticed that his crystal of fluorescent material was glowing brightly in the dark room. Somebody asked him what he thought. He replied, "I didn't think. I tried to see what would happen." He moved the crystal around, and found that through the black paper were coming rays that would likewise pass through his hand, throwing a shadow of the bones. Thus came the discovery of the X rays.

Here you have the case of the cautious man, apparently not very imaginative. He was rather of the careful investigator type who was not going to be satisfied with something that he was not sure was right. That was why he was testing out the findings of Lenard.

The consequences of those experiments of Roentgen were enormous. In the first place the X-ray tube was glowing with a fluorescent light. That prompted Henri Becquerel in France to try out other fluorescent materials to see whether he could find coming from them a radiation that, like X rays, would penetrate ordinary opaque materials. So Becquerel tried all the fluorescent materials he could think of. He happened to have some uranium salts, which are notably fluorescent. He found that they would blacken a photographic plate through black paper. Thus the discovery of radioactivity was made. Later it was found that neither X rays nor radioactivity has any relation whatever to fluorescence. That was a pure coincidence. Here, however, is the value of a hypothesis even when it is false. It was not so important that Becquerel should have had a correct hypothesis; it was rather that the idea of fluorescence stimulated him to action. Though his hypothesis was wrong, it led him to a significant result—accidental if you please, but the kind of accident that happens only to one who is actively working on something and has his eyes open.

Other people started working with X rays. They found that electroscopes were discharged in the presence of the X rays. This meant that X rays make the air electrically conducting. J. J. Thomson and Ernest Rutherford, working at the Cavendish Laboratory in Cambridge, England, found that there was a limit to the amount of electric current that the air would carry. From this observation they deduced the phenomena of ionization. That is, they got the idea of molecules being broken into positively and negatively charged parts. They worked out the consequences of this hypothesis; and when they tested them, their predictions were confirmed. Their experiments showed evidence of molecules more convincingly than any experiments that had as yet been done, not only electrically charged pieces of molecules but also noncharged molecules.

The Cavendish Laboratory was now buzzing with new ideas. There must be some elemental unit of charge carried by the ions. Was not this the same as the charge of a particle of cathode rays? Thus was born the concept of the electron.

At the place where the electron theory thus originated was at the time gathered together the largest and most highly organized research group in the world. It was a group that J. J. Thomson had built around him in Cambridge, starting about 1885, and which by 1896 was going strong. There were some remarkably brilliant men in that team: Thomson himself, Rutherford, Townsend, Bragg, Bose. Within the group there was an intense feeling of competition. Each person was on his own, and Thomson had the sagacity to keep the organization one in which everyone was free.

Another remarkable member of this Cavendish team was C. T. R. Wilson. I talked with him some twenty or thirty years later about how he happened to invent the "cloud chambers" with which we first were enabled to see the paths of individual atoms and electrons. He had been wandering over the hills of his native Scotland and had watched clouds forming on the hills as the moist air would blow over them. He said of himself: "I can make similar clouds in the laboratory. I will take moist air and expand it, and a cloud should be formed as is happening here." When he returned to the laboratory at Cambridge, he tried the experiment and he found that a cloud was formed as he had expected. But the cloud would form only under certain conditions. If the air was very clean, he could not make the cloud except when there were some X rays around. Then the droplets formed in lines, obviously the paths of moving particles. Thus the tracks of individual atoms and electrons were first made visible. What had happened was that a particle of some kind would move so rapidly through the gas that it would break up the molecules into ions, and those ions would form the nuclei on which droplets would form. The paths of various kinds of particles thus became visible. So C. T. R. Wilson's cloud chamber became a very useful tool in many different kinds of experiments.

So much for the ionization caused by X rays. The X rays themselves were used by the Braggs, father and son, by reflecting them from crystals. By such reflection they studied the arrangement of the atoms in the crystals. The structure of crystals and later the structure of many molecules thus became an open book.

But X rays also told us about the nature of light. The X rays, as we know now, are like light rays, but of a thousand or ten thousand times greater frequency. That gives them certain characteristics sharply different from those of ordinary light. The old electromagnetic theory developed by Maxwell had made it possible to interpret most of the experimental results that were being obtained with light. When the same experiments were performed with X rays, unexpected difficulties were encountered.

It was at that stage that I became involved in the problem. Professor O. W. Richardson, with whom I had started my doctor's thesis, had suggested that I look into the field of X rays. The Braggs had just been doing the work with the study of crystals. I thought that if one could find the arrangement of atoms in crystals it should be possible to find the arrangement of electrons in the atoms by the same kind of approach. According to theory, the clearest results should have been obtained by avoiding a crystalline structure and working, for example, with a gas or a liquid. I tried a variety of such experiments, but the X rays were not scattered as I had expected. Then, while I was working as a research engineer for the Westinghouse Lamp Company, I came upon a paper of Charles Barkla, an Englishman, who had tried an experiment on the absorption of X rays. He found that the X rays were being absorbed less strongly than the electron theory of that time could possibly account for. I was troubled by this paper of Barkla. I tried one hypothesis after another to account for it. After many unsuccessful trials, I found a hypothesis that worked. These X rays were found to have an unexpected kind of echo. We may think of it this way. Light comes from a lamp onto a piece of paper and is reflected into the eye. It is the same color as the light from the lamp. But if the lamp were an X-ray tube, the light coming from the paper would not be of the same color. It would be of a longer wavelength. Now that does not sound right in terms of echoes. There are a certain number of waves per second coming from the source, and we expect the echo to have the same number of waves. Actually, the echo of the X ray is of a different number of waves per second. That was what troubled me. In the end I found that the change in wavelength could be accounted for by a wholly different assumption; i.e., that light was coming in particles that bounced off the electrons in the scattering material.

The idea that light was composed of particles was as old as Isaac Newton, and had been reintroduced into the physics picture by Einstein on the basis of evidence that was suggestive but not convincing. Here was more evidence along the same line. It was one of the steps that led toward the development of what we now call the quantum mechanics. The quantum mechanics, therefore, in a rather indirect way came out of this discovery of the X rays. Thus from one discovery by this simple, meticulous scientist, working by himself in the laboratory in Würzburg, developed a whole chain of phenomena leading to a very large part of what we call modern physics.

## NUCLEAR PHYSICS

Let me go quickly into a second case, that of the nucleus of the atom. In this case, the central figure is Rutherford. His key experiment was the bombardment of matter by alpha rays from radium. I have already told how C. T. R. Wilson had made the tracks of particles visible in the cloud chamber. Those tracks for the most part were gradual curves; but every once in a while they would make a sharp bend. In an effort to explain the shape of these tracks, it was found that the gradual curves could be explained as a cumulative result of a multitude of collisions with molecules. This explanation, however, could not account for the sharp bends. Rutherford wondered what would happen in the case of very high-energy particles, such as alpha particles, with speeds roughly 10 per cent the speed of light. So he passed these particles through very thin materials, like sheets of gold leaf or aluminum leaf. Occasionally the particles were deflected quite sharply. Sometimes the alpha particles bounded almost directly backward. In studying the phenomenon quantitatively he found that the number of particles that were deflected at large angles could be explained by the assumption that the alpha particle came close to something that acted on it according to an inverse-square law of attraction, like comets deflected by the sun. But when he calculated the distance to which these two particles must approach each other in order for this theory to be correct, the distance was very much smaller than the size that had been calculated for an atom. The size of an atom is $10^{-8}$ centimeters— about one hundred millionth of an inch. This seems incredibly small, but the distance between these particles according to Rutherford's calculation had to be not $10^{-8}$ but $10^{-12}$ centimeters, that is, a distance ten thousand times smaller than the diameter of the atom itself. Thus he was confronted with something that was subatomic yet had a mass greater than the mass of the alpha particle. So he got the picture of a hard kernel within an atom. This he called the nucleus of the atom. It was a straightforward deduction. The hypothesis of the nucleus had been made before by Nagaoka, a Japanese physicist, but without any convincing evidence. J. J. Thomson had introduced the hypothesis of a diffused distribution of positive electricity within the atom. But here was clear evidence of a dense core of positively charged matter.

Among the members of the team that Rutherford brought together at Manchester was Niels Bohr. Bohr was stimulated by Rutherford's results to work out a new theory of the structure of the atom in which he had the idea of quantizing, as we say, the motion of the electrons as they revolve in orbits about the atom's nucleus. This was the beginning of our understanding of how the atom is put together. Bohr's theory has been modified many times since, but it was a firm beginning. Other experimenters joined in the exciting task. Moseley tried the X-ray spectra of different elements and found, using Bohr's theory, that he could measure the charges on the atomic nuclei. Thus the idea of atomic number was developed.

A natural extension of Rutherford's experiments was to bombard various elements with alpha particles of the highest available energy. Rutherford tried one substance after another. In one of those experiments, off flew some pieces that were neither alpha particles nor the substance that they had hit. These first exciting results were obtained by bombarding nitrogen, from which he got hydrogen and oxygen. Rutherford saw that he was actually breaking up the nucleus of the atom. He wrote to one of his friends in the United States—this was in the midst of World War I: "I've just performed a new experiment which I truly believe has more meaning to it than the result of the war that is now on."

Thus the first artificial disintegration of the nucleus of an atom was achieved. Later [1932] two of his men, John Cockcroft and Ernest Walton, obtained similar results by using artificially accelerated ions rather than natural alpha particles. Then [1932] James Chadwick found that when certain substances were hit by alpha rays a new kind of particle was emitted that had a mass about equal to that of hydrogen but that had no charge at all. This was the neutron. Almost immediately Enrico Fermi, working by himself in Rome, found that if the target were surrounded with paraffin which slowed down the neutrons, they could, because of their electrically uncharged condition, penetrate atoms readily and produce various isotopes. Many of these isotopes were radioactive, a completely new phenomenon. When Fermi tried to attach neutrons to uranium, he thought that he had got some atoms heavier than uranium. Later this was found to be false, but it was as a result of his experiments that Otto Hahn and Fritz Strassmann did their remarkable work [1938] of finding that when neutrons attach themselves to uranium a product comes out that can only be interpreted as due to the splitting of the uranium nucleus into parts. Thus the fission of uranium was discovered.

By this time Fermi had transferred to Columbia University in New York. When Niels Bohr brought to him word of uranium fission, Fermi and those associated with him at Columbia got busy. First they found that an immense amount of energy was associated with the fission of uranium. Then they found also that neutrons were emitted when the uranium nucleus breaks apart. At that stage physicists all over the world knew that a chain reaction could be effected. The only question was when and under what conditions.

Fermi had entered the picture with his experiments on the capture of slow neutrons while he was professor at the University of Rome. At that stage, thanks to Mussolini, he found it desirable to get out of Italy. He came over to the United States, and so he was here when we needed him for the chain reaction.

Now another actor comes onto the stage—Ernest Lawrence. At the beginning of the war, Ernest Lawrence saw the possibility that this chain reaction could be made of importance in connection with our military development. He was, I suppose, the first to see the feasibility of making an atomic bomb in time to affect the outcome of the war. But let me go farther back. Lawrence has more drive than almost anyone I know. Out at the University of California he had conceived the idea of making an electric motor with the usual magnetic field but with the armature consisting of electrical particles going round and round between poles of the magnet. This was the cyclotron. People were skeptical, but he made a little model, and it worked. Then he made a bigger model. But what he wanted was a cyclotron that would produce particles that would have tens of millions of electron volts of energy. This idea came from a book by Sir Arthur Eddington, another member of that powerful team at the University of Cambridge. Eddington in the 1920's had published a remarkable book called *Stars and Atoms,* in which he gave convincing evidence that the heat from the stars and the sun comes from some atomic nuclear process. He saw that at very high temperatures in the interior of the stars changes in the nuclei of the atoms were taking place. He made some estimates of what the energies of these particles must be in order to

| 187 |

account for the phenomena that we observe, and came to the conclusion that these energies were of the order of ten million electron volts. Now in an X-ray tube you have about one hundred thousand electron volts. The light rays coming from an incandescent lamp have two or three electron volts. So you may well understand that ten million electron volts is an energy that is obtainable only with difficulty. The highest voltage being used in the laboratories when Lawrence was developing his cyclotron was about one million.

Lawrence saw in his motor with its electrical particle armature a device whereby he could get these immense energies. But how big did it have to be? The estimate was of the order of a hundred tons. Nobody had ever seen in a university physics laboratory a thing weighing a hundred tons. That did not bother Lawrence a bit. He went out and got somebody to supply the funds. Having made such a cyclotron, he went to the Rockefeller Foundation and said: "This isn't big enough yet. We need a giant cyclotron that will weigh several hundred tons." Thus he made it possible to make many different kinds of isotopes and to create many new kinds of matter.

At this stage, Mark Oliphant came over from England, and talked with Lawrence during 1941 about some calculations on the possibility of making a chain reaction in uranium 235. The British had calculated that a smaller amount of uranium 235 was necessary than was previously believed. Then in Lawrence's laboratory Glenn T. Seaborg and Joseph W. Kennedy and Arthur C. Wahl found a new kind of element produced when uranium was bombarded with neutrons. This new element, which we now call plutonium, would not only undergo fission like uranium 235, but also, as a chemically different substance, it could be separated chemically from the uranium and thus avoid the difficult isotopic separation of uranium 235.

Armed with this information, Lawrence came to Chicago when James Conant and I were there. The three of us met in my home on an evening in early September. Lawrence told us: "Now this can be done. With a relatively small amount of uranium 235 you can make an atomic bomb, and its destructiveness is going to be such that it could make all the difference between losing and winning the war. We know the Germans are already at the job. I think we've got to get at it."

I recall Conant's turning to him and saying, "Ernest, do you think the job is so important that you're willing to put the next five years of your life into it?"

Lawrence replied, "If you agree that it's as important as I think it is, I'll do it."

That was the start of the atomic project as a war program. It occurred to me that the best way of getting that uranium 235 was by magnetic separation. Lawrence was the person who had the magnets in his big cyclotrons. He took up that idea, which had been independently urged by Smyth of Princeton, and with the help of some very active industrial organizations established in Oak Ridge for that purpose, turned out the first quantity production of uranium 235. It is typical of the way scientific research goes that the chain reaction that Lawrence saw could make plutonium was turned over to me to carry through and with Fermi's help we developed the nuclear chain reaction at Chicago. The Du Pont Company put it on a production basis, and it went ahead from there.

These urgent war tasks were on so large a scale that they could not be done by lone workers. Thus we used teams. With Lawrence's group at California, our group at Chicago, a group under Harold C. Urey and others at Columbia, and other groups of scientists in many parts of the country, with engineers from many different industrial companies, and finally with the Army, we had a venture with many different kinds of people working together in a hastily assembled organization. Yet we came out quickly with a favorable result. People have often asked me, "How was it that you could get an organization together so quickly that would work effectively on a research job?" The answer is that the people concerned were so very eager on the job. The prime incentive was to keep from losing the war or to get the war over as quickly as they could. Their contribution toward it was going to be making the atomic weapon, and it became a crusade with them. Thus in order to develop the idea that came from a lone investigator, in this case Rutherford, many thousands of different people in many parts of the world worked together as a large group.

In that large group likewise there was some very creative work done. I think of the work of Crawford Greenewalt and his Du Pont colleagues in connection with the development of the chemical method of the separation of plutonium from uranium. It was an exciting and thrilling piece of work. Greenewalt, as most of you know, is a person accustomed to working with large organizations and he knew how to bring results from a cooperative effort.

### FLUORESCENT LIGHT

I am going to give just one more illustration, a briefer one, that of the fluorescent light. I want to tell of this because it is typical of something that often happens in the case of a research laboratory.

| 189 |

Fluorescent light had been known for a long, long time. It had been noticed and studied by Hittorf and Plücker, back in the middle of the nineteenth century. It had never been considered very exciting. Plücker, who was a glassblower, liked to put fluorescent materials inside his tubes in order to get pretty colors.* But the colors disappeared rather rapidly, and the fluorescent materials that were used became stagnant. Many of you will remember the old fluorescent screens and discharge tubes that quickly became dark. Such experiences made one feel that fluorescence was a temporary phenomenon.

Then came two things. The first was the development of the theory of fluorescence. It had been supposed that fluorescence occurs by the emission of light when a substance changes from one molecular form to another. In that case no more light would be emitted after all of the material had been changed. But now came a new theory. It was based on Bohr's idea of the atom as extended to molecules, namely, that you could have excited states in molecules and excited states in crystals. This would mean that you could put energy into these crystals or these molecules, raising them to a higher energy state; then as they returned to their lower energy state, light would be emitted. The raising to the upper energy level would be the result of absorption of a quantity of short wavelength of light. As the material went back to the lower energy state, a longer wavelength of light would be emitted. Since the molecules would merely be returning to their former state, this process could be repeated any number of times.

The other new aspect was the result of an experiment. People became interested in television and were making television screens, which use fluorescent material. In the investigation of these fluorescent television screens a surprising amount of light was found to be coming off. As an interesting demonstration, by the General Electric Company, Ltd., in London, a Plücker-Hittorf tube was made with this new fluorescent material on the inside. I happened to be in England and saw this demonstration. When I asked how much light was coming off, I was told about three times as much as comes from an ordinary lamp using the same amount of power.

Then I asked, "How about the life of the fluorescent material?" I was told, "It decays after a certain period, but as we improve the material, its fluorescence lasts longer, and we believe we can make it so it will last for a very long time."

That was what was needed. I brought their experiments to the attention of the General Electric Company at Cleveland * and suggested some things that they would have to think about. I think it was Jim Rand who was commenting today on the barriers to picking up these new inventions. There was such a barrier here. The incandescent lamp had for many years been the stabilizer of the electrical industry. It carried on in depression times because lamps burn out and have to be replaced, while transformers, motors, and other heavy equipment do not have to be frequently replaced. But here was a lamp that you might install as you install the plumbing and that would last for a long time. Commercially it was thus a dangerous thing to play with, but practically it was one of those things you knew was going to come because it was good, and so you had better be in on it first. So the General Electric Company with both feet jumped into the task of developing a fluorescent lamp. This decision was made by the director of the laboratory, William Enfield. Within a couple of years they had some lamps on the market. This was how it was possible to have fluorescent lamps in time for the war period when you had to put up great new plants and had to have more efficient interior lighting.

Where was the invention in this case? I would say the critical point, if you pinpoint it at all, was the creative action taken by Enfield. It was the decision to go ahead with the job. No one had made any basic invention, anything specific that you could patent.

## NEED FOR INITIATIVE AND SELF-DISCIPLINE

Here then are some things that stand out as I consider this group of typical cases. First of all, to my mind the thing that is the essence of creativity is the decision to do something about it when you are irritated. I would agree that irritation is the first step; but the decision to do something about it—that is the essence of creativity. The conditions favorable for making such a decision include, of course, an opportunity to understand what the possibilities are, freedom and facilities to make use of the opportunities, and a setting in which one feels the real importance of doing what one sees may be done. To be a creator in research one must decide for himself what he is going to do, because nobody else can tell the research man what it is that he should do. Give him freedom and give him the necessary equipment to do with reasonable ease the things that he needs to do. Many of the other considerations, such as whether he finds himself in an easy financial position or a difficult one, whether the surroundings are pleasant or unpleasant, are rather beside the point; but he must have the opportunity to gain the thrill of doing the creative task that he sees needs to be done.

I will just emphasize that by telling a story. Toward the close of the recent war, in our atomic project we had a very heterogeneous group of scientists, engineers, Army and Navy men, and laborers. Though they were eager to do the job, it was not easy to get them working smoothly together. After a rather discouraging day, General Leslie R. Groves made this comment: "Compton, you know you scientists don't have any discipline."

I asked, "General, what do you mean?"

He said, "You don't know how to take orders and give orders."

I thought a minute before I replied: "General, I suppose that's right. We don't know how to take orders and give orders. But we do have a different kind of discipline. You see, there isn't anybody who can tell a research man what it is that he should be doing. He's got to figure that out for himself. But when he's figured it out for himself, he's got to make himself do it. The difference between a good scientist and a scientist that isn't so good is whether he will make himself do the thing that he sees needs to be done."

It seems to me that here is perhaps the most important element in creativity. The creative man must have within himself the incentive and the self-discipline to do the thing that he sees needs to be done.

# 17. Michelson, Millikan, and Richardson

## 1931

A student of Richardson and for many years a colleague of both Michelson and Millikan, the author was invited to comment about the work of the three scientists who, with himself, were the first residents of the United States to be awarded the Nobel prize for their work in physics.

Michelson was honored in 1907,* Millikan in 1923,* Compton in 1927,* and Richardson in 1928.* Though Richardson was a British citizen, it was in the United States that he carried out the investigations for which he is chiefly known.

Arthur Compton began his doctoral thesis with O. W. Richardson at Princeton in 1914. It was Albert Michelson, then head of the department of physics at the University of Chicago, who in 1923 invited him to become a member of one of the strongest physics departments in the nation. The research interests of Robert Millikan and Arthur Compton had several parallels, most notably their interest in cosmic rays.

With the passing on May 9, 1931, of Professor Michelson, there closes a chapter of history that is noteworthy in that it has marked the coming of age of American science. Not that the United States has in earlier years been without men of science. We are justly proud of our Franklin and Henry and Gibbs and Chamberlin among others; but it has only been during the last heroic generation that our nation has become a world leader in the growth of human knowledge. Such national leadership can be won only through the personal achievements of individuals and energy. In the work of Michelson, Millikan, Richardson, and others like them, American men of science have found their inspiration.

## A. A. MICHELSON

Albert Abraham Michelson [1852–1931] was born at Strelno, Prussia, in 1852, was brought to this country at the age of two, and entered the

United States Naval Academy at Annapolis when nineteen years old. The greater part of his long and brilliant scientific career was spent at the University of Chicago, where he was director of the physics department from its organization in 1892 until he resigned his position in 1929 at the age of seventy-seven. He had the distinction, unique in university circles, of having never earned an academic degree but of having almost every possible honorary degree and other distinction awarded him.

Michelson's scientific activities are succinctly described in *Who's Who* by the single word "light." His whole scientific career was centered on the study and application of its characteristics. First and last of his investigations was the speed of light. More than half a century ago, at the United States Naval Academy, while preparing a class demonstration of Foucault's method of measuring the speed with which light travels, he found that his own simple apparatus was giving more precise results than did Foucault's classical experiments. Young Michelson reported his results in a paper on "A Method of Measuring the Velocity of Light," in *Silliman's Journal* for May 1878.

His original speed-of-light apparatus went through many refinements, culminating in an experiment in 1926 in which a beam of light was reflected from a mirror on a mountain twenty-two miles away, and one now in progress in which the ray is reflected back and forth for many miles in a vacuum. From his bed, two days before he died, assured by the reports of progress that this experiment was a success, Michelson dictated the introduction to the report of his final measurement. Centuries ago Galileo attempted to measure the speed of light by noting the time required to signal with lanterns from one mountain to another and back again. In Michelson's experiment the lanterns were replaced by a Sperry arc of the same kind as that used in the Lindbergh beacon, with a mirror on the distant mountain, and instead of the signaler, a rapidly rotating mirror, which presents successive faces ten thousand times a second. How fast does light travel? Seven times around the earth in a single second, or as Michelson would say, 186,284 miles per second, with the last mile somewhat uncertain.

Why should Michelson want to spend so much time in finding precisely the speed of light? "Because it's such good fun," was his own reply. But behind that is the fact that the speed of light is perhaps the most fundamental of all the constants of nature. In connection with the astronomers' recent evidence that the very distant stars are receding, there is a suggestion that the velocity of light may itself be slowly changing. If this is true an experiment such as Michelson's, repeated after a century or so, should reveal the change. It is only by precision measurements of this kind that we can learn how reliable the world of nature is.

Most of Michelson's work, however, was centered around his interferometer, which he considered his greatest invention. This is an instrument by means of which distances can be measured in terms of light waves. A beam of light is divided into two parts by a mirror, and by reflection from other mirrors the parts are brought together again. If both parts have gone exactly the same distance, they will form again a strong beam of light; but if one ray goes farther than the other by as much as the length of half a light wave, the recombined beams will interfere with one another and darkness will result. Since it takes fifty thousand light waves to make an inch, this affords an exceedingly delicate means of measuring short distances.

For many years the international standard of length has been the distance between two scratches on a bar of platinum-iridium kept at the International Bureau of Weights and Measures at Sèvres, near Paris. Michelson measured this standard meter with his interferometer and found it to be 1,553,164.13 wavelengths of red light from a cadmium arc. Fourteen years later Benoît, Fabry, and Perot remeasured the meter and found a value differing by only a small fraction of one wavelength. This is the equivalent of having two surveyors repeat measurements of the distance from New York to Chicago to within a foot. If any catastrophe should damage the standard meter, it could now, thanks to Michelson, be replaced with great exactness.

His interferometer enabled Michelson, working with H. G. Gale and F. R. Moulton, to measure the rigidity of the earth. This they did by measuring the tides in a large buried pipe 500 feet long. If the earth had no rigidity, no tides should appear, for the moon's attraction would distort the earth's shape as much as that of the water. If, on the other hand, the earth were perfectly rigid, the tides in the pipe should follow a definitely calculable rule. The observed tides, only a few thousandths of an inch high, were a fraction of those calculated for a rigid earth, indicating that the earth has about the same elastic properties as steel. This supports the evidence obtained from measurements on earthquake waves, that the interior of the earth is a huge lump of iron.

Another striking application which Michelson made of his interferometer was measuring the diameter of a star. The highest power telescopes that have been made, including the great 100-inch instrument at Mount Wilson, have failed to show the fixed stars other than as points of light. The stars are too far away to appear as disks. Yet by placing two interferometer mirrors on a 20-foot beam, mounted on a telescope, Michelson made an instrument whose resolving power was as great as that of a telescope with a lens 50 feet in diameter. With this powerful instrument he measured the size of the star Betelgeuse (which marks Orion's shoulder), and his collaborators have since measured Antares, Arcturus, and others.

Yet the work for which Michelson will probably always be best known is his famous Michelson-Morley experiment, carried out in collaboration with Professor E. W. Morley of the Case School of Applied Science. This experiment more than anything else was the occasion for the development of the theory of relativity.

Light was known to consist of waves, and these waves were supposed to be propagated through a medium of unusual elastic properties known as the ether. The earth in its yearly course around the sun must be moving through this ether, and this motion should affect the speed at which light seems to travel on the earth. Michelson conceived the idea of staging a race between two light rays, one moving parallel to the earth's motion and the other at right angles. If two equal rowers start together, the first rowing a half mile upstream and back, the second a half mile across stream and back, the one going across stream should win the race. In Michelson's experiment the two light rays raced a dead heat. No effect due to the earth's motion could be detected.

How was this tied race to be explained? FitzGerald and Lorentz pointed out that if all distances in the direction of motion were contracted a little the effect of the motion could not be detected. To Einstein, on the other hand, the experiment suggested that perhaps motion relative to the ether is of no significance, that it is only when a thing moves relatively to some other material object that its motion has meaning. In the Michelson-Morley experiment there was no relative motion between the source of light and the apparatus, and thus no effect should be expected. Thus this famous experiment became the occasion for the development of the relativity theory.

Recently Dayton C. Miller, who collaborated with Michelson in some of his early experiments, presented evidence to the effect that the race between the two light rays is not quite a tie but that there remains a minute difference much smaller than the ether theory predicted. Michelson was thus spurred on to repeat his original experiment with even greater precision, and his conclusion that no difference is present larger than his very small experimental error has been accepted by the large majority of his colleagues. As yet, however, Miller's experiments are not accounted for, and the court of science cannot give a final verdict.*

The confidence of the scientific world in the reliability of Michelson's results is astonishing. This is illustrated by the fact that his great Michelson-Morley experiment, though its results were contrary to expectation and later became fundamental to the theory of relativity, was not repeated by anyone other than his own collaborators for almost thirty years. This confidence probably resulted from striking confirmations of his other measurements. The almost perfect agreement of Benoît, Fabry, and Perot's measurement of the standard meter with Michelson's earlier result has been mentioned. An even more remarkable example was his analysis of the fine structure of certain spectral lines by means of his interferometer. This analysis required accurate observation and judgment of the brightness of dark and light bands. Other experimenters using similar apparatus were unable to duplicate Michelson's results. Yet when years later new optical instruments enabled the structure of these spectral lines to be directly seen, his earlier analysis was completely confirmed.

Michelson in his pursuit of science, as in his art and sport, had always the spirit of the true amateur. He was guided by the imagination of an artist, and did his work for the love of it. Yet he had schooled himself to take interest in the things of enduring value. It was his love of the search for truth and his confident faith in the value of scientific endeavor, perhaps even more than his own great achievements, that made Michelson an inspiring leader.

## ROBERT A. MILLIKAN

Robert Andrews Millikan [1868–1954] was born in Illinois in 1868, was graduated from Oberlin College in 1891, received his Ph.D. degree from Columbia University in 1895, and after a year of study in Germany went to the University of Chicago. Here he worked for twenty-five years as a colleague of Michelson and made, in addition to many other researches, his measurements of the charge of the electron for which he is chiefly noted. In 1921 he went to Pasadena, where he has been chairman of the executive council of the Calfornia Institute of Technology. In spite of his arduous administrative duties he has actively continued his investigations, notably in the field of cosmic rays. During the world war [i.e., 1914–18] Millikan volunteered his services and was made chief of the science and research division of the Signal Corps, with the rank of lieutenant colonel.

Not only in the activities of American scientific organizations, but also in stimulating international cooperation on scientific problems, Millikan has taken a leading part. His laboratory has always been a haven for scientific men searching for an inspiration and a place to carry on their own investigations. Perhaps no scientist has ever personally guided the researches of more young men than has Professor Millikan. He is one of those rare spirits who can envision the political and economic significance of science and at the same time keep that personal interest in his fellows which enables him to give them welcome encouragement.

Millikan's most important contribution to science was his precise measurement of the charge of the electron. In 1895 J. J. Thomson had given convincing evidence that the "cathode rays," appearing when an electric current passes through rarefied gas, consist of streams of minute particles carrying electric charges. These particles came to be known as electrons. Rough estimates of the charge carried by each electron indicated that it was probably the same as that carried by a hydrogen ion when water is dissociated by an electric current. Further studies suggested that all electricity was probably divided into such "electronic units." To test this assumption, however, it was necessary to make accurate measurements of individual unit charges.

Approximate measurements of these charges had been made by J. J. Thomson, H. A. Wilson, and others, but their methods needed refinement before the precision could be attained that Millikan wanted. A tiny drop of oil from an atomizer was made to catch or lose an electron, and its motion was watched when between two parallel electrified plates. From the rate of this motion the size of the electric charge could be calculated. Many drops of various sizes, charged in different ways, were measured. The oil drop was replaced by a drop of mercury. Always the charge on the drop was a small whole multiple of a certain unit. From the average of all the readings the unit charge could be measured to about one part in a thousand.

Why should we want to know this constant exactly? First because the electron is one of the three fundamental elements of which it seems the world is made (electrons, protons, and photons). The electric charge carried by the electron is its most characteristic property, and hence is one of the basic facts of nature. Second, if this electronic charge is known, we are able to calculate with precision many other interesting things, such as the number of molecules in a cubic centimeter of air, the weight in grams of any atom, the distance between layers of atoms in a crystal, and other quantities with which scientists concern themselves. The charge of the electron is thus a quantity which is second only to the velocity of light as a fundamental constant of nature.

Millikan's determination of this constant has been criticized from time to time, and many have failed to see how its precision can be as great as he has claimed. However, though new and independent methods have been devised for measuring the electronic charge, the value which he obtained seventeen years ago seems to be the most reliable that has yet been obtained.*

The thorough experimental methods employed by Millikan have enabled him and his collaborators to make marked advances in many other fields. Especially noteworthy are his precision measurements of the speed of the electrons in photoelectric cells, which verified more completely a theory of Einstein based on the conception of light corpuscles. At one time also he held the record for having obtained the shortest wavelength ultraviolet light that had been observed. Recently he has devoted his main attention to the study of cosmic rays, those mysterious messengers that seem to come from interstellar space. It is perhaps fair to say that the work of Millikan and his collaborators has given the first strong evidence that these rays come from outside the earth, though such an extraterrestrial origin had long been suspected. Though the true meaning of these cosmic rays is yet uncertain, Millikan's investigations have served to focus the attention of the scientific world on them as a problem of fundamental importance.

## O. W. RICHARDSON

Owen Willans Richardson [1879–1959] was born in Yorkshire, England, in 1879, and studied at Cambridge University for nine years. It was during this period that he started his work on thermionic currents. This became of great practical as well as theoretical importance, since it is basic in the development of the vacuum tubes which are essential in radio, long-distance telephony, and other modern industries. His famous Richardson's law of thermionic emission was first proposed at Cambridge in 1901, though it required the experiments of more than a decade for him to satisfy himself and others that his theory of the emission of electrons from hot filaments was correct.

In 1906 Richardson went to Princeton University as professor of physics, and it was during his eight years there that he performed the crucial experiments in thermionics and photoelectricity for which he is chiefly known. It was his influence also that was largely instrumental in making Princeton a leading center of physics research, a tradition since maintained by the efforts of his colleagues and former students. Thus, although his residence in this country was brief, we feel justified in counting Richardson as a leader among American men of science. In 1914, however, he accepted a call to the University of London, where he continues his investigations.

There probably is no other living physicist who has to his credit as many important contributions to the scientific journals. His prolific writings have shed light on difficult problems covering almost the whole field of fundamental physics: thermionics, photoelectric effect, magnetism, emission of electrons by chemical action, electron theory, quantum theory, spectroscopy, X rays, atomic structure, in addition to others. In each field he has shown himself a master. Richardson is no man of public affairs; he has wedded himself to his science. Yet because of his sound scientific judgment and his versatility of thought his advice on problems of physics is very highly valued.

Richardson's studies of thermionic currents and of the photoelectric effect deserve particular mention. It has been known for centuries that air near a hot body is electrically conducting. Observations had been made by Guthrie, Elster and Geitel, Edison, and others, and in 1899 J. J. Thomson showed that the current from an incandescent carbon filament was carried by negative electrons. The suggestion occurred to Richardson that these electrons were evaporating from the filament, escaping because of their high-speed motion when the temperature became high. On this hypothesis he devised his Richardson's Law, which has now been amply verified. He and his collaborators showed that when the electrons evaporate, the filament is cooled, just as moisture drying from one's face makes it feel cool. Likewise, when the electrons condensed on a metal surface, it was heated, just as one's hand may be scalded if live steam condenses on it.

It was these experiments on the currents emitted by hot filaments that led Fleming to devise his electron valve and led to the radio tube in use today. Coolidge's X-ray tube, now almost universally used, depends upon the same principle. Were it not for this work it would not now be possible "that a man should hear around the whole earth and half of heaven."

It was also the experiments of Richardson, working with K. T. Compton, that gave the first strong evidence that light is corpuscular in character. When ultraviolet light falls on metals such as zinc or sodium, they acquire a positive electric charge, owing to negative electrons being thrown from their surface. Einstein saw that it was hard to explain this photoelectric effect by the action of light waves, and suggested in 1905 that the light really consists of little particles (photons we now call them), and that each of these photons may eject a single electron. Technical difficulties prevented an adequate test of his predictions based on this idea until seven years later when, helped by improvement of vacuum technique, Richardson and [K. T.] Compton carried through the necessary experiments. Einstein's theory was vindicated. The number of photoelectrons was proportional to the intensity of the light, and the speed with which the electrons were ejected followed the law that Einstein had predicted.

A comparison of these three leaders of American science is of unusual interest. There is Richardson, a man of few words and of retiring modesty, disliking publicity and crowds and large audiences, yet enormously versatile in his own field. His research is his very life. Millikan, the man of affairs, who organizes cooperative work, a public speaker who thrills great audiences because he transmits to them some of his own enthusiasm, a friend who encourages his colleagues and students to their own best efforts, yet who finds time amid a busy life to carry on his own fundamental investigations. To him the human side of science is all-important. Michelson, the artist and amateur, who saw in nature the beauties of the infinite and the infinitesimal, the master of measurement, who loved a sweet, smooth-running machine as well as an elegant mathematical equation, of versatile ability in sport and art and music, but essentially a lone worker in his own field of light. He lived for the enjoyment of nature. Each is inspired with enthusiasm for the search of truth, and each has an intuitive sureness of the value of science. Such are those who are helping America write her chapter of scientific history.

# 18.  Ernest Rutherford

## 1937

After working for two years as a research engineer in an industrial laboratory, Arthur Compton decided to return to university research to pursue his investigations into the electronic structure of the atom. Rutherford, and the unique group of research men assembled at the Cavendish Laboratory, drew him to Cambridge in 1919, where he had the opportunity to work directly with one of the scientific giants of all time. Upon Rutherford's death, Mr. Compton recalled some of the qualities of his genius in this article for the *Scientific Monthly*.

The name of Ernest Rutherford [1871–1937] will be forever identified with radioactivity and the nucleus of the atom. In a scientific generation whose great problem was the structure of matter, Rutherford directed the newfound powers of nature to uncover her innermost secrets. Rutherford approached his scientific problems with vigorous directness, steering straight to the heart of the matter, using whatever tools were most suitable, pressed on by a burning urge to find the truth. His genius was to plow through a tangle of data and guesses and bring into obvious view the underlying facts. Himself a great leader in science, he has passed the blazing torch to hundreds of younger men.

Lord Rutherford was born in 1871 as Ernest Rutherford near the little town of Nelson, in the South Island of New Zealand. He made a brilliant record at Canterbury College of New Zealand University and went to Trinity College, Cambridge, in 1895. His studies during this first Cambridge period included work on electric waves, in which he developed a detector of increased sensitiveness, and important observations on the ionization of gases, in collaboration with J. J. Thomson. From Cambridge, Rutherford went to McGill University as Macdonald professor of physics, where between 1898 and 1907 he did his most important work on radioactivity. The next period of twelve years was that in which he developed the nuclear concept of the atom. As Langworthy professor at Manchester, he not only performed his own brilliant experiments on the scattering of alpha rays, but also stimulated the equally fundamental work of Bohr and Moseley. After the war, he accepted an urgent request to go to Cambridge as Cavendish professor, where he was destined to make the Cavendish Laboratory, already notable for the great researches of Maxwell, Rayleigh, and Thomson, pre-eminent in the worldwide attack on the structure of the nucleus.

If the record of his discoveries is to be paralleled in the annals of physics, it will be only by a Newton or a Faraday. Consider some of them. Working with J. J. Thomson on the effects of X rays, Rutherford gave the first convincing proof that electric current passes through gases because of the presence of charged "ions." This was the foundation stone of our knowledge of the mechanism of the conduction of electricity through gases. His brilliant researches established the existence and the nature of radioactive transformations. He was the leader in the analysis of the rays from radioactive substances into the alpha, beta, and gamma rays, and the identification of these rays as doubly charged helium atoms, electrons, and electromagnetic radiation, respectively. An incident in this work was his measurement of the electronic unit of charge with a precision many times greater than that of earlier determinations and adequate for the contemporary needs of the electron theory. Using alpha rays as his tool, he established the theory that the atom has a concentrated, electrically charged nucleus that possesses nearly all the atom's mass. He tested the laws of electric force for subatomic distances and measured the electric charges of his atomic nuclei. That these nuclei were not elemental things he proved by disintegrating them with alpha rays, discovering in the process that the proton, the nucleus of the hydrogen atom, is a component of the heavier atomic nuclei. Under his immediate encouragement were performed Moseley's remarkable X-ray experiments that showed the meaning of atomic number in terms of nuclear charge, Chadwick's discovery of the neutron which forms a part of the nucleus, Cockcroft's artificial disintegration of nuclei, and Niels Bohr's development of his theory of the atom. A large part of the development of modern physics thus occurred within his brain and was established by tests made with his own hands.

Strength and contagious enthusiasm were outstanding characteristics of Rutherford. His interest was an inspiration to those who worked with him. While not infallible in his inferences and conclusions, his clear physical intuition was at times almost uncanny in its accuracy. His powerful physique suggested a lethargy that was belied by his nimble wit, which on more than one occasion was effective in exposing the pretensions of too careless theorists.

Rutherford's great powers were not used in the laboratory alone. In his later years he took an active part in applying science to the public welfare. As president of the British Association for the Advancement of Science and for a number of years also of the Royal Society, he was an effective public exponent of science.

Universities, societies, and academies at home and abroad were pleased to have Rutherford accept their honors. He was knighted in 1914 and received the Order of Merit in 1925. It was with no little hesitancy that in 1931 he allowed himself to be created first Lord Rutherford of Nelson. His characteristic democracy, however, enabled him to keep close to his scientific colleagues, and he felt that he should not make it too difficult for his nation to recognize the importance of the contribution that was being made by science.

According to a recent British commentator, Rutherford "was by far the greatest living experimental scientist, and the greatest the world has seen since Faraday." This is a judgment that will be shared by most of those who know his work. In an age whose great achievement is its science, it would be fair to consider him as having been the world's first citizen.

# 19. J. C. Stearns

## 1948

In 1923 Joyce Stearns, already a teacher of remarkable promise, enrolled at the University of Chicago to seek a graduate degree in physics with Professor Compton, whom he considered to be one of the nation's inspiring teachers. Thus began the close friendship and productive association in many important tasks that was to span a quarter century.

Joyce Clennam Stearns died at his home in Webster Groves, Missouri, on June 11. He had served as director of the "Metallurgical" Laboratory * at the University of Chicago during the last year of the war, and since July, 1945, had been dean of faculties of Washington University in St. Louis.

Stearns was born in Meadville, Missouri, in 1893, studied liberal arts at Kingfisher College, took his master's and doctor's degrees in physics at the University of Chicago, and taught successively at Albion College and the University of Denver, where he was professor and eventually chairman of the department of physics. He was among the first to be drawn to Chicago in January, 1942, when the atomic program was set up as an active war project. Here his work was concerned chiefly with employment of personnel, with the training of new men in the new field of atomic science, and later with maintaining the strength of the laboratory at the crucial stage of the preparation of the bombs, when the heaviest demands were being made upon it for trained men to work at Los Alamos and Hanford and high-pressure work had still to be done at the home base.

The climax of his professional career was at Washington University, where as dean of faculties Joyce Stearns was the guiding spirit in rebuilding the staff after the disruption of the war. If the students and faculty of this university have the courage and the forward look that comes with growing strength, it is to a large extent because of the respect for scholarship, for firm justice, and for practical human values which he brought with him.

Stearns made notable contributions in his special field of science, as a distinguished educator and as an able administrator. His first major scientific work was a classic demonstration that magnetization of iron makes no considerable change in the positions of the atoms or the electrons of which the iron is composed. This result ruled out the older theory of magnetism based upon the Bohr atom, according to which the electrons revolving in orbits constituted the elementary magnets that were oriented by the applied magnetic field. It was consistent, however, with the later theories, according to which the electrons are themselves magnets that become oriented when the iron is magnetized. Stearns's experiment consisted of magnetizing a crystal of iron from which a beam of X rays was reflected. He found that no change in the strength of the reflected beam as great as one part per thousand was caused by magnetization, whereas changes of several per cent should have been expected if the orbits in which the electrons revolved had followed the magnetic field.

Stearns also carried on several interesting experiments with cosmic rays, including tests of possible directional effects from the sun, and of east-west asymmetry of cosmic ray showers. His most notable achievement in cosmic ray studies, however, was his establishment of the high-altitude laboratory on Mount Evans, just west of Denver.* Stearns secured the cooperation of the Denver City Parks in building a road to the top of the mountain and in preparing the site for the laboratory. He persuaded the University of Denver, Massachusetts Institute of Technology, and the University of Chicago to cooperate with Mr. John Evans in building and maintaining the laboratory. He gave valuable aid to the many expeditions to Mount Evans from several universities by offering his own laboratory at Denver as a low-altitude base of operations and by helping with the experiments in many ways. It would be a fitting tribute indeed to name the Mount Evans laboratory after him.*

Few physicists have earned as high a reputation in the field of teaching. His work at Denver was chiefly with undergraduates. But many graduate schools learned to look to Stearns for sending them well-trained students with live interest in their science.

At the Metallurgical Laboratory, Stearns was one of the invaluable men who without consideration of their own personal interests would put their full effort on the tasks that needed most to be done. Thus he served successively as director of personnel, director of the physics division, and director of the laboratory. His understanding of human nature, his keen sense of humor, and his forthright honesty made him one whom all respected. One of his most notable services was organizing and carrying through the training program for the engineers who were to build and operate the Hanford plant that would use the atomic chain reaction for producing plutonium. Mature men had to learn a new art and science from their not always too patient juniors. The skill with which these engineers later met their difficult assignments spoke eloquently for the effectiveness of their training.

At Washington University the teaching staff of most of the schools had been dispersed during the war. In certain of the schools the faculty had in fact almost ceased to exist. With the help of those who remained, Stearns had the task of reorganizing effective groups of teachers to meet the rush of postwar students. He brought with him not only a familiarity with educational problems, but also administrative experience and a remarkable ability to get things done. He undertook this extraordinarily difficult assignment because he saw the urgent need to develop in this central area of the nation a powerful agency for giving education that would help in bringing lasting peace. He had the satisfaction of seeing a good growth in the direction of his efforts and of feeling a warmth of friendship from his colleagues such as is rarely experienced.

# 20. Albert Einstein

## *1949*

❧ On the occasion of the seventieth anniversary of the birth of Albert Einstein [1879–1955], Unesco prepared a special radio program paying tribute to him as a man, a scientist, and a pioneer of the human spirit. Three international leaders in science were invited to participate in the program, which was broadcast on radio stations throughout the world. Einstein's contributions to peace and to international understanding were emphasized by Jacques Hadamard and Niels Bohr, while Mr. Compton spoke of Einstein as a scientist.

I want to say a word about Albert Einstein as a scientist, for it is as one who has greatly clarified man's view of his world that Einstein will always be remembered. Einstein's great contributions to science are his principle of relativity and his theory of particles or "quanta" of light. These are fields of knowledge so specialized that most persons consider them too abstruse to understand and too theoretical to affect human life. It would be possible to tell how these theories have indeed aided the advance of practical physics and chemistry, and how they affected the outcome of the recent war. But this would put the emphasis in the wrong place.

Einstein is great not because of any effect he may have had on our habits of life but because he has shown us our world in truer perspective, and has helped us to understand a little more clearly how we are related to the universe around us.

In 1921 the Nobel physics prize was given to Albert Einstein "for his discovery of the law of the photoelectric effect." This was selected as an aspect of his theoretical study that was subject to precise test and had been thoroughly verified by experiment. It is, however, his principle of relativity that has properly brought to Einstein his great fame.

About 1900, new properties of rapidly moving objects were discovered that did not fit with the long accepted ideas of physics. Typical of these properties was that the mass of an electron was found to increase greatly if it was set in motion at very high speed. One special assumption after another had been introduced to account for such effects, but these special assumptions themselves had no justification.

Then, in 1905, Einstein suggested that the laws of physics as we observe them may be in no way dependent upon how fast we are moving through space. It is only how fast an object is moving relative to us that, in his view, can affect the way things on this object appear to act. The mathematical consequences of this simple assumption were found to fit with the changes in the properties of objects moving at very high speeds. No further special hypotheses were needed. Accordingly, since Einstein, science has given up the idea of any framework of space, such as a fixed ether, relative to which we might think of ourselves as moving. The only motion that has any meaning, according to the special theory of relativity, is the motion of one object relative to another.

Among the unexpected consequences of this theory is that the mass of anything is proportional to its energy, a result now well verified by experiment. It was this principle that led Lise Meitner to find the enormous energy associated with atomic fission.

Hardly was the scientific world becoming accustomed to think in terms of this "special" relativity when, in 1915, Einstein introduced a general theory of relativity. This took into account not only the speeds but also the changes in speed, or "accelerations," of objects relative to each other. One of the remarkable unexplained coincidences of physics had been that the weight of anything, that is, the pull on it by gravity, is proportional to its mass; whereas mass is measured by the force with which an object reacts against an imposed change of motion. By putting these two properties together, Einstein introduced a new concept of weight: According to Einstein, the weight of anything is itself nothing but the reaction against an enforced change of motion.

This concept meant that in the neighborhood of a massive body, such as the earth, toward which objects fall if left to themselves, there must be a natural state of motion that is different from that at distances far away from such masses. This natural state of motion near the earth Einstein found could be described by modifications of space and time in its neighborhood, modifications that correspond roughly to the curvature of the parallels of latitude on a globe. What is more, there was only one way in which such curvature of space and time in the neighborhood of a gravitating body could be fitted into the requirements of geometry, and this curvature corresponded precisely to an attraction inversely as the square of the distance, the law of gravitation that Isaac Newton had found many years before. In the new theory, however, differences were to be expected for fast-moving objects, amounting to twice as great an effect of the sun's attraction on a ray of light passing near it as might have been expected on Newton's theory. This effect was first tested by the British expedition to observe the solar eclipse of 1919. The delicate astronomical studies made then and since have confirmed this and other predictions of Einstein's "general" theory.

This general theory of relativity also has its remarkable consequences. One of these is that there cannot be an endless amount of matter in the universe. Not only is the space near the earth and sun curved, the space including the whole system of stars is also curved; and this curvature puts a definite limit on how many stars can be in the universe and over how many light-years of distance it can extend. Further studies, especially the theoretical studies by de Sitter of Holland and the astronomical observations by Hubble in the United States, seem to give a rather definite picture of how big this universe of ours is.

Thus Albert Einstein has made it possible for man to see himself in truer proportions. His concept of light quanta has helped us understand the atoms that make up the world of which we are a part. In his special theory of relativity he has taught us that we must think in terms of objects that we see, not in terms of some imagined framework of space. By his general theory of relativity he has unified our laws of motion and our law of gravitation, and has opened the way for us to see with new clarity our universe, finite now in extent, but vaster by far than had been dreamed before his thoughts stimulated the imagination of the scientific world.

Einstein continues his studies. He hopes to bring all the forces that physics knows, gravitational, electrical, and nuclear, into one unified formula. As yet that goal is not achieved; but in his progress toward the goal he has greatly expanded our horizons.

# 21. Robert A. Millikan

## *1950*

&#10086; At the age of eighty, after more than a half century of active scientific work, Robert A. Millikan published his autobiography. In his review of Millikan's book, Mr. Compton stresses not only Millikan's importance as one of the most influential native-born scientists but also the book's importance as a contribution toward an understanding of the scientists whose work is so rapidly changing the world.

It would be difficult to find a person whose life is more representative of the course of modern history than is that of Robert A. Millikan [1868–1954], whose work in science has helped to change the world's thought, and whose contributions as a citizen have substantially strengthened our nation. The great event of modern history is the emergence of a democratic society in which life is vastly influenced by science.

"I suspect," writes Millikan, "that the changes that have taken place during the last century in the average man's fundamental beliefs, in his philosophy, in his conception of religion, in his whole world outlook, are greater than the changes that occurred during the preceding four thousand years all put together."

Why? *Because of science and its applications to human life,* for these have bloomed in my time as no one in history had ever dreamed could be possible." Millikan's autobiography illustrates the growth of this scientific influence, in which the author himself had a powerful hand.

Science owes its origin to men from many nations. A remarkable aspect of its recent growth, however, has been the increasing importance of the part played by Americans. When Millikan began his study of physics in 1893, Europe had many great figures making notable contributions. American scientists were rare indeed. Toward the close of his career he finds his compatriots occupying a leading place. Noteworthy also is the fact that some sixty per cent of the present leading American scientists have originated in the Midwest, so the author's birth and upbringing in the Mississippi Valley is representative of the majority group of American scientific men. Statistically typical of the training of our scientists are likewise the facts that he was the son of a Protestant minister whose six children later moved to various parts of the country, and that his initial education was in the public schools and in a denominational college.

Thus it is that Millikan's story gives an example of the characteristic contributions that America has made to the growth of modern thinking, and an understanding of some of the factors that have brought America into its present position as a world leader. One factor is that our men of action have been carrying on the pioneer tradition. To the pioneer the world was what he could make of it. He asked little help from outside, and he built for the future. During Millikan's boyhood the men who controlled the affairs of his community were themselves the pioneers. There was no other thought than that they could shape their world to their needs. This they were doing, and they expected the rising generation to carry on the program of making theirs a better world. Such was the author's heritage.

A corollary was devotion to duty, the prime virtue both of the pioneer and of the American Protestant. A priceless example is afforded by Millikan's account of his wedding. I know personally something of his admiration and affection for his charming wife. Yet his description of his marriage is confined to the following statement: "On April 10, 1902, I married Greta Blanchard. I was just then getting my *Mechanics, Molecular Physics and Heat* ready for the printer, and in order to finish it before going to Europe I read proof until 6 P.M. on my wedding day. . . . I had a bad ten minutes when I found the exit door locked, but finally located a janitor and got out in time to appear at the Blanchard home to play the assigned role."

It is an expression of this devotion to duty and love for his science that the major part of Millikan's autobiography should be taken up with stories of the great events in which he participated. These events include the growth of physics from a dormant classical subject to a dynamic, growing field of research; the work of the American scientists as they took their effective place in the First World War; the establishment of the National Research Council and the development of the National Academy of Sciences into an effective agency for advising the government; and the creation of the California Institute of Technology, which has brought new life to technical industry in California and has afforded the nation a valuable pattern for engineering education.

Of special interest to the scientific reader will be the author's account of his own remarkable researches. His proof that all electrons bear precisely the same electric charge and his accurate measurement of that charge is one of the classic experiments of modern physics. His precision measurement of the ratio of the energy of a photoelectron to the frequency of the light that ejects it reinforced the evidence for Einstein's theory of the photoelectric effect, and was an important step in establishing the photon theory of the nature of light. His spectroscopic studies of high-voltage sparks in a vacuum not only extended greatly the experimental knowledge of spectra but also made possible a better understanding of the properties of highly ionized atoms. He performed a great service to science in calling attention to the significance of cosmic rays, and with the help of his students, in using them effectively for revealing new ele-mental components of matter. He tells of this work in his well-known manner, full of personal anecdote and rich with references to his con-versations with the world's scientific leaders.

Since the time of Benjamin Franklin there have been few if any native-born Americans whose researches have affected more significantly the development of scientific thought.

Not the least of Millikan's contributions has been the writing of scien-tific books. Written in cooperation with others, these have included college textbooks on physics, a translation of Drude's classic work on optics, a monograph on cosmic rays, and a masterly discussion of the relation be-tween science and religion. His writings that have perhaps had the greatest influence have been his *First Course in Physics*, originally done in co-operation with Henry Gale, which during its successive editions has been studied by millions of students, and his own *The Electron*, which in later editions included also the other fields of experimental physics covered by his versatile research.

The latter volume became a handbook for those following similar lines of study. His colleagues have good-humoredly referred to it as "Happy Days and Nights in Millikan's Laboratory," thus indicating both the point of view from which he wrote and the fascinating story of intellectual ad-venture that he told. In the present volume he tells of the conditions under which these books were written, the urgent need for adequate texts, and the importance of presenting in understandable perspective the work upon which he was engaged.

It is fortunate that the author has used his autobiography to express his mature thought on certain major issues, such as the requirements for peace, the essentials of a good education, and the vital place of science and religion in life. Let him speak for himself:

> I said then [1914] as I say now, that if the democratic, peace-loving peoples who in the long climb upward from savagery toward civilization

have outgrown the ideology of conquest and are trying to replace it by rational procedures have not the intelligence to unite to defend themselves when they are attacked by the wild beasts of the jungle who propose to thwart that effort and to perpetuate the ideology of war and conquest, then there is no hope for the future of mankind.

Millikan does not anticipate important economic consequences of atomic energy, but he considers most significant its effect in deterring people from attempting to solve disputes by war:

> The great service to mankind of the advent of the atomic bomb has been to make as clear as crystal, to all classes and conditions of men the world over, the necessity . . . to find a substitute for war in the handling of its international relations . . . [this] in itself, without reference to further inventions of any kind, will make a new world; and its influence in making a new world will probably be greater than all other influences combined.

Millikan's view of education is that it exists primarily to prepare men for actual jobs including that of effective living outside one's job. In sharing in the development of the California Institute of Technology, he had an opportunity to put this idea into practice. The result is an institution in which engineering students learn the scientific basis of technology, and at the same time participate in such cultural studies as English, history, economics, philosophy, and ethics.

It is a matter of serious concern to Millikan that our nation's expenditure for alcoholic drinks is twice as great as the total cost of our public and private schools of all levels. The often expressed thought that more and better education for all of our citizens costs more than we can afford he considers preposterous, and a sad reflection on our sense of values.

We can make our educational opportunities adequate to the demand, he believes, only if we will steer away from higher education those not fitted for intellectual pursuits, and give them advanced training of a manual and commercial type, accompanied by an understanding of the opportunities and privileges of free citizens. Thus we can meet the conditions required to build a great democracy.

I should add that the form of Millikan's own institute shows that he recognizes clearly the other essential aspect of education in a great democracy, namely that of making available for those destined to become the leaders of our thought the most adequate and stimulating education that we know how to supply. This superior education cannot be given to many, for those competent to give it are necessarily few. Thus if such education is to be used to good effect, a wise and careful selection must be made of the students to whom it shall be offered. In our present educational pattern, this is perhaps the most important responsibility of private education and it is that toward which Millikan has directed his attention.

Perhaps, however, in no field are the author's comments of greater significance than in that of science and religion. He places "(1) the *spirit* of religion, (2) the *spirit* of science (or knowledge)" as the pillars upon which rest human well-being and all of human progress.

The contrast between this view, typical of a large group of American scientists, and that of the European positivists is striking. To the positivists, religion is a superstitious delusion that is the antithesis of science. To those represented by Millikan, religion and science form two distinct aspects of man's life, inspiration and knowledge, which while mutually related cannot be inconsistent.

For one with Millikan's background, the assumption that goals and ideals are significant is taken for granted, and the task of religion is to select these goals wisely and to make them effective in life. Science becomes useful in giving a reliable basis for one's choices, and for implementing one's purposes with the strength that comes with knowledge. Traditional religious doctrine is useful so far and only so far as it aids in understanding and cultivating the possibilities for good that lie in the human spirit. It is with this in mind that he quotes a statement which he helped to formulate in 1923, and which was signed by forty-five leaders of religion, science, and human affairs:

> The purpose of science is to develop, without prejudice or preconception of any kind, a knowledge of the facts, the laws, and the processes of nature. The even more important task of religion, on the other hand, is to develop the consciences, the ideals, and the aspirations of mankind.

This latter sentence would in fact seem to constitute the author's definition of religion, that which is concerned with "the consciences, the ideals, and the aspirations of mankind." When this meaning is grasped, the great importance that he places upon religion becomes evident. The common essential of all good religion he selects as "the attitude of altruistic idealism." "It is so to shape my own conduct at all times as, *in my own carefully considered judgment,* to promote best the well-being of mankind as a whole."

"Never in history," he writes, "has mankind faced a situation which forced every person on earth to ask himself so insistently the question, 'How can I help to make a better world?'" Here is evidently the key to the remarkable ardor, diligence, and persistence with which Robert Millikan has worked and lived for the eighty years of which he writes. He has had a burning passion to help make a better world.* He has thus carried on in the spirit of the pioneer community into which he was born. With regard to physical powers he has indeed helped men to improve their lot. If they will also catch his vision of a more worthy life toward which they can work, they will have progressed also in well-being.

For those who would understand the scientists that have played so large a part in changing our world, I do not know where to find a more illuminating book than this. It is authoritative and eminently readable. It includes valuable source material regarding not only the history of modern science but also the great events of the last half century as recorded by a keen, reliable observer. Only in certain matters of minor significance, such as his pessimistic view of the future possibilities of atomic power, would the reviewer consider the thoughts expressed by the author as misleading. Taken as a whole, this autobiography is an important contribution to the understanding of what is perhaps the greatest age of history. I expect it to be read for many years to come.

# 22. C. J. Davisson

## 1958

Davisson's discovery of the diffraction of electrons by crystals (1927) was an important step in the development of the quantum theory, as was the author's research on the scattering of X rays. In this biographical memoir for the American Philosophical Society, Mr. Compton discusses Davisson's influence upon his scientific colleagues.

Clinton Joseph Davisson [1881–1958] was a scientist of the type that scientists admire. As stated by his long-time associate at the Bell Telephone Laboratories, Mervin J. Kelly:

> His inner driving force was always seeking complete and exact knowledge of the physical phenomena under study. The rapid tempo of the work [in wartime] with the necessity of accepting partial answers and following one's nose in an empirical fashion were foreign to his way of doing things. As a war necessity he yielded to it, and performed as a good soldier. His interests were almost wholly scientific, but the needs of the situation forced upon him somewhat of an engineering role for which he had little appetite. As an adviser and consultant, he was unusually effective. In this he has few equals among scientists of my acquaintance. I believe that his success here is due to the high level of his interest in solving problems, to his broad area of curiosity about physical phenomena, and to his warm, friendly, and unselfish interest in the scientific aspects of the work of his associates.[1]

Those of us who have known Davisson personally will recognize the correctness of this description of his attitude toward his science. He always held the highest possible standard for himself in his work and his innate modesty gave him a tendency to undervalue the importance and scope of his contributions.

In spite of his retiring characteristics, the influence of Davisson upon

[1] *Bell System Technical Journal*, 30:4 (October 1951), p. 780.

his colleagues was quite extensive. There were several factors that contributed to this influence. First of all, there was the remarkable research that he performed in discovering the diffraction of electron beams by crystals. This opened up fields of study, both experimental and theoretical, that have engaged the interests of many men and have had a fundamental effect upon the scientific interpretation of the world of nature. In a similar category come Davisson's investigations of thermionic emission from metals. Using meticulous care in securing clean, gas-free metallic surfaces, he and his co-workers were able to make a crucial distinction between two laws of thermionic emission as enunciated by O. W. Richardson. The form of the law that they confirmed was the one that assumes a distribution of electron velocities in the metal that is not Maxwellian but rather follows a distribution law that was proposed some years later by Fermi and Dirac. He thus established a firm background for replacing the classical laws of statistical mechanics with a quantum modification of these laws. There was a practical consequence likewise of Davisson's studies of thermionics that is of high importance. This had to do with the long life of electron tubes that is vitally important in connection with telecommunication work. In 1917, when Davisson began his thermionic studies for the Western Electric Company, electron tubes were in their infancy. Though they had already demonstrated their importance, their use was severely limited by shortness of life and variability of characteristics. Davisson concentrated his attention on the understanding of the oxide-coated cathode and did not leave this field of investigation until it had become possible to build these tubes with such uniformity and reliability that they could be used with confidence in complex electronic equipment. The straightforward matter of developing such high reliability has been a major factor in the rapid development of the electronic art.

I can speak with firsthand knowledge of the unusual effectiveness of Davisson as an adviser and consultant with regard to physical problems. In the Bell Company laboratories he was recognized as exceptionally effective in this regard. He always showed a friendly interest in the problems placed before him and rarely left the visitor without benefit from the discussions. Occasionally, when an answer was not forthcoming, he would continue his study of the problem and would come back later to give the questioner the benefit of his more mature consideration of the problem. His success as a consultant does seem to have been due in large measure to the high level of his interest in solving problems, the broad area of his curiosity about physical phenomena, but especially to his warm, friendly, and unselfish interest in the scientific work of his associates. Davisson thus became a major factor in building up the *esprit de corps* of his laboratory and of other scientists throughout the world in cooperating on similar problems of electronics.

Yet another important factor in his influence on his colleagues was the reputation that he established for unwillingness to settle for anything less than a full understanding of the phenomenon under investigation if such an understanding was attainable. This implied unusually high standards of perfection in Davisson's experimental work. It became well recognized among Davisson's colleagues that it was, in fact, this high standard of perfection that was the secret of his success in solving various unusually difficult experimental problems. It may be fairly said further that Davisson has had an important effect on the pattern of research in American industrial laboratories by demonstrating the importance of the understanding of fundamental principles in the developing and practical construction of instruments that these laboratories have been developing. Typical was his work with the oxide-coated cathode and with the surface characteristics of metallic crystals that have become so important in connection with electron emission. As Kelly says:

> It is a tribute to Davisson's overpowering interest in science, and to his steadfastness in the pursuit of knowledge through the scientific method of experiment and analysis that during the pioneering and rapid expansion years of our laboratories, when development demanded the attention of most of our scientists, he gave almost undivided attention to the scientific aspects of our work. Throughout his career he has remained a scientist and has maintained a working knowledge at the forefront of a wide area of physics.[2]

It was in the course of a systematic investigation of the surface properties of metallic crystals in vacuum tubes that Davisson made the epochal discovery of the diffraction of electrons by crystals, for which he is best known. He and his co-workers were interested in the secondary electrons that come from a surface bombarded by a beam of electrons. Working with C. H. Kunsman in 1921, he reported the scattering of electrons with prominent peaks in certain directions, these directions depending on the speed of the electrons. In his effort to explain the occurrence of these peaks, Davisson was led to think of the nickel surface as made of a complex of small crystals. Some years later, owing to an accident, the nickel surface with which he was working became overheated and became recrystallized in a small number of larger crystals. As he was endeavoring to explain the change in the pattern of the distribution of electrons scattered by the new nickel surface he came in contact with the work of Erwin Schrödinger on wave mechanics and became convinced that the

[2] Ibid., p. 784.

phenomenon that he was observing could be interpreted only in terms of some form of quantum theory. A German physicist, Walter Elsasser, who had been following Davisson's publications, put forward the suggestion that the remarkable results that Davisson was obtaining were to be interpreted in terms of Louis de Broglie's electron waves. While Elsasser was unable to show quantitatively that such an interpretation was correct, Davisson instituted a program of thorough search that showed that Elsasser's hypothesis was indeed correct but that the diffraction of electrons occurs from only the layers of atoms in the crystal that are nearest the surface. This work was done in the year 1926-7 in cooperation with L. H. Germer. At about the same time G. P. Thomson, then at the University of Aberdeen, using an entirely different technique, demonstrated the diffraction of electrons as an electron beam was passed through thin layers of gold and aluminum. In 1937 the Nobel prize for physics was awarded jointly to Davisson and Germer and to G. P. Thomson for the discovery of electron diffraction.

This discovery was truly epochal in its significance. For a generation electrons had been known as particles. Henceforth it was apparent likewise that they had the properties of waves. Ten years earlier it had been demonstrated that X rays, whose wave characteristics were already familiar, had the characteristics of particles whose paths could be followed from one electron to another with which they collided. It now became apparent that the dual properties of particle and wave were characteristic of all the fundamental elements composing matter. Following the lead of Davisson and Thomson, similar diffraction has since been demonstrated in the case of protons, hydrogen atoms, neutrons, helium atoms, and hydrogen molecules. In the effort to understand these dual particle and wave aspects of matter it has been necessary to introduce the fundamental assumptions on which the quantum theory of matter and energy is based.

Davisson's interests, however, did not carry into the development of these theories. The observing of optical properties of electron beams led him rather into the study of the optical characteristics of electrons, including electron diffraction, refraction, and lenses. By building lenses suitable for focusing electron beams, he contributed to the development of the electron microscope. In this study he made one of his few technological developments. He also applied the principles he had developed to the construction of a cathode-ray tube of great precision. By virtue of the fundamental design of the beam and deflecting system, his tube provided an extremely small rectangular spot on the fluorescent screen that remained in sharp focus over the entire screen area and had a much improved response characteristic. This tube proved to be a useful tool in the evaluation of picture impairment resulting from different types of signal distortion.

Davisson was born October 22, 1881, at Bloomington, Illinois, the son of Joseph Davisson, a craftsman, and Mary Calvert Davisson, a schoolteacher. Young Davisson attended the Bloomington public schools and on graduation was awarded a scholarship at the University of Chicago in mathematics and physics. He received the B.S. degree with a major in physics from Chicago in 1908. In 1911 he received his Ph.D. from Princeton University, where his research was supervised by O. W. Richardson of thermionics fame. Immediately after receiving his degree, he married Charlotte Sara Richardson, a sister of O. W. Richardson. They had three children, James Willans, Elizabeth Mary Dixon, and Richard Joseph. Leaving Princeton, he became an instructor at the Carnegie Institute of Technology in 1911, but in 1917, in World War I, entered the Western Electric Company's engineering department, which subsequently became Bell Telephone Laboratories. He remained at Bell Laboratories until his retirement in 1946. In addition to the Nobel prize, Davisson received many other honors, including the Comstock prize of the National Academy of Sciences, the Cresson medal of the Franklin Institute, and the Hughes medal of the Royal Society of London. He likewise received honorary degrees from several universities. During World War II he was engaged in the study of the theory of electronic devices for the Armed Forces.

In 1946 Davisson retired from the Bell Telephone Laboratories and became a visiting professor of physics at the University of Virginia in Charlottesville. In 1929 he had been elected to membership in the American Philosophical Society. By his death in February 1958, the Society has lost a member who has contributed substantially to strengthening the foundations of modern physics.

# 23. E. O. Lawrence

## 1958

A bold innovator in science, Ernest Lawrence, who invented the cyclotron, is ranked by the author as one of America's most imaginative scientific leaders. The paths of Ernest Lawrence and Arthur Compton first crossed at the University of Chicago in 1926, when Lawrence was a graduate student in physics. Later Mr. Compton helped him secure funds to construct his 184-inch cyclotron, and during the war years both were importantly involved in the development of nuclear energy. Lawrence's unique contributions to science are assessed in this memoir for the American Philosophical Society.

Ernest Orlando Lawrence [1901–1958] may well be remembered in the history of science above all for his demonstration of the effectiveness of the organized research team as a means of studying academic problems of physics. George Ellery Hale, in organizing Mount Wilson Solar Observatory, had done a corresponding task for astronomy, though astronomy had long understood the value of large telescopes and organized research teams in their observatories. Similarly, Simon Flexner had put new life into American medical education and research when he organized the Rockefeller Institute for Medical Research and insisted that medical schools must have adequate equipment in order to qualify for first-class teaching. Herbert Hoover credits Thomas A. Edison with initiating the organized research team as a tool for industrial research. But the long tradition in physics had been that academic research should be performed during a teacher's spare time using apparatus designed for classroom instruction that was at the moment idle. This tradition, with an emphasis on use of only such added equipment as could be thrown quickly together using string and sealing wax, had been followed by J. J. Thomson's notable research school at Cavendish Laboratory, with the remarkable effectiveness that has given Cambridge University its unique place in modern physics.

It was not that Lawrence was primarily interested in building a major research team. He was concerned with research that required building and using large-scale physics equipment and for whose construction and operation a research team was necessary. His most striking scientific contribution was the invention and use of the cyclotron, an original invention of strictly first rank. The problem to be solved was to impart to atomic particles energies of ten- to a hundredfold greater than had been attainable in electrical discharge tubes. A. S. Eddington and others had found indications that reactions between the nuclei of atoms were occurring in the interior of stars and had reasoned that such reactions should occur when the energies of these particles became of the order of a million electron volts. Cockcroft and Walton demonstrated that such reactions do indeed occur in electrical discharges of very high voltage. The energies of the particles that they were able to obtain were however not high enough to explore the consequences of this discovery in the region of yet higher energy particles. Lawrence's cyclotron in principle should be able to shrink the size of a particle accelerator to such dimensions that it could be housed in a laboratory room of generous size. As in the case of many revolutionary inventions, many of his scientific colleagues predicted freely that it could not work. After its feasibility had been demonstrated on a small scale there were those who argued that to build full-scale equipment would exhaust the resources of any laboratory and would thus curtail other lines of research. Others complained that Lawrence was making gadgeteers of men who might be making useful contributions to physics experiments. Lawrence's answer was simply to build his cyclotron and apply its unique power to the study of the properties of particles of higher energy than had previously been available.

First, he produced a series of artificial isotopes, most of which had never before been observed. Thus was made possible the work with tracer atoms, a technique that has become of great importance during the past decade not only in physics but also in chemistry and biology. The invention of one instrument of this type stimulated the development of a series of other high-voltage accelerators and has opened up a great new field of research using high-energy particles. Important among their findings have been the remarkable properties of mesons and other subatomic particles of mass greater than that of the electron.

The construction and use of a heavy, powerful piece of apparatus such as a cyclotron becomes an engineering problem on a major scale. It was a part of the genius of Ernest Lawrence that he drew to himself physicists of like interests who were eager to share with him the task of building and using this equipment. He thus found himself directing a team of voluntary research men who were glad to accept his assignments with the hope of contributing to the scientific advances that the team would make. Many came to him from distant laboratories with the hope of learning his techniques. These he welcomed, for, he reasoned, the research task in hand was a big one and the more that entered upon it the greater would be the excitement of the chase.

His research organization was in full swing when World War II began to throw its shadow over the world. There was hardly a major nation that did not have one or more research men who had been trained by Lawrence. Lawrence himself was keenly aware of the threat to the freedom of thought and the freedom of life that was inherent in the development of the totalitarian nations. He was one of the first to sense clearly the military importance of atomic energy. And, while others were discussing the conditions under which nuclear energy might be released, Lawrence came forward with a proposal of a feasible method for building an atomic bomb. It had not yet been demonstrated that uranium 235 could be separated from its twin, uranium 238, in sufficient quantity for building atomic bombs. Lawrence proposed that plutonium 239 be made in a chain-reacting pile and then separated by chemical methods from its parent, uranium 238. His evidence was good that the amount of plutonium that would be needed would not be too much to produce and extract by this method. Already the importance of atomic energy had been brought to the President's attention. But with Lawrence's proposal of a feasible method for constructing a weapon that might well be of decisive importance in the war, what had been considered a research program of secondary importance became accepted by the government as a matter of highest priority. The successful carrying through of the whole wartime atomic program was greatly indebted to the initiative and drive imparted by Lawrence. His own part in the wartime research was concentrated primarily on a magnetic method of separating the isotopes of uranium, while the method that he had proposed for producing plutonium was assigned to another.* But at every stage his confidence in the success of the end result and his intent to let no barriers prevent the progress of the program gave heart to the entire atomic research team. The giant cyclotron that he had been building for research with high-energy particles was temporarily turned to use as a magnetic separator that gave us our first tangible quantities of uranium 235 for experimental purposes. One of his cyclotrons of intermediate size supplied us with the first samples of plutonium by means of which chemical experiments on its properties could be performed.

A major interest of Lawrence was biological studies of the effect of neutrons and other rays excited by his cyclotrons, a task in which his brother, Dr. John Lawrence, shared his efforts to find new and useful means of therapy.

Brilliant as were the scientific achievements and discoveries coming from Lawrence's laboratory, perhaps the most lasting effect will be his cultivation of an increased cooperativeness among scientists engaged in similar tasks. Lawrence had little room for scientific rivalry except as such rivalry might stimulate more active research. He was always ready to go out of his way to aid a colleague by counsel on techniques, by assistance in the building of equipment, or by suggesting some fruitful line of research.

There is little that is extraordinary in Lawrence's personal history. Ernest Lawrence was born August 8, 1901, in the small town of Canton, South Dakota, of the third generation of Scandinavian immigrants. His father, Carl G. Lawrence, was at one time president of the Northern State Teachers College at Aberdeen, South Dakota, while South Dakota was still a territory. His early education was in the Canton public schools, St. Olaf College, and the University of South Dakota. He started his graduate work at the University of Minnesota, and when W. F. G. Swann moved to the University of Chicago, Lawrence moved with him. After a year at Chicago, he went to Yale University where he received his Ph.D. In 1928 he was called to the University of California at Berkeley as associate professor of physics, advancing to a professorship in 1930. It is greatly to the credit of that university that it was able to help him secure the generous grants of equipment and other funds that made it possible for him to carry on his unusual research program.

In 1929 he began work on his first cyclotron. With its success, he was able to draw financial help from many different sources to support his imaginative but expensive researches. It is indicative of Lawrence's interests that immediately after the war he reorganized his research team at Berkeley to attack with full vigor the fundamental research problems of high-energy particles.

Lawrence was a lover of good company and enjoyed discussions, especially with his academic colleagues at the faculty club of the University of California. With industrialists and businessmen he was at home at the famous Bohemian Club, which meets in a redwood grove near San Francisco. Here on occasion he served as a genial host, showing the same kind of human interest in his guests as he did in his students of physics.

In 1932 he married Mary Kimberly Blumer. Their family consisted of six children, John Eric, Margaret Bradley, Mary Kimberly, Robert Don, Barbara Hundale, and Susan. A favorite form of relaxation was outings with his family in the woods. He also enjoyed tennis with his colleagues, a game that he played until the last year of his life.

Lawrence was awarded the Nobel prize for physics in 1939 and received high honors from scientific organizations of England, France, Russia, Belgium, and Ireland, as well as the United States. For his outstanding work toward victory in World War II, he received the Presidential award of the Medal for Merit. A member of many scientific societies at home and abroad, he was elected a member of the American Philosophical Society in 1937. His death on August 27, 1958, removed from our ranks a bold and adventurous scientific explorer whom we could ill afford to lose.

# 24. Alfred Nobel and the Nobel Prize

## *1948*

The St. Louis Chamber of Commerce honored the city's five Nobel prize winners at a testimonial dinner on November 29, 1948. On this occasion Mr. Compton discussed the history and significance of the Nobel prize.

There is something to contemplate in a man who expended his life energies in perfecting instruments for destruction and who in death encourages service to mankind and the search for peace. Such a man was Alfred Bernhard Nobel, a pacifist who was the creator of tremendous power for evil and an advocate of the forces of good.

The manufacture of dynamite, Ballistite, smokeless propellant powder, guns, shells, and aerial torpedoes does not, in the ordinary mind, add up to peace. But to Nobel, for the first sixty years of his life, products of devastation were the components of the equation of peace. His ultimate goal was to make war so horrible that no nation would consider waging one. In his mind munitions factories would end war before peace congresses would. "The day when two army corps can annihilate each other in one second, all civilized nations will recoil from war and discharge their troops," had been his words and his driving force. He held to this belief until it was modified in his late years by a woman and the book she wrote. The woman was Baroness Bertha von Suttner, who for a short time in the early days of Nobel's success had been engaged by him to become his secretary. The book she wrote was *Lay Down Your Arms!*, which became a watchword in war-sapped Europe. Through the book's powerful message and the Baroness' personal onslaught on Nobel's thinking, he finally came to the realization that as long as people regard some things as dearer than life itself there will be war. Thus it was that for the last few years of his life Nobel was active in the encouragement of peace congresses, and his peace prize was undoubtedly the outgrowth of his many arguments with Baroness von Suttner, who herself was the recipient of this least-awarded Nobel prize in 1905.

There is proof that Nobel did not altogether abandon his long-cherished idea of making wars so terrible that nations could not afford to fight. He maintained that when war could become a "sword of Damocles hanging over the head of each individual" that would be the day wars would cease.

Alfred Nobel was born in Stockholm in 1833 of a Swedish peasant family. His father, Immanuel, was an architect and builder who held a whole series of patents, but whose greatest fame and fortune came from the construction of mines used by the Russian government for land and naval warfare in the Crimean War. Alfred, a sickly child, liked to read Shelley and to write Shelleyan-style poetry. It was not expected that he would reach manhood, much less become his father's good right hand.

It was the taming of nitroglycerin so that it could be used practically and with safety that made Alfred Nobel one of Europe's richest men and controller of one of the world's largest trusts. The heavy, colorless liquid that looked like salad oil was discovered in 1847 by an Italian scientist, Professor Ascanio Sobrero, who gave up his investigation of the "explosive oil" after four hundred grams accidentally exploded. Fifteen years later the Nobels, Immanuel and Alfred, began their experiments; but it was Alfred who, in 1863, developed a mixture of gunpowder and nitroglycerin that performed reasonably well. In 1864 an accident in his workshop killed his brother and four other persons. It was then that he formulated his philosophy that enabled him to overlook other disasters occurring in various places all over the world and that made him strive on in the face of government bans on the purchase and storage of his explosive. His belief was that each new invention, each advancement in scientific thinking and technical skill, would ultimately be used for the good of mankind. "Every new discovery modifies the human brain and makes the new generation capable of grasping new ideas." Through knowledge of every type man becomes more nearly perfect, and is not peace a main feature of perfection? Through knowledge, peace—so reasoned Alfred Nobel.

Three years after the workshop explosion, Nobel hit upon the version of dynamite as we know it today—nitroglycerin absorbed in a type of clay prevalent in northern Germany. This product was so manageable that it was labeled under the name "Nobel's Safety Powder," and it brought its inventor royalties amounting to over $50 million.

Nobel died in Italy, on December 10, 1896, and a great deal of interest attended the publication in January of this strange genius' will. It directed that the capital of his estate was to be invested and the interest distributed each year in the form of prizes without regard to nationality, to those who shall have rendered the "greatest service to mankind" in the realm of physics, chemistry, and physiology or medicine; who shall have produced in the field of literature the "most outstanding work of an idealistic tendency"; and who shall have done the "most or the best work for fraternity among nations, for the abolition or reduction of standing armies, and for the holding and promotion of peace congresses." Nobel had written his will without the aid of an attorney, and it is not known when he first conceived the idea for such a bequest.

Each year, on December 10, Stockholm becomes for a day the capital of the world of achievement. It is then that men high in the fields of government, education, and science gather in an atmosphere both festive and hallowed to honor those who have been selected for their service to mankind. There in the flower-bedecked Concert Hall, while the royal family looks on and the royal orchestra plays, the Swedish Academy of Science awards the prizes for physics and for chemistry, the Caroline Institute presents the prize in physiology and medicine, and the outstanding literary achievement is honored by the Swedish Academy. (The Peace prize is awarded in Oslo by a committee of five, elected by the Norwegian Storting [parliament], whose task it is to select the person or institution most nearly carrying out the ideals Nobel set forth.) After the presentation of the awards and the gold Nobel medallions, a banquet is held in the City Hall where, following the customary toast to the King, the Crown Prince leads a silent toast to the memory of Alfred Nobel, king of dynamite and architect of peace.

Nominations for the prizes must come from "competent quarters," such as members of leading national scientific and art academies, government circles, and past recipients of the awards. Each prize—which is usually worth about $40,000—may be divided among two or three individuals should the committee so decide.

Since the first awards were made in 1901, two hundred thirty-two men and women and six institutions, representing twenty-three different countries, have received Nobel prizes.* Only eleven of the Nobel laureates have been women.* St. Louis' own Gerty Cori is the only woman to hold this honor in medicine. Marie Curie, a most remarkable scientist, received the prize twice—once in physics in 1903, sharing the award with her husband and Henri Becquerel, and once in chemistry in 1911. She is the only person to have been so honored.*

German scientists have won the coveted award over forty times. It is interesting to note, by the way, that in 1937 the Nazi government prohibited its citizens from accepting the prize.*

Of the thirty-seven Americans * who have received this honor, six of us are with you tonight. Five are now living in St. Louis.

Because of the importance to the world of each contribution, it is, of course, impossible to list a few names and say that their work is of greatest importance. Let me remind you, nevertheless, of a few winners in each field.

In medicine St. Louis is well represented by four Nobel winners.* Edward Doisy in 1943 shared the award with Henrik Dam of Copenhagen for the isolation, analysis, and synthesis of vitamin K. In 1944 Joseph Erlanger shared the prize with Herbert S. Gasser, former professor of pharmacology at Washington University and until recently director of the Rockefeller Institute for Medical Research, for their investigation into the manner in which nerves carry messages. Their best-known contribution is the development of the application of an instrument known as a cathode-ray oscillograph to the study of nerves. In experimenting with glycogen, Carl and Gerty Cori discovered a new enzyme, phosphorylase, and this work was considered of such importance that they shared the prize in 1947 with B. A. Houssay of Argentina. Many others should be mentioned, but time does not permit. I cannot, however, pass this important field without calling to your attention the work of Behring on serum therapy against diphtheria, Golgi for his work on the nervous system, Pavlov for research in the physiology of digestion, Ross for his work with malaria, and Einthoven, who gave us the electrocardiograph.

In the field of chemistry the contributions of Rutherford, of the Curies on radium, and of Hahn on uranium fission are of especial note.

While the sciences are well represented among those persons receiving awards, of equal or greater importance are those who devote themselves to the quest for peace among all nations and peoples. In this group we find such American names as Theodore Roosevelt, Elihu Root, Woodrow Wilson, Charles Dawes, Frank Kellogg, Jane Addams, Nicholas Murray Butler, John R. Mott, and Emily Balch.

T. S. Eliot, grandson of the founder of Washington University, will receive the Nobel prize in literature for 1948. Those who have preceded him include such names as Rudyard Kipling, Anatole France, John Galsworthy, Pearl Buck, Eugene O'Neill, George Bernard Shaw, and Sinclair Lewis.

In my own field of physics, may I remind you that Roentgen was recognized for his discovery of X rays; Becquerel as the pioneer of radioactivity; Marie Curie, among other things, for her work on the phenomena of radiation; Pierre Curie for his discovery that all substances change their magnetic properties at a certain temperature; Marconi for his development of wireless telegraphy; Albert Einstein, not for his relativity theory, but for his theory of the photoelectric effect; and it was Niels Bohr's theory of atomic quanta, which led scientists to a fruitful explanation of the spectra of light emitted by the various chemical elements, for which he was awarded the prize in 1922.

Alfred Nobel once wrote of life:

> . . . a precious gift
> A gem that Nature gave to each of us
> That we might polish it until its sheen
> Should finally reward us for our pains.

His bequest gives continual encouragement to those individuals of each generation who polish best the gem of life that nature gave them so that the sheen may be shared by their fellow men.

# 25. Thomas Jefferson as a Scientist

## 1946

❧ The Jefferson National Expansion Memorial, located on the Mississippi riverfront at St. Louis, commemorates the nation's third President, the Louisiana Purchase, and the westward expansion of the United States through the St. Louis gateway. In a ceremony at the site of the memorial on the eve of the anniversary of Thomas Jefferson's birth, the author spoke of some of the unique qualities of Jefferson's vision.

We are meeting today to honor the memory of one of our greatest Americans. In honoring Thomas Jefferson we are preparing a memorial that will give to the nation a richer cultural life that Jefferson valued so highly. The great Central West of the United States, which Thomas Jefferson made a part of our nation, will through this symbol of Jefferson's spirit be inspired to enrich still further our American life.

Jefferson was a philosopher and a humanitarian, a scholar, and a great leader. He had a thorough understanding and appreciation of the principles of science and of the practical value of precise knowledge. To a man of lesser stature, his own achievements in the field of science would have been significant. To him they were, for the most part, incidental.

The most serious scientific study by Jefferson of which we have record is that connected with the introduction of the decimal system into American coinage and his recommendation of its use in weights and measures. His recommendation that the dollar be established as the central monetary unit—with a ten-dollar gold coin, a one-tenth dollar silver coin, and a one-hundredth dollar copper coin—was eventually adopted by Congress. His arguments against continuing the use of the pounds and pence system of the British were convincing. It is unfortunate that his equally valid argument favoring a decimal system of weights and measures was not likewise adopted.

Jefferson reported to the Congress on the problem of weights and measures in 1790, at a time when this question was a live international, as well as an important American, issue. The colonial system, borrowed from the English, varied from place to place and was unsatisfactory. The French had not yet adopted the meter, though this was already under discussion. Jefferson wanted to find a unit of length that could be duplicated anywhere on earth.

Thus, Jefferson described his fundamental units of time, length, and mass: The second is the appropriate fraction of the mean solar day. The inch is one-fiftieth of the length of a rod which suspended at one end will beat a second; the foot is ten such inches, which works out to be almost identical with the English foot. The ounce is the weight of a cubic inch of water, and is almost identical with the English ounce.

Jefferson developed this system in detail with recommendations of multiples and submultiples of the various units, comparing their values precisely with those in existence in various British systems. He thus had a series of weights and measures similar in principle to those later adopted by the French in their metric system. If these had been introduced at that time, they would have eased the tasks of generations of industry and would have relieved the headache of many a schoolboy.

I have been especially interested to note the true grasp of the methods of science that Jefferson showed in his discussion of weights and measures. It was a matter of major importance to him that his fundamental units be such that they could be precisely duplicated without reference to artificial standards. There was no such basis for the British system of weights and measures. The French advocated a unit of length based on the length of a quadrant of the earth's surface. Jefferson pointed out that the size of the earth is much more difficult to measure precisely than is the length of a "second" pendulum. He was careful to explain that each of his units could be determined by a direct physical operation, such as measuring the length of a pendulum or building a cube with a one-inch edge and weighing the water that it would contain. These were important points. History has shown that his fundamental basis for the unit of length was a sounder one than that later chosen by the French and now used in our American system of weights and measures. It has become practically necessary for us to make use of a replica of the French meter as the basis of our system of measurement.

I must not take time to describe such other work of Jefferson as his development of methods of determining longitude, his invention of a plow, nor even his study of natural history with particular relation to the remains of prehistoric mammals. More important is his interest in stimulating the use of scientific observations as practical assets.

Of especial interest is Jefferson's concern with the encouragement of inventions through the development of a patent system. He saw the high importance of reward to inventors. He wanted to guarantee these rewards and, at the same time, to set up a legal system that would give an equitable adjustment of claims of different inventors. Of equal interest was his concern with obtaining a detailed census. In 1800, as president of the American Philosophical Society, Thomas Jefferson sent a memorandum to the House of Representatives, calling attention to the great value that might come to the nation by learning more details about its population. He wanted not only an enumeration of the number of citizens, he wanted also to know their ages, where they had come from, and their occupation. Thus, he pointed out on behalf of the Society, we might learn what the relative conditions of health are in various parts of our country, and where within our nation we should look to find persons capable of doing appropriate tasks.

Most particularly, however, I should like to remind you that Jefferson was primarily an advocate of freedom. To him anything that would advance freedom was something to be encouraged. He saw such advance in education. He saw it in the growth of industry. He saw it in the development of science. To Jefferson the great task of the American nation was to show the world a way of developing a life of greater value than had been possible under the old restrictions of Europe.

These ideas he epitomized in his memorandum * describing the stone that he wished to have erected over his grave:

On the faces of the Obelisk the following inscription, & not a word more:

HERE WAS BURIED
THOMAS JEFFERSON
AUTHOR OF THE DECLARATION OF AMERICAN INDEPENDENCE
OF THE STATUTE OF VIRGINIA FOR RELIGIOUS FREEDOM AND FATHER
OF THE UNIVERSITY OF VIRGINIA.

. . . because of these, as testimonials that I have lived, I wish most to be remembered.

Jefferson worked that men might be free. It is this task that we in St. Louis are now trying to carry on. We want our citizens to be alive to greater values. For this reason, in establishing a memorial to Thomas Jefferson, we would make it a memorial of beauty, one that will be an inspiration to greater effort, and one that will call attention to the deeper satisfactions of the human spirit.

It was essential to Jefferson that he was the father of the University of Virginia. In the program of that university he included, along with the study of the humanities, also the study of the sciences. He saw that this was necessary for freeing the spirit of the students who enjoyed the privileges of that institution. To him education and religion were basic to true freedom. In science Jefferson saw the truth that gave strength; in education he saw the knowledge that would enable men to balance one value against another; in religion, and especially in the free approach to religion, he saw the inspiration to work for greater human value. Such was the great vision of the man we are honoring today.

# VI

## Science and the
## National Interest

Scientific research means more than its practical results in increased living comfort. The future of our nation is not merely a question of the development of our industries, of reducing the cost of living, of multiplying our harvests, or of larger leisure. We must constantly strengthen the fiber of national life by the inculcation of that veracity of thought which springs from the search for truth. From its pursuit we shall discover the unfolding of beauty, we shall stimulate the aspiration for knowledge, we shall ever widen human understanding.

HERBERT HOOVER

# 26. Our Nation's Need for Scientific Research

## *1918*

༺༻ Five years after his graduation from the College of Wooster, Mr. Compton spoke to the Wooster Honors Society on the values he had come to see in scientific research. He was at that time employed by the Westinghouse Electric and Manufacturing Company as an engineer in its research laboratory, which was one of the first of the great industrial laboratories to be established.

There has been before me for a number of years a problem that may involve our nation's security. Its solution will certainly be fundamental in forming our future civilization. I wish to bring this problem before you tonight because I believe that you can help me solve it, and I am confident that you will find its solution worthwhile.

Especially at this crucial time, our nation is greatly in need of trained investigators of nature. My problem is to find them. To show the need for these investigators, it will be necessary to point out the value of scientific research. The great dearth of workers in this country in almost every line of scientific investigation will become evident as we discuss the kind of men who have done valuable scientific work. It is with the hope of encouraging to further effort those already at work in this field and of encouraging new men to enter it that I speak tonight of the nation's need for scientific research.

After I had completed my studies in college, I felt a great interest in the work that was being done in modern physics. I had an ambition to follow this work to the limit in a graduate school. But I was unable to see that such study would enable me ever to do work of any considerable value in the world. After learning all the physics that I could, I might teach the subject to someone else, who might in turn study and teach. But I wanted to prepare myself to do some kind of work that would be of material value to my brother men. As a result I laid my plans to spend a year of graduate study in physics for a thorough foundation, and then to enter an engineering college. I am certainly thankful that by the time I had completed my first year of graduate study I had come to see in physics research a field of the greatest possible promise so far as achievements of real and permanent value are concerned.

Allow me to speak then of some of the reasons for changing my attitude toward the value of scientific research. Direct evidence of its worth confronted me when I made a trip to Schenectady, New York, and was shown through the research laboratories of the General Electric Company. I found there scores of men who were employed by this great organization to do nothing but investigate the different physical and chemical problems that arose. It is true that the large majority of the men were working at problems that belonged to engineering rather than to pure science; but the half-dozen men who were working in pure science had, from the by-products of their work, made improvements and inventions that paid many times over for the whole expense of running the research laboratory. Later I visited the United Gas Improvement Company at Philadelphia, which found it profitable to employ several men to study from a scientific standpoint the physiological effects of light as well as problems of general illumination. From there I went to the Western Electric Company at New York and saw a laboratory fully equipped to study questions of sound production, reverberation, and absorption, with the idea of improving the quality of the telephones they manufacture. Since that time [1917] I have been employed in the research laboratory of the Westinghouse Electric and Manufacturing Company and have talked with men from the laboratories of the Eastman Kodak Company. The outstanding fact in every case is this: each organization is finding that the results obtained by trained experimenters in the branches of science that underlie its business are of sufficient value to justify an increasingly large expenditure for such work. This is sufficient evidence to prove the *practical* value of industrial research.

As I have already suggested, the greater part of the investigation done in industrial laboratories has more or less directly a practical end in view. Valuable as this industrial research is, however, I wish to point out that, even from a practical standpoint, the results of pure scientific investigation are in the long run more useful.

Not long ago the readers of *Popular Mechanics* selected the eight greatest wonders of the modern world. The following were chosen in order: wireless, the telephone, the airplane, radium, antiseptics, antitoxins, spectrum analysis, and X rays. How were these wonders originated? In every case the foundation was laid by men whose whole interest was in the investigation of the facts of nature for their own sake.

The theoretical basis of wireless telegraphy was laid by Clerk Maxwell when he explained light in terms of electromagnetic waves in the ether. It was in seeking to test this theory of Maxwell that Professor Heinrich Hertz found that a spark in one Leyden jar produced an effect in a similar jar at a distance. Hertz had no thought of improving by this experiment the telegraph or the telephone. The chief value of the experiment to him was rather that it was a verification of Maxwell's theory. When he had added to our knowledge the results of this purely scientific investigation he had laid the foundation for a Marconi.

Before Bell could produce a telephone it was necessary to have a Helmholtz to study the properties of sound. It was Helmholtz who showed that all the intricacies of pitch and quality in human speech have their counterpart in the waves and ripples of the air, and that these waves and ripples can be made to produce vibrations in a diaphragm. Oersted, a Danish professor, noticed during a lecture that a wire carrying electricity made a magnetic needle move when brought near it. Ampère in France, and Gauss and Weber in Germany, quickly went on with this little phenomenon, studying perhaps because of pure curiosity exactly what is the magnetic effect of an electric current. It still required the study of Professor Henry at Princeton, and of Faraday in England, to show that an electric current could be produced by moving a piece of iron near an electromagnet. None of these men in their investigations ever dreamed of such a thing as a telephone. They were studying nature for the sake of adding something to our knowledge. Yet their results had to be common knowledge before Bell could begin work on his invention.

In a similar manner we might go through the whole list. The airplane, an invention of the Wright brothers, was based on the scientific work of Professor Langley, who was testing a law of Newton concerning the pressure exerted by wind on a surface. Mme Curie's discovery of radium and Rutherford's study of its unusual properties were the result of a systematic investigation of certain remarkable attributes of matter. The necessity of antiseptic and aseptic conditions in surgery was brought out as a result of Pasteur's disinterested but highly interesting study of chemical reactions produced by certain bacteria. No one ever dreamed of being able to analyze a star into its chemical constituents until Fraunhofer, interested in the colors produced by light passing through a prism, noted that in sunlight certain colors were absent and that these colors were absorbed by certain vapors. Or who would have thought of rays that would pass through a book or a man's body before X rays were discovered? Obviously Roentgen was not trying to obtain such rays; he knew not what to try for.

He was studying the discharge of electricity through high vacua when he just happened to notice the existence of these rays.

Every one of these modern world wonders is based on the results of investigation performed merely for the purpose of adding to our existing knowledge. Nor is this all. Not only are all of these marvels traceable directly to some pure scientific research, but each of these researches is also the basis of other advances. Thus the laws of electromagnetic induction, which were discovered by Henry and Faraday, besides being fundamental to the development of the telephone, make it possible to produce electric current by means of a dynamo, to run a motor in our home, or to communicate by wireless with ships at sea. Who knows where or when the results of the researches of these men will cease to develop for the benefit of mankind? Truly, though the hanging gardens and the pyramids of the ancient world may disappear, the foundations of these wonders of the modern world shall last to the benefit of man as long as he remains on earth.

It is an ambition worthy of any man to seek thus to add to the world's knowledge something that will be of eternal material value. But what is perhaps of greater weight with most scientific men is the fact that when some idea suggests itself to them they cannot rest until they have worked it out. They catch a glimpse of what God was thinking when he planned his world, and they must follow that thought as far as he will permit them. The ambition to know more of the world in which we are placed, and to help others to know more of it, is the chief source of inspiration for the true man of science. And rightly so. For who can say that the development of a man's spirit in striving to think God's thoughts after him is not of greater value than the greatest of material blessings? These are some of the considerations that have led me to believe that pure scientific research is worthy of the best efforts of any man.

In order that one may fit himself to do really valuable scientific work, he should see what has been the training of those who have been successful in scientific investigation. The first thing that becomes evident is that virtually every scientific discovery of importance has been made by men of the most thorough training who have spent years at this kind of work. Thus, of the fifteen men who laid the foundations of our modern wonders, eleven were university professors, thoroughly equipped with all the training available, and the other four were supported by government grants to spend their whole time in scientific research. It seems to be a habit of Americans to think that all that is necessary to make a worthwhile discovery or invention is to put the problem up to a man of ingenuity. We too often forget that not only is ingenuity needed but training as well.

# 27. The Birth of Atomic Energy and Its Human Meaning

## 1952

A key figure in the development of atomic energy and one of a handful of men who actually witnessed the drama of the first nuclear chain reaction, the author reviewed the history of this work and considered its peacetime implications on the tenth anniversary of the event.* The critical experiment took place at the University of Chicago on December 2, 1942. Mr. Compton's remarks were made at a luncheon meeting of the Chicago Association of Commerce and Industry, which recognized the anniversary by sponsoring a series of meetings devoted to the industrial applications of atomic energy.

Arthur Compton was one of the first scientists to become involved in the wartime atomic energy program, and he took a leading role throughout its development. In April 1941, he was appointed chairman of a committee of the National Academy of Sciences to evaluate the possible military usefulness of atomic energy.* Following the committee's favorable report, on November 6, he became one of six members of the "S-1 Committee," * organized under the government's Office of Scientific Research and Development, to recommend action on fission research. On December 6, he was assigned responsibility for initiating research on atomic bombs (later delegated to Robert Oppenheimer), for developing methods for the production of plutonium, and for investigating the possibilities of atomic power. The plutonium research group was centered at the "Metallurgical" Laboratory at the University of Chicago, and it was there, under the west stands of Stagg Field, that the first self-sustaining nuclear chain reaction was achieved.

Just ten years ago, in a temporary laboratory at the University of Chicago, was produced the first self-sustaining nuclear chain reaction.

| 243 |

This event may properly be considered to mark the opening of what has been called the Atomic Age. It is appropriate that we should pause to assess the meaning of this event and see in how far our achievements are matching the opportunities opened by atomic technology.

Let me first review with you the dramatic story of the birth of atomic power, which I was fortunate enough to witness. I shall then consider what the ten intervening years have accomplished and look ahead to what we may expect future years of the atomic age to bring.

## THE BIRTH OF ATOMIC ENERGY

### The feasibility of atomic weapons

In September 1941, Ernest Lawrence of the University of California met President James Conant of Harvard and me in our home in Chicago. He told us of calculations indicating that an atomic bomb of great effectiveness could be made using much smaller amounts of uranium 235 than had previously been thought necessary. The British scientists responsible for these calculations were so convinced of their significance that they were eager to get going on a full-scale effort to produce the required U-235 and to make the bomb. Lawrence told us further of the discovery, just made in his laboratory, that the new element plutonium that Seaborg, Kennedy, and Wahl had made with the California cyclotron has the same fission characteristics as does U-235. But this new element might be produced in a nuclear reactor and be separated chemically from its parent uranium. Here was an alternate approach to making the material for an atomic bomb that would not require the very difficult process of isotope separation.

We all became convinced that these possibilities called for quick and thorough examination. Conant turned to Lawrence. "Ernest," he said, "does this seem important enough to you to devote to it the remaining years of the war?" Lawrence paused, and swallowed hard: "If you tell me that's my job, I'll accept it."

Conant then turned to me. "Arthur," he said, "it's up to you to get together the people who can judge the merits of this atomic bomb proposal, study it with all the available data, and give us a report on its importance and feasibility. And don't lose any time. If the possibilities are what they seem to be, with the head start the Germans have, it may well be a race for the key to victory. We have no time to lose."

That was September. Enrico Fermi, then at Columbia University in New York, gave his quick calculations about the bomb. Harold Urey and John Dunning supplied the latest reports on isotope separation. Engineers from Westinghouse and General Electric gave practical counsel. In November we turned in our report. The bomb could probably be made. It might well be of decisive effect in the war. Three or four years of all-out effort would be needed, at a cost of roughly a billion dollars. If the Germans got there first, they might yet snatch victory out of the hands of defeat.

Vannevar Bush went to the President. Our report paralleled closely one from the British. On December 6, 1941, several of us were called to Washington and were given instructions from the President to put all possible effort into experiments that would show how U-235 could be separated and how an atomic bomb might be made.

After the meeting I lunched with Conant and Bush. I explained that there was just a chance that producing plutonium by means of a nuclear chain reaction might be a cheaper and quicker way of getting the material for the bomb than by separating the uranium isotopes. We discussed the enormous difficulties involved—setting up a controlled nuclear chain reaction, which was as yet only an idea on paper, learning the chemistry of plutonium, and developing a method for separating it from other substances in the presence of lethal rays of tremendous intensity. Difficult, but not impossible, we agreed. Thus, as an afterthought, I was commissioned to bring together the physicists who would endeavor to set up the chain reaction and the chemists who would look for a method of extracting the plutonium after it was produced.

## Pearl Harbor alerts the nation

Coming away from Washington the following day I learned of the Japanese attack on Pearl Harbor. The nation was alert. Our project became to us more vital than life or death. From all parts of the country men competent in the field rallied to give what help they could. At the University of Chicago campus was the nucleus of the effort, but at Princeton, Iowa State College, and many other places supporting groups were active.

By December 1942, preliminary experiments had shown how a chain reactor should be built. Pure uranium metal had been obtained in tons, where a year before hardly an ounce was available. Methods had been developed for starting, controlling, and stopping the nuclear reaction, and for measuring its rate of production of power. For years it had been as-

sumed that producing the first atomic chain reaction would be an extremely hazardous experiment, with a good chance of producing either an
atomic explosion or developing ionizing rays of lethal intensity. Our men
were convinced that the experiment could be done safely, and the pressure of time prevented setting it up in a remote location.

## The critical experiment

On the morning of December 2, a reviewing committee of eminent
engineers came to my office. They had been charged with recommending
to the War Department whether actual construction of atomic bombs
should be undertaken, having in mind the half-million man-years of effort
that the task would require. Their visit to the Chicago laboratory was to
see whether they could recommend proceeding with the project with the
full resources of the nation.

The reviewing committee met me in the conference room. "Where
is Fermi?" they asked. Enrico Fermi was the great Italian physicist who
eight years before, working in his laboratory in Rome with the help of a
single assistant, had shown how to handle the neutrons that play the
vital role in the nuclear reaction. He was now directing the construction
of our experimental atomic reactor. "I'm sorry," I replied, "Fermi is engaged in his laboratory and has asked to be excused. Perhaps I can answer
your questions." After an hour of discussion the telephone rang. It was
word from the research team. "We are ready to try the critical experiment." I took with me the youngest member of the reviewing committee,
Crawford Greenewalt of the Du Pont Company, and walked over to the
laboratory.

We entered the balcony at one end of the room. On the balcony some
twenty scientists were watching the instruments and handling the controls. Across the room was the large cubical pile of graphite and uranium
blocks in which we hoped the atomic chain reaction would develop. In-
serted into openings in this pile of blocks were the control and safety rods.
When inside the pile these rods absorbed so many neutrons that the chain
reaction could not start. Just beyond, standing on a platform overlooking
the pile, was the "suicide squad." These men were armed with equipment
to destroy the pile and thus quench the chain reaction if all went wrong.
A hundred feet away, behind two concrete walls, was a third group of
men who followed the experiments with remote-control instruments, and
who could set off the electrical mechanism for throwing in the safety rods
in case the reaction became too violent.

After a few preliminary tests, Fermi gave the order to withdraw the control rod another foot. We all knew this was the real test. The Geiger counters registering the neutrons from the reactor began to click faster and faster, until their sound became a rattle. Now the galvanometer pointer, indicating the current in the ionization chambers, began to move, at first slowly, then faster and still faster. The reaction grew until there might be danger from the rays coming from the pile. "Throw in the safety rods," came Fermi's order. Immediately the pointer moved back toward zero. The rattle of the counters fell to a slow series of clicks. For the first time atomic power had been released, and it had been controlled and stopped. It was only half a watt—infinitesimal in comparison with the atomic power that, for more than eight years at Hanford, Washington, has now been heating the streams of water flowing into the Columbia River. But it showed that man had the boundless energy of atomic fission under his control.

The men in the suicide squad breathed an audible sigh of relief. Eugene Wigner handed Fermi a bottle of Italian wine. A little cheer went up.

## Reactions of the scientists

What I shall not forget was the expressions on the faces of some of the men. It was Volney Wilson who had called me over to see the experiment. Two years before, at my request, he had prepared a report in which he had concluded that a nuclear chain reaction using ordinary uranium might be produced. "But," he had added, "please take me off this work. It is going to be too destructive." So we had shifted him to work on radar. But after Pearl Harbor he had asked to return to do his part in using atoms to defend the nation. Now Wilson's face was troubled. He knew the destruction that we were preparing, and he could not like it. With many of us, he had cherished the hope that something ultimately would make the nuclear reaction impossible. If impossible for us, it would be impossible also for the Germans. Now what he dreaded was on the way to reality, and duty demanded that he help see it through.

Then there was Fermi's face. There one saw no sign of elation. The experiment had worked just as expected, and that was that. But what about the next steps? Data must be obtained to make the working reactors. Time must not be lost. The men were tired and might make mistakes. He told them to go home and get some sleep. Tomorrow we will get on with the job. Cool and collected, Fermi's face was that of the competent man of action busily engaged on the one important job.

But most memorable was the face of Crawford Greenewalt. His eyes were shining. He had seen a miracle. And a miracle it was indeed—the dawn of a new age. As we walked back across the campus to join the reviewing committee he talked of his vision: endless supplies of power to turn the wheels of industry, new research techniques that would enrich the life of man, vast new possibilities that yet remained hidden. As Greenewalt entered the conference room, there was no need for him to tell his colleagues what he had seen. They could read the miracle in his face.

## The Italian navigator has landed

As the reviewing committee left I picked up the phone and called James Conant at Cambridge. He knew of the critical experiment on which we were engaged, but he had not expected results so soon. We talked as usual in an extemporaneous wartime code:

"The Italian navigator has just landed in the new world," I told him. "The earth was not as large as he had supposed"—meaning that the pile of uranium and graphite needed to bring about the reaction was smaller than anticipated—"so he arrived earlier than expected."

"Were the natives friendly?" Conant asked.

"Everyone landed safe and happy."

Such was the birth of atomic power. The rest of the story is familiar. A nuclear reactor was built at Oak Ridge to give working experience on a higher power level and to produce experimental amounts of plutonium. This reactor continues to serve as our main source of radioactive isotopes for research studies. Then came the building of the great nuclear power plants on the Columbia River, where the plutonium for the bombs was to be produced. Many were the new technical problems that had to be solved. The Du Pont Chemical Company took charge of the engineering and production, and with our laboratory at Chicago found solutions to these problems in time to avoid delay and serious errors. Other scientists, headed by Lawrence, Urey, and Keith, and working at the University of California, Columbia University, and a hundred other places, learned how to separate isotopes on a production scale. Other great industrial organizations, all now under the general control of the Army as represented by General Leslie R. Groves, built plants in Tennessee that produced the needed uranium 235. At a remote mountain site in New Mexico Robert Oppenheimer brought together a great international group of scientists who learned how to make bombs from the precious material that had thus been gathered.

## The moral issue

Frequently the question has come to me: How could peace-loving scientists turn their skill to building such terrible weapons as atomic bombs?

The answer is simple. These men found themselves with the power in their hands to stop the most disastrous war in history. Should they put that power in the hands of their nation's leaders, or should they withhold it and let the war continue to its normal conclusion with the death of more millions of men and women? Only one answer was possible to responsible men, and that answer was given. The terrible weapon was made, and used to the extent needed to bring the war to a quick end.

In the opinion of those best qualified to judge, by this decisive action some millions of Americans and Japanese were saved from destruction. By creating a balance of power in the postwar world, a third world war has been held off that would have meant the lives of many more millions and disaster for the entire world.

We who had the might of the atomic nucleus in our hands would have been traitors to mankind had we refused to build the bombs and use them to end the war. We should now be failing our evident duty if we did not give free men the means of maintaining their freedom.

I am reminded of the story of Nehemiah. It was he, you recall, who led the Jews as they rebuilt the walls of Jerusalem in order that they might go peaceably about their business within the walls. As the construction of the walls began, their enemies pressed on them from all sides to prevent the work from going ahead. So Nehemiah armed his men. To some he gave spears and shields. Others worked at building the wall; but these also were armed. With a sword in one hand and a trowel in the other they went ahead with the task. And so they built the wall.

Such is the world in which we also live. Our earnest desire is to go about our peaceful business of living. But in an unfriendly world the protecting wall must first be built; and as we build the wall, experience shows that we must be prepared to fight off those who would prevent us.

## THE CONSTRUCTIVE USES OF NUCLEAR ENERGY

### Defense

It is in this setting that I would consider the constructive uses of nuclear energy. As long as those who want to go peaceably about their business are actively threatened by enemies who seek to prevent their normal life, weapons of defense are necessary. It is for providing such weapons that the energy of the nucleus has thus far found its chief use. The introduction of atomic weapons has had two major effects on war. The first is that they supply a means whereby heavy blows can be delivered at targets remote from the home base. The second is that, combined with airplanes and guided missiles, they make it impossible to prevent an enemy from bringing great destruction to a nation however well protected may be its boundaries. This is at least the situation as we find it today, and it is likely to remain true for many years.

The result is that before entering upon a war that may develop into an all-out struggle, a nation must consider whether its objectives are worth the cost as measured by such destruction. The likelihood of full-scale war is thus substantially reduced. In fact, competent authorities, including for example Winston Churchill, have expressed the view that it is precisely this situation that has prevented a Russian attack against Western Europe.

On the other hand, postwar experience has shown that strictly limited war—such as that in Korea and Palestine, where circumstances make atomic weapons of little value—is little affected by these developments. It remains to be seen what will happen if or when tactical atomic bombs come into use for such purposes as destroying enemy planes or strongly held fortifications.

One thing is certain, and that is that the availability of atomic weapons has placed a high premium on great industrial potential. Only those nations whose technological facilities are very great can defend themselves in an atomic war.

Another point that becomes clear is the reason why the Russians continue their demand for outlawing atomic weapons while continuing a full construction program of tanks and fighting planes. The reason is that these conventional weapons are effective for them to use against their neighbors and they would provide no means for American retaliation. On the other hand, atomic weapons have little advantage over conventional ones when used near at hand, but they provide the United States with an effective means of striking across an ocean.

The net result is that as long as there remains the threat of major war a nation that wants freedom must be prepared to defend itself, and for many years to come it is evident that preparedness with atomic weapons will be an essential part of any adequate defense program. I, for one, am glad that in God's good wisdom it was the world of free men and not the tyrants who first had these weapons. My hope and prayer is that the free world may retain its atomic advantage until the nations shall have found a way to unite in controlling the use of *all* weapons so that the danger of disastrous war will be gone. There can be no doubt that such an end to major war is brought much closer by the development of atomic weapons. Whether the unified control of the world will be by the dictators or by those to whom man's person is sacred is what is now in the balance.

Thus, as we consider how atomic nuclei can be made to enrich men's lives, I would pause to give all honor to those engaged in building the atomic wall about our free world. Theirs is a noble and worthy task, and up to the present time theirs has been by far the most significant human use of nuclear energy. I believe that it is primarily to these men that we owe the prevention up to now of World War III with the catastrophic human tragedy that this would have meant. In similar measure I believe these soldiers will continue to hold back our hostile neighbors as we proceed to build a stronger and more humane society protected by their atomic wall.

### PEACEFUL USES OF THE ATOM

Now let us turn to the atom's peacetime uses. Four such uses should be mentioned. First is that of electric power derived from the heat of nuclear reactions. Second is other industrial use. Third is the use of nuclear radiations in medicine. Fourth is the use of atomic nuclei and their radiations as scientific tools. Taken together these applications are already of substantial importance and are sure to have a great future development.

In talking about the birth of atomic power I have spoken of what I lived through. In talking of the use of atomic weapons I have described what was the center of my life for four unforgettable years. But in speaking of the peacetime uses of atomic nuclei I shall be telling of what was to me but a dream for the future. It was the miracle that Greenewalt had seen and that had shown in his face ten years ago. Others during these ten years have gone far in making a reality of this dream of atoms at work for man. But such has not been my lot.

## Atomic power

I recall nearly forty years ago hearing Henry Norris Russell, the Princeton astronomer, tell of the riddle of the heat poured from the sun and stars. Too vast was this heat to have its origin even in the radioactivity of uranium or radium. I had then a vision of a laboratory where I might work with others toward making such enormous energy from the atom's nucleus available to man. A few years later, Ernest Rutherford transmuted nitrogen into oxygen by bombardment with alpha particles from radium and showed that energy was released in the process. In 1925 Sir Arthur Eddington published a book on *Stars and Atoms*. Here he showed convincing evidence that under the tremendous pressure and temperature of a star's interior the nuclei of atoms must be supposed to undergo changes, giving out the energy that keeps the star hot. He went further. He gave an estimate of the voltages at which such nuclear reactions should occur. These voltages were in the range of a million to ten million —higher than were then in use in the laboratory. Throughout the world physicists were encouraged by Eddington's studies to explore the effect of high-voltage bombardment on atoms.

In the new Eckhart Laboratory built at the University of Chicago in 1929, we included an oversize room for experiments with high-energy particles. A year later Ernest Lawrence started his work at Berkeley on the cyclotron, which became so important a tool for splitting atoms and producing neutrons. Neutrons were discovered by James Chadwick at Cambridge, England, in 1932. These neutrons, destined to play so important a part in nuclear reactions, may be described as atoms of a new chemical element of atomic mass one and atomic number zero. Enrico Fermi, then working in his laboratory at the University of Rome, learned how to work with these neutrons, making them combine with the nuclei of many kinds of atoms. Before the end of the decade, Hahn and Strassmann, working in Berlin, showed that such a neutron when captured by an atom of uranium made it divide into two roughly equal parts—the phenomenon of nuclear fission. From that discovery to the development of the nuclear chain reactor was the dramatic sequence of events already described. Such a chain reaction had already been suggested by Leo Szilard, and many experimenters shared in the work leading up to Fermi's epochal demonstration that we are celebrating.

I was called upon to bring together those who knew how to do the task, and with support from the government and the cooperation of the University of Chicago, to supply them with facilities for doing the job. Thus, by an unexpected turn of the wheel of fortune, I also had a share, even if second hand, in releasing the energy of the atom's nucleus for the use of man. The dream of my student days had become a reality. But how different was the actual setting from what I had imagined! Under the pressure of war, even before a chain reaction had been achieved in the laboratory, plans were being laid for its active use. Guided by the theoretical genius of Eugene Wigner and with the giant industrial competence of the Du Pont Company, three great reactors were built in the state of Washington as rapidly as the construction task could be done. Now for eight continuous years these reactors have been warming the waters of the Columbia River.

Thus atomic power on a tremendous scale came quickly into being. But the power had not as yet been used to drive the wheels of industry or light a city's lamps. At the war's close, when I forsook the atoms to help reorganize a university, we had ideas and hopes about nuclear power plants. Some of these hopes have already ben realized. A reactor has already been built that is now delivering useful electric power in substantial amount. Other reactors are under construction for driving ships. Engineering calculations have shown, in spite of great technical difficulties, promise of economic operation of nuclear power plants under favorable conditions, and estimates by competent industrialists indicate that within a few years atomic power plants will be in commercial use. Regarding these matters there are others who can speak much more authoritatively than I.

I should add this, however, for it seems to me a matter of very great importance. We have gone far enough already in our development of the use of uranium as a nuclear fuel to know that it will eventually become an economic source of electrical power, and that the amount of energy thus available to us is vastly greater than that available in the form of coal. By the end of the century I should suppose that uranium will to a large extent supplant coal as a source of commercial power and our coal reserves will become available for their much more distinctive use as a source of organic chemicals. What is more, the energy reserves in the earth that are thus available in the form of uranium are adequate for our use as far as we can see into the future.

By contrast I may note that no one now sees on the horizon any method of giving man control of the thermonuclear reaction of hydrogen into helium. We believe that in the sun's interior hydrogen is being continuously converted into helium, and that this is the source of the sun's enormous outpouring of heat. It seems possible for us to make the reaction occur explosively, as in the proposed hydrogen bomb. But unless some catalyst can be found that will make this hydrogen-helium reaction occur at temperatures and pressures that we can handle, it would not seem possible for us to use it on the earth as a continuous, controlled source of power. Whether such a catalyst is within the realm of possibility is as yet unknown.

## Other industrial uses

Regarding other industrial uses of the nuclear chain reaction and its products, the present developments are disappointing. One is reminded of the mountain that labored and brought forth a mouse.

The fact is that the most promising industrial uses that have been proposed, other than that of power production, are extensions of what we have had available to us for many years in the form of X rays and radioactive substances. There are certain advantages in using the gamma rays from cobalt 40 for testing castings and welds or for sterilizing pharmaceuticals without raising their temperature. But it remains to be seen whether the artificial radioactive elements will compete favorably in such tasks with the newer forms of electrical equipment such as high-voltage X-ray tubes and betatrons.

It may be that such materials as strontium 90, produced in abundance by an atomic reactor, may find wider use than radium or polonium for making luminous markers such as those frequently used on instrument dials. There is some real advantage also in keeping the gas in a fluorescent lamp permanently ionized. The lamp starts more readily. This can be done with strontium 90, for example. There are other relatively minor but nevertheless valuable industrial applications.

If these matters seem to be a small return for the billions of dollars that we are spending on nuclear energy, we must recall that the expenditure is paying for itself many times over in aiding our defense, and these by-products are the little extras. We may recall also that for the first fifty years after Michael Faraday discovered electromagnetic induction its most important commercial application was the parlor shocking machine with which the operator turned a crank while the victim held the electrodes in his hands to feel the electric current. It was after the first fifty years that Thomas Edison used Faraday's discovery to build electric generators to light up his lamps and thus introduced the age of electric power. One cannot tell what fifty years from now may be the practical use of the relatively vast amounts of radioactive matter that the atomic reactors can produce.

## Medicine

In the field of medicine the importance of the nuclear reactor is more significant, though here also it is far from revolutionary. Here again we are concerned with new and more abundant substitutes for X rays and radium. But the great human significance of these tools is little appreciated.

X rays and radium are used by physicians in two ways. The first is for diagnosis of disease and injuries. The second is for therapy, especially for cancer and other abnormal growths. All of us have had our teeth X-rayed, and many of us have had either minor or major X-ray treatments. It is impossible to give any precise figures; but it can be shown reliably that the number of people over the world whose lives have been saved by X rays and radium is roughly equal, within a factor of two or three either way, to the millions of soldiers and civilians who were killed in the two great world wars.

This is a striking fact to remember when someone speaks of the destructiveness of science. For the same science of atomic physics that gave us the atomic bomb gave us also X rays and radium.

I bring out the enormous importance of these radiations in saving the lives and aiding the health of hundreds of millions of men and women to show what it means when we improve their use. This is what the atomic reactor has done. It has given a wider choice of radiations, as illustrated by the cobalt-40 bomb for cancer treatment. It has supplied many kinds of radioactive isotopes, such as iodine for thyroid treatment and phosphorous for direct action in the blood stream. A promising experiment now in progress is to impregnate tumor tissue with boron that is made radioactive when the patient receives neutrons coming from a nuclear reactor. All of these things taken together, though they are not revolutionary, spell substantial advance in healing.

## Scientific tools

It is not unlikely, however, that except for atomic power the most important peaceful use of the nuclear reactor will be the scientific tools that it supplies. One of these tools is the beam of neutron rays that can be permitted to flow out from the reactor. Just as X rays have revealed to us many things that were hidden from ordinary light, so also neutron rays open up other new aspects of matter to our study. Among such new information now available is the location of hydrogen atoms in crystals and molecules, which is a substantial help to our chemists.

More generally useful have been found the "tracers." These are radioactive atoms, usually produced in a nuclear reactor. An important example is carbon 14, discovered at Berkeley by Martin Kamen. A growing plant in an atmosphere containing radioactive carbon dioxide can be exposed to light. Sugar will then be formed with this carbon as a basis. By tracing the growth of the radioactive sugar, much can be learned about the process of photosynthesis. Or again, a radioactive sugar may be synthesized and fed to an appropriate organism, resulting in a radioactive virus. The course of this virus in the development of a disease may then be followed by electrical instruments. In our laboratories at Washington University alone three books have been written describing the new chemical information that has thus been obtained. Those who use these radioactive tracers consider their importance in research comparable with that of the microscope.

## Significance of nuclear energy

On an occasion such as this, while it is appropriate that we celebrate an important achievement, it is appropriate also that we make an effort to appraise its relative significance. Here are some of my own judgments. As a scientific tool the importance of the nuclear reactor is comparable with that of the cyclotron. As a means of improving health it may reasonably be compared with the betatron, a new type of supervoltage instrument for producing X rays and beta rays. In industry other than power I would compare its value with the use of polarized light. In these respects the importance of the nuclear reactor, while truly significant, has probably been considerably overemphasized. As a means of defense, however, I would rate atomic weapons as comparable in importance with the airplane.

But the great significance of nuclear energy seems to me to be as a source of useful power, a field that has as yet barely begun to open up. Here I should consider its eventual importance to mankind to be hardly less than that of fire.

In considering the human meaning of an invention such as the nuclear reactor, it cannot properly be considered as standing alone. In war it is the combination of the atomic bomb, the plane that carries it, and the electronic devices that control it that makes it useful. In power production the nuclear reactor must activate an electric generator if it is to be made useful. Thus each new invention adds to the significance of all those that have come before.

Several of us have commented independently that the release of nuclear energy means that some form of world government must come into being within fifty or a hundred years, and that major war will then become very improbable. This statement is not based solely on the invention of the atom bomb, but rather takes into account the combination of this weapon with fast airplanes, long-range missiles, and radar.

Similarly, we have said that if peace can be kept for another fifty years the free world's strength will have developed so greatly that the threat of attack against it will have become much less serious than it is today. In saying this we have had in mind not only the effect of nuclear science on our growing industry, but also the effect of many other new developments. The description of how the work of many men in many countries contributed to the invention of the nuclear reactor is typical. Our hope for the growing strength of the free world depends upon giving competent men wherever they may be facilities for their work and opportunity to compare their ideas with their colleagues elsewhere. Restrictions that would have been unthinkable a generation ago have now been placed on the world's scientific men, not only in Russia but also in the United States. By such actions it may well be possible to stifle the growth of knowledge and of industrial advance that is normal in free society. If so, the balance of power could very possibly turn in favor of the dictators.

May I then summarize the human meaning of atomic power by saying that in my judgment its possession by the free world is affording a protection that should make possible a growth in strength until hostile attack by enemies of freedom becomes unlikely. The growth in strength of this protected free world will result partly from an extensive development of nuclear power for peacetime purposes. But the growth of the free world's health and strength and peaceful happiness will come from many interacting sources. As demonstrated in the atomic race between the United States and Germany, these forces work most effectively when men are free to think and act cooperatively toward common goals. Our greatest national danger seems to me to lie in placing unwise restrictions on such free cooperation among those who must be responsible for the development of our new ideas.

The central meaning of atomic power is thus that if men have the will to be free, they have in their hands the strength to protect that freedom and the opportunity to grow to ever greater human stature.

# 28.  On the Use of Weapons

## 1945

By early summer of 1945 the secret United States atomic energy project had progressed to the stage where a new weapon of devastating power would soon be available for use. On May 31 Secretary of War Henry L. Stimson convened the civilian group, known as the Interim Committee, which had been authorized by the President and was charged with advising him on the various questions raised by the imminent readiness of the atomic bomb and to plan for the longer term development and control of atomic energy. Mr. Compton was one of four members of a Scientific Panel assisting this committee. The others were Enrico Fermi, E. O. Lawrence, and J. R. Oppenheimer. At this meeting the Scientific Panel was asked to prepare a report stating whether it could devise any kind of demonstration that would seem likely to bring the war to an end without using the bomb against a live target. On June 16, after thoughtful deliberation, the negative conclusion was submitted to the Interim Committee. In describing the considerations that led to use of the bomb, Secretary Stimson quoted the essence of the report as follows:

> The opinions of our scientific colleagues on the initial use of these weapons are not unanimous: they range from the proposal of a purely technical demonstration to that of the military application best designed to induce surrender. Those who advocate a purely technical demonstration would wish to outlaw the use of atomic weapons, and have feared that if we use the weapons now our position in future negotiations will be prejudiced. Others emphasize the opportunity of saving American lives by immediate military use, and believe that such use will improve the international prospects, in that they are more concerned with the prevention of war than with the elimination of this special weapon. We find ourselves closer to these latter views; *we can propose no technical demonstration likely to bring an end to the war; we see no acceptable alternative to direct military use.*
>
> With regard to these general aspects of the use of atomic energy, it is clear that we, as scientific men, have no proprietary rights. It is true that we are among the few citizens who have had occasion

to give thoughtful consideration to these problems during the past few years. We have, however, no claim to special competence in solving the political, social, and military problems which are presented by the advent of atomic power.*

The following outline, reflecting some of Arthur Compton's thoughts * during this period, is taken from a personal memorandum dated June 10, 1945. The handwritten memorandum was preserved among his personal papers, but it is unlikely that he intended to publish it. It was Mr. Compton's habit to write such memos for his own use, as he felt the effort required to prepare them helped to clarify his thinking. No special significance lies in the fact that the outline appears to be incomplete, as it was not unusual for Mr. Compton's memoranda to himself to remain unfinished. The writing of personal memos, characteristically a slow and reflective process, was undoubtedly especially slow in this case. It is possible that he felt there was no further help to be gained from the written analysis.

## CONSIDERATIONS

    a. Lasting peace
    b. Minimum domination of one group by another
    c. Saving lives, especially American lives
    d. Quick return to peaceful pursuits
    e. Maintaining good relations with world

## POSSIBLE PROCEDURES

    a. Use weapon most effectively to destroy enemy
    b. Make military demonstration with minimum human damage and ask for surrender
    c. Make technical demonstration to Allies and neutrals, and ask for surrender
    d. Make secret tests only, then retain secret without use

## HOPES AND FEARS

If *a* is followed:

Hopes:

    1. Force Japs to quick surrender by making them impotent to fight back, thus shortening war and making Japs harmless for a long time.

2. By showing effectiveness of weapon at its primitive stage, the world would have a more realistic picture of what future wars would mean, and prepare to prevent them.

Fears:

1. World will fear U.S. because of its power, and combine against it.
2. By doing unnecessary damage to enemy, our nation will become hated, as ruthless and inconsiderate of human rights of others.
3. Start an armament race which will absorb undesirably great fraction of our and world's strength for many years.
4. As result of armament race, world psychology will be toward further war, rather than toward growth of human culture.
5. Unless U.S. grabs world power, first, the end result of such a race must be disastrous to us. Possibility of avoiding this disaster:
   a. Grab power and hold it when we can, and under our tutelage educate the world toward lasting peace. (*Pax Romana*)
   b. Get alliance with powers we can trust, e.g., British Empire and some minor states such as Switzerland, Holland, etc., as to methods of development and control.

      If this procedure is to be followed, steps in that direction should be made before first use, to make clear our intentions.

If *b* is followed:

Hopes:

1. If we offer opportunity to surrender, after showing what we can do, the Japs might prefer to resign in order to avoid complete destruction. In this case the war would be brought more quickly to a close than by fighting it out. Less destruction to our own men and to the enemy would be caused, and we should not be open to the charge of ruthlessness and inhumanity.
   a. If we are to get the Japs to surrender, it would appear that we will need to tell them what the conditions will be. This would enable them to "save face." The conditions could be as severe as may be considered advisable: e.g., evacuation of Asia, Formosa, Hainan, etc., complete control of Jap Islands by Allies with elimination of all Jap military, but with fostering of Jap agriculture and light industries under allied supervision. *We should in this case abandon unconditional surrender, but make terms severe.*
   b. If surrender does not come, then we should proceed as in case *a*, to reduce enemy to complete impotence.
2. This also would afford some demonstration of what future wars might mean, though perhaps not as effective as *a*.

Fears:

1. No. 1 will remain as in case *a*, though fear may be less acute if opportunity to surrender is first given.
2. No. 2 will be avoided, because any demonstration will be only as required to show power. If enemy elects to go on, we have no alternative but its use.
3. The occasion for the armament race will be present, but we shall have shown our intention to find a common method of control, at least if we discuss intention with other powers before all-out use.
4. & 5. This proposal (*b*) would somewhat allay fears *4* and *5*, but they would be present. *b* would be in line with procedure *a 5 b*.
6. Fear of lengthening war is unfounded.
7. Fear lest Japan would revive and cause later trouble.

   If it is American intention to *destroy* or *enslave* Japanese people, procedure *a* is the only possible one. If anything less severe, we can state the conditions, see that an "honorable peace" can be made. By properly choosing these conditions we should be able to insure inability of Japan to become again a military threat.

If *c* is followed:

Hopes:

1. That Japs may choose to surrender, without needing to inflict more severe damage.
   a. Experience indicates Japs would not be affected by such a demonstration.
   b. Would give warning of attack and time for countermeasures.
2. That world will recognize our honorable intentions and collaborate better with us.
   a. Our all-out air attacks show enough determination and apparent ruthlessness that this gesture of restraint would hardly be understood.
   b. It might be interpreted as doubt on our part of its effectivenesss.

Fears:

1. Without military demonstration the world, and particularly the U.S., could hardly appreciate weapon's power. In this case:
   a. Support for further work would not be forthcoming.
   b. The incentive to careful attention to conditions for peace would be lacking.
2. This procedure (*c*) would reduce to a minimum world fears of U.S., especially if combined with an effort to agree upon some method of international control. Because it would be considered weak handling, we would be subject to scorn.

This is probably the *worst* solution, because it could start race, and would probably not quickly close war. Others would doubt whether we really have anything.

If *d* is followed:

1. No chance of affecting Jap war, and this might last for long time. War might be considerably more expensive in American lives.
2. World would not *know* of effectiveness of new weapon; but various *rumors* would be afloat.

Hopes:

1. By holding back this weapon it could be preserved for next major conflict, giving us important advantage at that time. This would be militarily right if it can have little effect on *this* war.
2. By refusing to use it, we could cause considerable delay in its knowledge by others. Results:
   a. We would advance further before enemy would . . .

# 29. American Visa Policy

## 1952

To express their concern about the barriers to the free interchange of scientific ideas resulting from the McCarran Acts and their administration, the editors of the *Bulletin of Atomic Scientists* devoted the entire issue of October 1952 to a consideration of this problem and its effect upon the nation. An editorial, which opens the issue, begins as follows:

> Through the two McCarran Acts—the Internal Security Act of 1950, and the Immigration and Nationality Act of 1952—and their excessively rigid, indiscriminate application by the State Department, the United States government and the American people are undoing with one hand what they are laboriously and expensively accomplishing with the other. While one part of American policy generously and farsightedly has sought to defend the free societies of the West through the Marshall Plan, the North Atlantic Treaty, and other measures, these two Acts, and particularly the clauses bearing on the entry into the United States of foreign scientists, scholars, and educators, in conjunction with the sheer ignorance and unconcern for consequences in some sections of the State Department, alienate our allies, comfort our enemies, enfeeble our free institutions, and traduce the principles of liberty.[1]

Included in the issue, among statements by prominent American and foreign scientists, was this statement by Arthur Compton.

No one who understands how science develops can doubt the detrimental effect of the present procedure on our scientific welfare. The chief stimulus to development in science is the free, rapid interchange of ideas; restriction on travel is one of the substantial barriers that can prevent such interchange.

[1] Reproduced with permission from "America's Paper Curtain" by Edward Shils,* which appeared in the October 1952 issue of the *Bulletin of the Atomic Scientists.* Copyright 1952 by the Educational Foundation for Nuclear Science.

One of the greatest assets of the United States in the century past has been the freedom of our scientists to move among those of other lands and our freedom to invite others to bring their ideas personally to us. It is in large measure this freedom that has made it possible for us to rise during this century from an almost insignificant position to a leading position in world science. In a period when our welfare and safety depend upon maintaining this leadership, it is of double importance that freedom in the exchange of ideas be maintained. An authoritarian state is much better able than are we as a democracy to develop its science in an atmosphere of secrecy, but such an authoritarian state is likewise retarded by barriers to interchange of ideas. Thus, one of our hopes for success in a period of intense competition is in the retaining of our scientific freedom.

Too often in the minds of those unfamiliar with scientific thought the freedom of exchange of ideas is confused with the release of technological information which may be applied directly to some military or industrial problem.

Though American industrial organizations have found it profitable to relax considerably their one-time tightly held industrial secrets, it nevertheless remains true that temporary advantage—and frequently an advantage over a considerable period of years—is retained by withholding such technological information. This is perhaps pre-eminently true in the military field.

This recognition, however, of the usefulness and necessity of withholding certain types of technological information must not be taken to mean that basic scientific facts and ideas should be withheld. Such facts and ideas nearly always require many years before they become practically important, and during these years the knowledge in any case becomes worldwide. The effect of retarding the flow of this knowledge is merely to discourage and make more difficult the scientific growth of those who are affected.

With this in mind, the scientist sees a loss to our country resulting from the barriers that recent political actions have imposed, which is many times greater than any possible competitive advantage that might result from compelling certain persons to keep their ideas and their knowledge at home.

# 30. In the Case of
Robert Oppenheimer

*1954*

During World War II Robert Oppenheimer, one of the world's leading theoretical physicists, was responsible for the design, construction, and testing of the first atomic bomb. In recognition of his service to the nation, he received the Medal for Merit, the highest civilian award then bestowed by the United States government. After the war Dr. Oppenheimer became director of the Institute for Advanced Study at Princeton, New Jersey. He continued to be a respected adviser to various government agencies, including the Atomic Energy Commission, serving as chairman of its General Advisory Committee.

In 1954 Dr. Oppenheimer became the most conspicuous victim of the excesses brought on by the cold war and the overzealous investigations of McCarthyism.* In late December 1953, the Atomic Energy Commission formally notified Dr. Oppenheimer of the suspension of his security clearance because his continued employment by the AEC might "endanger the common defense and security." He requested an opportunity to be heard before an AEC personnel security board, which began closed hearings in Washington in early April.

Arthur Compton was in Asia at the time of the hearing, participating in a four-month educational mission. When news of the suspension and hearing reached him, he sent the following letter to Gordon Gray, president of the University of North Carolina, who had been appointed chairman of an AEC review board to hear the Oppenheimer case.

At the conclusion of the hearings, in May 1954, two of the three members of the review board recommended that further security clearance be denied. The decision was widely criticized. On December 2, 1963, in a ceremony at the White House, President Lyndon B. Johnson presented Dr. Oppenheimer with the highest award of the Atomic Energy Commission, the Enrico Fermi award.

Istanbul, Turkey
April 21, 1954

President Gordon Gray
University of North Carolina
Chapel Hill, North Carolina, U.S.A.

Dear President Gray:

*Re: Evidence Regarding Loyalty of Robert Oppenheimer*

I was in Pakistan when the news broke regarding the suspension of J. Robert Oppenheimer from the Advisory Board of the AEC, and it was not until yesterday that I received sufficiently full information about the case to make a statement that I knew would be relevant. Because of my close association with Oppenheimer, I believe that some facts from my firsthand knowledge will be useful to your committee in judging his loyalty. These facts I am stating here with the same responsibility for their veracity that I would accept in the case of sworn testimony before a court of law.

## 1. WARTIME ASSOCIATION

I was responsible for appointing Oppenheimer to the task of organizing whatever was necessary for designing the atomic bomb. This was about the end of April 1942. (The dates given here are all approximate. I have here no notes regarding these matters, and all of my statements are from memory.) It was a month or two later that responsibility for the atomic development was assigned to the U.S. Engineers (Army), and it was in September 1942 that I recommended to General [Leslie R.] Groves that Oppenheimer be continued at this task, and that the responsibility be enlarged to include the construction of the bomb. This recommendation was in accord with that of others, in particular that of Dr. James Conant, and was accepted.

At the time of Oppenheimer's appointment the atomic development was, as you know, in civilian hands. By Dr. Conant, acting for the OSRD [Office of Scientific Research and Development], I was given complete responsibility for such appointments, reporting to him, however, regarding actions taken. For my guidance, within our *Metallurgical Project*, a personnel division had been established which investigated the loyalty background of employees. This investigation (and our other security measures) was carried on with the help of the Federal Bureau of Investigation. But we kept within our own hands the responsibility for the decisions in each case.

It was recognized that the task to which we were appointing Oppenheimer was not only of essential importance to the success of the total project, but also one in which a unique degree of discretion was required. It was my judgment that Oppenheimer's qualifications fitted him for such a post better than any other person who could be made available. This was after a diligent search for about a month, which included consultation with many top-level scientists.

That Oppenheimer had had contacts with Communists was well known to me. These contacts, as I knew them, were essentially as described in his letter as published in *The New York Times* of April 13. It was my impression that, as one eager to find a solution to world problems, he had investigated Communism firsthand to see what it had to offer.

The much more significant fact was that he had already become disillusioned with Communism by what he had found. In a conversation with him about another matter, in the spring of 1940 I believe, he had given me his reasons for not associating himself with a professional organization that had some Communist ties. Later, in 1941 I believe, he had told me of his efforts to persuade his brother, Frank, to dissociate himself from Communist groups. As I recall it, it was during the early stages of our conversations about the atomic program, before I had approached him about accepting the responsibility for the design of the bomb, that Oppenheimer told me he was breaking completely every association with any organization that might be suspected of Communism, in order that he might be of maximum usefulness on war projects.

It was my judgment that a person who had known Communism and had found its faults was more to be relied upon than one who was innocent of such connections. This was the more important because it was evident that his task would necessarily draw in many men of foreign background who were among those most competent in theoretical physics. Without the use of such men his task could hardly have been accomplished. A man with Oppenheimer's experience both in foreign countries and, in a limited way, with Communism, was in a most favorable position to recognize those whose loyalties might be directed elsewhere than to the United States and the free world.

The chief positive reason for selecting Oppenheimer for this post was that, after working vigorously on rallying the help of theoretical physicists to the design of the bomb, Oppenheimer had shown the most eagerness and initiative, he was one of the very few American-born men who had the professional competence, and he had demonstrated a certain firmness of character. While his administrative competence remained to be demonstrated, it looked to me promising.

Looking back on this selection, I do not believe it would have been possible to find anywhere a man better suited to carry through this unique job in the nation's interest.

## 2. POSTWAR ASSOCIATIONS

After the war was over I discussed with Oppenheimer several times the question of proceeding with the development of the H-bomb. Its possibility Oppenheimer had called to my attention in August 1942. This possibility was kept under the utmost secrecy; but before the war was over its suggestion had arisen spontaneously from so many sources that it was evident that it would arise in any group working seriously on nuclear explosions. In particular, it was evident that the basic principle of the fusion bomb would be known in Russia.

Immediately after the war our great consideration was to reach a reliable agreement with Russia that would rule out atomic weapons but permit the development of atomic power. During this period there was no immediate occasion to work toward atomic fusion.* The situation changed when Russia showed such reluctance that no atomic weapons agreement seemed feasible. We then recognized that Russia was working vigorously on her own atomic development. Presumably the H-bomb would eventually become part of her program.

I recall a conversation with Oppenheimer in 1947 or 1948 in which I was advocating the initiation of a program of active research and development toward the H-bomb. My point was that this development, if it was physically possible, was sure to come before many years, and it was important that the availability of this *super*weapon should first be in our hands.

I found Oppenheimer reluctant. His chief reluctance was, I believe, on purely moral grounds. No nation should bring into being a power that would (or could) be so destructive of human lives. Even if another nation should do so, our morality should be higher than this. We should accept the military disadvantage in the interest of standing for a proper moral principle.

He had other reasons: the development of fear and antagonism among other nations, the substantial possibility that the effort to create an atomic explosion would fail, questions regarding the H-bomb's military value. He hoped that no urgent need for its development would arise.

In this and other conversations Oppenheimer brought up precisely those questions that needed to be considered. His thinking seemed to be aimed solely toward finding what was in the best interests of the United States. He took for granted, as did I, that the United States' interests are those of humanity. There was no shadow of a suspicion that his arguments were subtly working toward Russia's advantage. I am confident that no such thought was in his mind.

With the explosion of Russia's first atomic bomb in 1949 the situation was sharply changed. I do not recall any firsthand discussions with Oppenheimer on this matter after that date.

## 3. CONCLUSION

Having known Robert Oppenheimer since his days in Göttingen in 1927, having worked with him closely during the war years, and having kept in touch with him occasionally since, it is my judgment that he is completely loyal to the interests of the United States, and that any activity in the interest of a foreign power at the expense of the United States would be thoroughly repugnant to him. It is my judgment, further, that he is, and has been since 1941, just as thoroughly opposed to Communism.

Yours sincerely,
*Arthur H. Compton*

# 31. The Loyalty Security Problem

## *1955*

Concerned with the erosion of liberties guaranteed by the Constitution, a Subcommittee of the United States Senate conducted a series of hearings on Security and Constitutional Rights, under the chairmanship of Thomas C. Hennings, Jr., of Missouri. Senator Hennings, an ardent defender of civil liberties and a leading critic of Joseph McCarthy, ultimately provided a basis for the censure of McCarthy by the Senate. Mr. Compton's testimony was presented before the Subcommittee in Washington, D.C., on November 16, 1955. He utilized the opportunity to state his conviction that indiscriminate questioning of the loyalty of scientists greatly reduces both the strength and the security of the nation.

I wish to bring out four points:

1. Screening programs involving political acceptability are interfering seriously with American participation in international scientific conferences. This is retarding to a significant degree the development of science in the United States.
2. Indiscriminate questioning of the loyalty of scientists is reducing (*a*) the effectiveness of scientists in their work, (*b*) the willingness of scientists to engage in defense research, (*c*) the number of young people entering science as a profession.
3. The screening programs and accusations of disloyalty are resulting in ignorance regarding matters vital to the nation's interest.
4. An impression seems to be widespread that science can best strengthen the nation by directing its prime attention to problems of national defense and other matters concerned directly with the nation's welfare. This impression is strengthened by the questioning of the loyalty of scientists. The reverse of this impression is true. Experience shows that science can best become a national asset by cultivating its search for all knowledge that is relevant to man. Because of the sharply rising significance of

science as a factor in the nation's strength, these deleterious effects of screening and questioning are matters of vital concern to the nation.

## SCREENING PROGRAMS AND INTERNATIONAL SCIENTIFIC CONFERENCES

Permit me first to show that international conferences play an important part in determining a nation's scientific strength. I shall do so by giving examples that I personally have noted of the effects of two such conferences. One of these was in the United States, and the other in Europe.

In 1931 I attended a conference on nuclear physics held at Rome. Present were physicists from a score of countries, including Europe, Asia, and America. At this conference it became clear that research on the nucleus of the atom should lead rapidly to important results. One consequence of my attendance at this conference was that I declined the offer of an important university presidency in order to continue my own scientific studies. Thus when World War II came, I was prepared to take an active part in the atomic bomb project. If I had not attended this conference it is doubtful whether I could have participated effectively in this wartime atomic program. Also at this international scientific conference in Rome in 1931, Professor Enrico Fermi and I became well acquainted. It was probably in part this acquaintance which encouraged Fermi to come to the United States in the autumn of 1938; and it was certainly my acquaintance with him, made at that time, which made it possible for us to work together effectively toward developing the nuclear chain reaction in Chicago in 1942, with all its important consequences.

In June of 1939 I organized an international scientific congress held at the University of Chicago. In attendance were physicists from Britain, Germany, Italy, France, and the United States. Recalling that in 1939 our prime political concern was that of the rise of Fascism, it is notable that two of the countries represented were Fascist countries. Particularly from the Germans who attended the conference the Americans obtained important information regarding their theoretical studies of nuclear fission. We became aware also of the distinctive political attitudes of several of our European colleagues. The scientific knowledge thus obtained enabled us in the United States to proceed more rapidly with our own development of atomic energy, and our acquaintance with the ideas of our European colleagues enabled us to anticipate more intelligently what we should expect from Europe when a few months later war engulfed that continent.

| 271 |

## International scientific conferences
in the United States

The effect of the political screening tests now applied to scientists who wish to obtain visas for entering this country presents a severe handicap in holding international scientific congresses here. I shall cite three examples.

1. In Geneva, Switzerland, in 1952 I attended an international conference of scientists and philosophers who were discussing "Man Facing Science." The interest was such that it was desired to hold a second conference on a similar topic. In response to my suggestion that such a conference might be held in the United States, there was a chorus of objections that it was too difficult to obtain visas.

2. An international physics conference was held in Glasgow, Scotland, in the summer of 1954. Many of those in attendance expressed regret that it was not possible to hold a similar conference in the United States because of the difficulty of obtaining visas.

3. In the autumn of 1954 I organized a conference at St. Louis on the subject "Science and Human Responsibility." Attending this conference were representatives from Britain, Germany, France, India, and China. The British and Chinese representatives were persons already in this country on visitors' visas. Because of his previous visa difficulties, and in order to avoid international embarrassment, I did not invite Professor Michael Polanyi of the University of Manchester, though he would have contributed substantially to our discussions and would probably have been willing to come. The German delegate, Professor Werner Heisenberg of Göttingen, made application for a visa about four months in advance of the date of leaving for the conference. When almost at the last moment no favorable response had been received, I called the matter sharply to the attention of American officials in Washington and in Germany and the visa was granted. If I had not had access to special channels there is no doubt that Professor Heisenberg would have been unable to attend. His presence was of prime importance to the success of the conference.

## Participation of American scientists
in conferences abroad

American scientists have been prevented from attending conferences in other countries by withholding passports permitting them to leave the

United States. In this regard, Professor Linus Pauling will, I believe, testify as to his own experience. I will cite that of Professor Martin Kamen, a member of the faculty of Washington University.

Dr. Martin D. Kamen, Associate Professor of Radiochemistry at Washington University, has been invited during the past several years to attend international scientific conferences, or to give scientific lectures, in Australia, Israel, and various countries in Europe. His passport was refused, presumably on the basis of questionable loyalty. When Dr. Kamen was refused his passport I was Chancellor of Washington University, and was in a position to have reliable knowledge with regard to the loyalty matters with which Kamen was charged. This was not only because I was his employer but also because I had been associated with him in his wartime research, about which the loyalty questions were centered. I was not consulted before the Congressional investigation of Kamen was begun. Because of my firsthand knowledge of the case, the questions introduced by Congressional investigation did not cause us at the University to lose our faith in Kamen. It was necessary, however, to press the investigation to a legal decision in order to clear his reputation from false implications of disloyalty. In the meantime, presumably because of the questions, his passport was denied and he was unable to attend the international conferences. There is no doubt that this has reduced his own effectiveness as an American scientist, as it has also retarded the development of science elsewhere. I know of no reasonable basis that ever existed for supposing that Martin Kamen's attendance at such conferences would have damaged the interests of the United States.

## DELETERIOUS EFFECTS OF INDISCRIMINATE QUESTIONING OF THE LOYALTY OF AMERICAN SCIENTISTS

### The effect on the work of scientists

As examples of the damaging effect on the work of the scientists that such questioning produces, I will cite two cases. The first is again that of Dr. Martin Kamen. This case is, I believe, properly called one of indiscriminate questioning, for had the committee conducting this investigation asked in advance for our knowledge of him, it is doubtful whether the formal questioning would ever have been undertaken. Evidence that the important charges against Kamen were unfounded is the court verdict last summer for damages against the Washington *Times-Herald* for publishing statements which they based on the accusations made against Kamen by persons associated with the investigation.

It is impossible to say what advance in his profession Kamen might have had if such accusations had not been made. It is possible, however, to point to one tangible effect.

In 1954 the Public Health Service began to cut off grants from investigators about whom "derogatory" information existed in the security files. One of the cases was that of Martin Kamen. He had a three-year commitment from the Public Health Service for support of his research. In 1954 this support had continued for two years. It was then discontinued. This discontinuance had the effect of removing the funds from which an assistant to Professor Kamen was being paid his salary. Thus his assistant, Dr. Leo Vernon, lost his position, and the work of Kamen was interrupted. Later it was possible to continue Kamen's work by funds from a private source. But in the meantime Vernon had left to take another position.

Following the clarification of Kamen's loyalty status, he has received a grant from the National Science Foundation in support of his research. This is one of the rare cases in which the Congressional questioning has been followed up with sufficient determination to clear the status of the individual concerned.* It was not cleared by the Congressional investigators themselves.

As the second example of the effect of indiscriminate questioning of the loyalty of scientists I will cite my own experience.* In the winter of 1952 in Houston, Texas, I took occasion to speak favorably of the work of Unesco. A letter to the editor of a Houston newspaper noted that I had been listed as a member of certain organizations on the Attorney General's list. The writer thus wished to discount the value of my testimony. It appeared that she had received her information from a report published in the *Congressional Record* which contained a list of names presented by the Dies Committee in about 1942. These names were persons reported to have taken part in questionable activities. I had learned of this report and had filed an affidavit with the Attorney General affirming that to the best of my knowledge I had never had any connection with the organizations or activities described, and had thus presumably cleared my record.

The point is that when a Congressional committee raises publicly the question of a person's loyalty, even though the question may in due time be answered to the full satisfaction of those concerned, damage is nevertheless done to the individual's effectiveness. Nor is there any possibility of undoing this damage completely once it has been done.

## The unpopularity of government scientific work

The question of the loyalty of scientists is one of the factors that has tended to make scientific work for the government unpopular. That this is true is largely a statement of my personal judgment. It is, however, a judgment in which many of my scientific colleagues join.

Thus Dr. John Manley, when in 1947 he left Washington University's Department of Physics to accept a position at the Los Alamos Scientific Laboratory, told me that he did so to strengthen research in an important government enterprise which was being left weak in part because loyalty questionings had made it unacceptable to so many of his colleagues.

I should explain that the scientists' objection to the loyalty questioning is not because they consider themselves disloyal. The objection has two main sources: (1) unfounded accusations that have been made against persons whom the scientists consider loyal; (2) an impression that the loyalty questions are determined to large extent by political considerations in which science should have no part.

## The false impression of disloyalty

Questioning concentrated on the loyalty of scientists has inevitably had the effect of creating the false impression that scientists, more than others, are apt to be disloyal to the country. The profession of scientific research thus loses its appeal to young men and women who are concerned with advancing our nation's strength and welfare. It is difficult to measure the magnitude of this influence. Nevertheless, at this time when science is so important a factor in building our strength, it would have been much better for the country's welfare to call attention to the substantial contributions that scientists have made to the nation rather than to focus public attention on supposed cases of disloyalty. To the best of my knowledge, not one of the supposed cases of disloyalty of a scientist has been established, at least to the extent of a court decision.*

### SCREENING PROGRAMS HAVE RESULTED IN
### IGNORANCE ABOUT MATTERS VITAL TO
### THE NATION'S WELFARE

That the screening programs have resulted in ignorance with regard to matters vital to the nation's welfare is illustrated by two examples. The first is my discovery in Europe in 1949 of a paperbound edition of a book by Eric Ashby on Soviet science. This book, written by a former scientific attaché of the British Embassy in Moscow, had been available in Britain and Europe for some years. It dealt with matters that it was important for me as head of a major American university to know. This information was necessary for guiding the development of our scientific and technological studies. There is no doubt that this book would have had profitable sale in American bookstores if it had been available, but its existence had not come to my attention. I do not know that this book was specifically prevented from admission to the United States by any legislation. But the atmosphere, created largely by Congressional investigations of these matters, was such that its circulation was frowned upon. That this was true is indicated by the fact that when I returned to the United States, I kept the book hidden from the Customs inspectors lest questions should be asked. Here is one of the reasons why it has been possible for Soviet science and technology to take us by surprise with the rapidity of its growth.

A second and even more serious effect of the loyalty questioning was explained to me by a junior member of an American consulate in Asia. I was talking with him in the winter of 1954, shortly after certain respected members of the American foreign diplomatic corps had been removed because of charges of disloyalty. This young man told me that he had a wife and children. He said that he was not going to report information that might get him in trouble in Washington. By this he meant he would not transmit information that was distasteful to those who were responsible for conducting investigations. I should add at once that I did not see any indication of such a cowardly attitude on the part of the more highly placed diplomatic officers in our American foreign service. But there is no doubt whatever that the effect of the loyalty screenings at that time was to make difficult the obtaining of reliable information in Washington regarding critical matters in the Far East.

## SCIENCE MUST BE OPEN IN ORDER
## THAT IT SHALL BE STRONG

A striking example of the weakness that develops when science is narrowly confined is shown by what happened in Germany preceding World War II. During the late 1920's science in Germany developed until in many fields Germany was leading the world. At this stage German science had the full support of the government and of German industry. With the coming into power of Hitler and the Nazis there developed the concept of "German" science as opposed to "Jewish" science. German science was described as that directed toward the strengthening of Germany. Jewish science, by contrast, was that directed toward universal understanding, and hence of equal value to all nations. The immediate effect was to develop German technology, especially in the field of conventional weapons. Already by 1939, however, the strength of general science in Germany had fallen to such a low ebb that in the new fields of electronics and atomic energy Germany could not match Britain and the United States. Within less than ten years the importance of these new and unforeseen scientific developments had become so great as to be of determining influence in World War II.

## SCIENCE STRENGTHENS THE NATION

It is those scientists who are searching for basic knowledge who are perhaps contributing most to the strength of the American nation. Their science is itself independent of national boundaries. The experience of World Wars I and II shows that in times of national danger these scientists have been among the first to see the danger and to rally to the nation's defense.

May I conclude by stating as clearly as I can why I consider the screening programs, and the publicized investigations of loyalty as they have been conducted during recent years, damaging to the true security of the nation.

From the point of view of true national security, the fact is that survival of our American way of life depends most importantly upon whether we can grow in strength more rapidly than our rivals. At present, the free world and the Communist world are approximately equally matched in military strength. The economic strength of the free world is at present considerably superior, but that of the Communist world is growing rapidly. It is clear that our relative standing a generation hence will depend upon which social order can develop the more rapidly.

In this contest it is new ideas and the development of vigorous initiative that are our chief hope. The great danger from inquisitions and restrictions on freedom of travel and exchange of ideas is that they retard the development of original ideas and dampen the initiative of those who put such ideas into effect.

The safety and health of the free world accordingly depend upon the encouragement, not the restriction, of those on whom this growth of our strength depends.

# VII

# Implications of

# Nuclear Energy

A world of change is a world of hope. . . . A narrow preoccupation with the Bomb is myopic because it fails to see the potential heights of human achievement.

DAVID E. LILIENTHAL

# 32. The Atomic Crusade and Its Social Implications

## *1946*

In the belief that an understanding of the forces of social change may help direct the trends and lend stability to the social order, the University of Michigan presented during the summer of 1946 a series of lectures on "The Social Implications of Modern Science." The author was invited to discuss atomic energy as a part of this effort to take stock of scientific advance and to anticipate its social consequences.

Much has been said regarding the implications of atomic energy. It is worth calling special attention to the unusual sequence of events that led to making atomic energy useful and that has made a group of scientists become a significant factor in our political and social life. This sequence of events is indeed a social movement, motivated primarily not by considerations of economic and political power, but by social objectives and ideals. For this reason the correct connotations are given by characterizing the movement of which the atomic bomb was an incident as the "atomic crusade."

In considering the social implications of this atomic crusade, it is important to note why it was possible for the movement to develop and succeed in its wartime objectives in the United States, while it was not similarly successful elsewhere. This will lead us into a consideration of its form of organization and of the factors favorable to its strength. What are the future implications of such features as the highly organized research, the close cooperation of science, industry, and government, and the imposition of secrecy on research that is traditionally free? But perhaps of greatest interest is the way in which the atomic crusade epitomizes certain major social trends, such as growing specialization with its implied coordinated cooperation, increasing emphasis on better training and education, and the growing awareness of the need for generally accepted social objectives as coordinating principles in setting a pattern for our social and political development.

The dramatic use of the atomic bomb on Hiroshima was unique with regard both to the startling newness of the weapon and to its decisive effectiveness. Perhaps the bomb merely gave the Japanese a convenient excuse for resigning from a struggle which their leaders already knew was lost. Nevertheless, it changed literally at a flash the world's attitude toward war. Our enemies had not overlooked the possibility of an atomic bomb. In fact, their progress in this direction was the spur that goaded us into its development. Their own wartime investigations had, however, convinced them that the construction of such a weapon could not actually be accomplished. In our own country the atomic bomb was one of the last major developments of war research to be undertaken. It was conceived as a practical undertaking only after other urgent war tasks had made heavy demands on the nation's major scientific talent. Thus it was the more remarkable that so complex an undertaking should have been carried to a decisive conclusion so quietly and in so short a time.

### FAITH IN THE GOAL

The atomic program was in fact a crusade. This is why it was so effective. It was not necessary to have a highly refined organization to get cooperation. The goal was recognized as so important that personally favored ideas were willingly scrapped when it became clear that better progress could be made by working along other lines. Individual scientists, leaders of the government, the Army, universities, and great industrial organizations successively caught the vision of great achievement. They could see that success might spell early victory and that to lose the race might well mean defeat. They were glad for a chance to share in what was instinctively recognized as one of the great human adventures of all time.

Many have wondered how the secret was so well kept that both our enemies and the American public were taken completely by surprise. Probably some thousands of persons—a fraction of a per cent of the million who worked on the job—knew, or guessed, that atomic bombs were being prepared. Though very few were acquainted with such essential details as delivery schedules, objectives, and timing, the vigor of the prosecution of the work showed that the use of the bombs in this war was expected. Of course, care was used in selecting those who would have to know the purpose of what they were doing. But the real explanation for the tightness of the secrecy was that when by accident someone learned what was going on, he was awed by its significance. A simple suggestion was enough to make him understand that "here is something I must not tell. The safety of the world may depend on the tightness of my lips." He had himself become a part of the crusade.

As in the case of a holy war, so also the atomic crusade was the expression of a widespread faith that had developed over many years. Among the scientists this was a faith in the reliability of their methods of prediction, a confidence in their ability to accomplish a task that theory showed was possible, combined with a conviction that the release of atomic energy would eventually become one of the greatest gifts that science could ever provide to man. Generations of experience with the growing applications of science gave the representatives of government and industry a faith in the considered judgment of scientists. Other marvels as great as this had appeared. All those in responsible positions were determined to avoid any chance of losing the fight for freedom. If for no other reason than that they might be right, the predictions of the scientists must be listened to. Faith, expressed in complete support, was called for.

## ATOMIC POWER IN PEACE

It would be a mistake to suppose that either the scientists or the government set out initially to build an atomic bomb. This was indeed the central military objective of the great atomic war effort. The bomb was, however, only the wartime aspect of a much greater vision. This vision began to take shape with the discovery fifty years ago that within the atom lies a storehouse filled with energy vaster by far than that which shows itself in such chemical processes as the burning of coal. Many a physicist in his heart of hearts hoped that he might have a share in presenting this wealth of energy in useful form as a Promethean gift to mankind. Perhaps nothing that physics could ever do would be of so great practical importance. Dreams were dreamed of a more abundant life, of greater knowledge to control disease, of greater freedom to build a better world. When uranium fission was discovered, it seemed that these dreams might be made real. Atomic power to drive the wheels of industry? Yes, and to propel ships over the seas and to supply heat in the arctic wilds, making more of the planet available to man.

But uranium fission came at a time when war, the defense of all that was dear, compelled everyone's attention. The possibility of atomic explosions had been thought of only as terrors to be avoided, disasters that might overcome the bold experimenters who first would start the atomic chain reaction. Could atomic engines win the war? Hardly. By the time they were developed in usable form the war should be over. Nor would the use of such engines be of decisive importance. But the sudden release of atomic energy might make a bomb that would give to its user an enormous advantage. When this advantage was clearly seen, fear lest the enemy might first build such weapons called for a great effort. The atomic war program quickly took shape and into it was thrown all the strength that could be spared from other vital tasks.

To those who had been working with atoms for years, however, even the winning of the war was only one step in the use of the newfound strength. Victory was necessary so that people should be free to work for a better world. Among the essential features of that better world stands prominently the freedom from fear of war. The atomists knew that from here on war would be so destructive that its waging would be madness. The world must see that this is true and be compelled to find a way whereby war can be prevented. With this as a greater objective, the years they spent at making atomic bombs prepared those who were making them to burst into a vast missionary call for peace as soon as the war was won. The little group of atomic physicists had now grown to a crusading army, with the strength of the many thousands of humanity-minded men and women who had shared their war effort.

Nor is peace itself the final goal. Many have been the frustrations of science. Improved methods of supplying food and shelter and other essentials to needy humanity have failed to achieve their promise because of the failure of society to use them for the common welfare. Here in atomic energy is a new, great opportunity to enrich life. Those who have brought this new child of science into being are determined that they shall not be frustrated again. It is not the rich, not the clever or the powerful, not the United States, Canada, or Britain alone that shall prosper from this new gift. The whole world shall have peace and, as far as the new advances of science and technology can bring it, prosperity and a more complete life. It is this great goal that the atomists hold before them. Atomic energy gives perhaps the greatest opportunity they will ever have to work effectively toward that goal. This opportunity must be used to the utmost. Such is the spirit of the atomic crusade.

## MOBILIZATION OF THE ATOMIC BOMB PROJECT

In his official report on the use of atomic energy in war, Professor H. D. Smyth has given an authentic account of the way in which the atomic program was organized. For the purpose of this article it will be useful for me only to call attention to certain distinctive features of that organization.

It was the civilian scientists actually engaged on studies of atomic fission who first called attention to its potential importance in war. Previous to the discovery of the fission of uranium, the hopes for releasing atomic energy were so vague that no one considered seriously the possibility of making it useful in a practical way except after long continued fundamental research. Such research was indeed progressing, but without any of the urgency associated with war or even with imminent peacetime applications. With the discovery of the fission of uranium, however, physicists throughout the world looked for rapid developments. When in the spring of 1939 reports from Europe and America showed that this fission was accompanied by the emission of more than one neutron per disintegrating atom, the physics world was aware that an atomic chain reaction was possible. How it could best be achieved and how it could most effectively be used had yet to be explored.

Atomic power, radioactivity in abundance, and bombs were thought of and discussed in all quarters of the globe. Those whose interests lay solely in pure physics thought of atomic fission as just one more property of matter that needed exploration. But those who were alert to war developments took quick action. In Germany the resources of the Kaiser Wilhelm Institute at Berlin were turned to isotope separation with an eye alert to possible use for a chain reaction. In the United States the government was persuaded to give modest support to the enterprise while its objectives were as yet vague. But until 1941 the primary initiative in this country continued to come from civilian scientists and the universities. To the physicists of Columbia University, Princeton, and the University of California goes the chief credit during these early years for proceeding with this vital program as far as limited support made possible while a study was being made as to what military applications of the energy might be developed.

These early explorations were conducted almost wholly by civilians, under the cover of a secrecy initiated and imposed by the scientists themselves. Their work showed that U-235 might be concentrated by gaseous diffusion, that plutonium could be made which would be similar in properties to U-235, and that with a suitable combination of uranium and graphite it might be possible to make an atomic chain reaction. Until the summer of 1941 no serious attempt had been made in this country to see how such a chain reaction might be made effective in the war, and lacking such an objective, government interest in the program was casual.

## The government sponsors atomic research

Then came the report from England that her physicists had calculated that a bomb of enormous destructive power could be made from a surprisingly small amount of U-235. Our data supported theirs, and indicated further that the U-235 could be separated by any one of several processes that looked industrially feasible. A reviewing committee,* appointed by the president of the National Academy of Sciences at the request of the Office of Scientific Research and Development, reported favorably on the feasibility of making atomic bombs of U-235 that might be decisive in the war, and gave a rough but reliable estimate of the time and the cost required to make the bombs. It was on the basis of this report and of a similar recommendation from the British * that President Roosevelt authorized Vannevar Bush, as director of the Office of Scientific Research and Development, to proceed with full vigor with what experiments were needed to see whether the proposed atomic program was indeed practicable. This order, which became effective just before Pearl Harbor, was the start of the atomic development as an active war project.

Vannevar Bush asked James Conant to see that the program was organized and carried through. Conant appointed an executive committee of six persons,* of whom three were assigned responsibility for carrying through major divisions of the bomb development task. Of these three, Harold Urey at Columbia University centered his work on the diffusion process for separating U-235. Ernest Lawrence at the University of California at Berkeley undertook to try the magnetic separation of the isotopes. I had the joint task of designing the bomb and developing a method for making plutonium. This work was organized at the University of Chicago.

A major handicap faced by the atomic program was the fact that other tasks were already in hand which had scoured the country for competent research men. The radar and electronics studies, antisubmarine research, and the ordnance laboratories had taken the first choice of men with the needed qualifications. The atomic program was fortunate, however, in two ways. First, a considerable nucleus of the leaders in atomic research had not left the field, and they rallied to the newly established centers. And second, the previous laboratories had drawn chiefly from the Atlantic and Pacific coasts and had not exhausted the extensive research talent from the middle of the country.

Industry as well as science had to be recruited. With evidence of government interest, this industrial support was gratifying. Consider, for example, the case of Company A,* which was uniquely qualified to carry through a new and difficult process that had been developed in the laboratory. Speed was of the essence. The task would demand a considerable part of the company's total strength at a time when it was already heavily loaded with important jobs. One morning the need was described to the head of the company. That afternoon the engineers started with the work. The day after the delivery of the first order was completed, well ahead of schedule, the contract was signed determining the price and other details. Company A had become a part of the crusade.

After six months of intensive effort, the scientists had gained further confidence in the feasibility of a bomb using either U-235 or plutonium. Hopeful progress had been made toward separating U-235. The evidence was convincing that a pile of uranium and graphite could be built that would give a chain reaction and supply a source of plutonium.

When President Roosevelt was presented with these findings by Vannevar Bush, he set aside the needed funds and instructed the War Department to do whatever was necessary to build atomic bombs. To General Leslie R. Groves and Colonel (now General) K. D. Nichols of the Corps of Engineers was assigned the responsibility for putting the President's order into effect.

## Army, industry, universities cooperate

It was necessary for General Groves to determine which of the various methods for producing U-235 or plutonium should be put on a production basis, the scale of the production program, how this production should be carried out, and under what conditions the bombs should be built. He made these decisions with advice from a series of reviewing committees composed of highly qualified scientists and engineers who in turn discussed the problems with the research men who were engaged in the development of the processes. His major decisions were in turn reviewed by a Military Policy Committee (Bush, Conant, General Styer, and Admiral Purnell). Messrs. James Conant, R. C. Tolman, W. K. Lewis, and C. A. Thomas acted as frequent consultants to him on technical aspects of these problems, though a large part of his advice came directly from the leaders of the various development projects.

Because of the short time available, the policy adopted was that of proceeding immediately with the building of production plants which, if all went as hoped for, would make available at the earliest possible moment enough atomic weapons to be of decisive military value. For the sake of speed and sureness, three methods of separating U-235 were carried through to production. While only one method of producing plutonium was completed, alternative methods were under development until the chosen process looked certain of success. Placing the bomb production unit in a completely isolated area, under the direction of a theoretical physicist (Robert Oppenheimer) who in spite of his evident competence was untried in such a major administrative task, was one of General Groves's many major decisions which, if wrong, might have meant the failure of the enterprise.

In order to secure the full cooperation of industry, General Groves chose the Du Pont Company as a leader, and requested this organization to undertake the construction and operation of the plant for producing plutonium. Representatives of the company were given full opportunity to study the state of development of all aspects of the bomb program.

After two months of such study, in a meeting at Wilmington, a vice-president of the company officially told General Groves that if the Army insisted, the Du Pont Company would proceed with constructing and operating the plutonium plant, but that he must state that in the judgment of the company the chance was not greater than one in a hundred that useful results would come from the work during World War II. The vice-president explained that as yet (November 1942) no laboratory demonstration of a chain reaction had been made, and no laboratory process for separation of plutonium had been developed. To assume the establishment of such unknown processes on a production basis before the war would be over seemed quite unrealistic. Fortunately, within two weeks the chain reaction was operating in the laboratory, the reviewing committee brought in a favorable report, and the Du Pont Company, at the Army's urgent request, undertook the contract, devoting to it the best talent in its organization.

Other major industrial organizations were similarly brought into the enterprise. Sometimes parts of the task looked almost hopelessly difficult. Occasionally one of the operating companies or one of the leaders of the scientific program would become discouraged about an essential part of the work. General Groves and Colonel Nichols, however, never faltered in their determination to carry through.

From the beginning of the task, the universities had been taking an active part. Now they were asked to undertake new burdens. Especially at Chicago, California, and Columbia the undertaking assumed proportions comparable with or greater than all the rest of the universities' activities. It was not obvious that the type of work to be done was appropriate to a university. Nevertheless, here were corporations that were prepared to operate the new mushroom research organizations. In the emergency the heads of these institutions felt that they must help if they were needed. As one spokesman said, "We will turn our university inside out if necessary for winning this war."

Thus the Army, American industry, and the universities joined the atomic crusade.

## Decision on use of bomb

As the time approached when the bombs would be complete, fateful decisions were necessary. Though the atomic program was initially stimulated by fear of Germany, the European war was now drawing to a close. In planning for the use of the bombs against Japan, President Truman acted on the advice of a civilian committee of highest level. Originally the program of developing and building the bombs had been authorized by President Roosevelt, in consultation with Vice-President Wallace, Secretary of War Stimson, Chief of Staff General Marshall, Vannevar Bush, and James Conant. As the work proceeded and large expenditures were required, members of the Military Affairs Committee and a few others were informed as to plans, progress, and intentions.

Shortly after the death of President Roosevelt, President Truman appointed a civilian "Interim Committee" to advise him regarding the atomic program. The Secretary of War was chairman of this committee, with George L. Harrison as his alternate. Other members were James F. Byrnes, later Secretary of State; Ralph A. Bard, former Under Secretary of the Navy; William L. Clayton, Assistant Secretary of State; Vannevar Bush, James B. Conant, and Karl T. Compton. Advisers to this committee were General Marshall, General Groves, and a Scientific Panel consisting of Ernest Lawrence, Enrico Fermi, Robert Oppenheimer, and Arthur Compton. The use of the bombs by the Army was ordered by President Truman, closely in accord with the recommendations of this Interim Committee. The committee likewise outlined the broad policies for the further development of the possibilities of atomic energy. Their policies continued to serve as the government's guide until Congress enacted new legislation.

### STRENGTH AND WEAKNESS OF
### RESEARCH ORGANIZATION

The atomic program is an excellent example of the usefulness of both free and organized research. That the possibility of releasing atomic energy was discovered is a triumph of free research. That this possibility was so quickly applied is a phenomenal achievement of organized research.

The Nazis introduced the distinction between "German" and "Jewish" science. German science was that which was distinctively capable of advancing the relative strength of the German nation. Jewish science was that which was of value only for general understanding, or of general human benefit. Science of the former type was practical; science of the latter, theoretical or broadly basic in its interest. It was partly because of Nazi scorn of such basic science that many students of science left Germany for countries such as Britain and America, where they might pursue their studies with freedom.

Nuclear physics, whose growth has made atomic power available, is a combination of the studies of atomic structure, the theory of relativity, and the quantum theory. None of these was considered by the Nazis to be German science. Uranium fission was discovered * in a German laboratory, the Kaiser Wilhelm Institute, which was almost unique in continuing the support of fundamental science. In the United States, however, scientists remained free to work in whatever fields seemed to them of greatest value. Our universities, in fact, encouraged whatever studies might aid in the understanding of the physical world. Because of the high value that they place on freedom of thought, our scientists, especially those of foreign origin, were doubly eager to work with their full strength for the survival of our nation. It is thus fair to say that the strength that comes because of freedom was a vital factor in enabling the United States to initiate and carry through its atomic crusade. At the same time, cooperation in research was called for to an unprecedented extent. How was such cooperation possible in a country where freedom of effort was so highly valued?

A part of the answer is to be found in the spontaneous growth of our voluntarily organized research programs. The centers where the atomic research program developed most productively were those such as at Berkeley and Chicago where there already existed strong nuclei of scientists who had come together voluntarily because by cooperative effort they could work more effectively on their chosen tasks of nuclear physics or cosmic rays. The atomic laboratories were merely greatly expanded organizations of the type which had already become a pattern for modern science—voluntary research teams, the members of each team following willingly the plan set by its captain.

It is important to note that these war research teams were also composed of volunteers. They came together not because of orders, but because they saw that only by such cooperative effort could they do the job that they felt was so urgent. While this might have resulted in weakness because of poor coordination of effort, it turned out to be a source of strength.

General Groves once complained that these scientists were undisciplined: "They do not know how to take orders or give orders." It was explained to him that they had instead a different kind of discipline. The scientist is essentially an initiator. It is his function to find out for himself what needs to be done and to exert the self-discipline required to do it without instructions from anyone.

The technique of directing the activities of such a group of self-starters so that their work will be effectively coordinated toward a single goal is very different from that of commanding an army or bossing a crew of laborers. Instead of telling a man what his job is and how he should do it, the research man needs first of all to know what the objective of his task is, why it is important, and what the interests and abilities of his collaborators are. Then he can intelligently choose for himself where he can best contribute to the program. It takes more effort thus to keep a program oriented; but having chosen his task, the scientist assumes a responsibility and an enthusiasm for its accomplishment which are not to be found among those who work merely under orders.

An important but rarely mentioned feature of the war research organizations was frequent staff discussion of technical and policy problems. When the plutonium project was at its height, such meetings were held regularly twice a month, usually at Chicago, but occasionally at Oak Ridge or elsewhere. A hundred or more persons would attend with representatives from the scores of widely distributed centers at which collaborative work was going on. Papers were read, some dealing with the progress on important problems, and some with technical or scientific information that had been found. At the policy meetings, with attendance limited to some thirty heads of laboratories or divisions, the state of the atomic program was regularly reviewed and plans for the future were discussed. While at all of these meetings representatives of the Army were present, the notable fact was the freedom and thoroughness with which all the relevant problems were considered. Perhaps more than any other aspect of the organization, it was these regularly scheduled general discussions, combined with frequent group discussions at each major center, that kept the work progressing on the direct road to success.

## Difficulties under Army control

When the atomic program was transferred to the Army's shoulders, there were many discussions as to the advisability of inducting many or all of those engaged in it into the Army, so that they might work under military directives. Such action would, I believe, have made it enormously more difficult to maintain the freedom necessary for effective progress. Even without such direct militarization, the evident need for concentration on the direct line of attack to solve the problems promptly led to much more regimentation than would ordinarily have been acceptable over so long a time to research men. By keeping the top direction in the hands of men who were themselves familiar with research, however, it was possible to maintain a highly coordinated program without coercion and with persistently high morale.

The difficulty of organizing such a research program within the Army's accustomed secrecy rules, however, amounted practically to an impossibility. Prominent among the military principles of secrecy is that of compartmentalization. No one must know anything that is not necessary for performing one's own task. If, however, one is to choose one's task and take the responsibility for performing it so as to give the results needed by others, one's view of the over-all effort must extend well beyond one's own immediate compartment. On the other hand, the sense of responsibility that goes with understanding the significance of one's work gives unusual earnestness in avoiding leaks of information to those outside the project. The result was that within the research groups knowledge of what was going on was inevitably much more widespread than the security officers desired. Yet if any leak of significant information was traceable to the workers in the research laboratories, it was never mentioned by the security officers.

On the other hand, it would be unfair to say that secrecy as imposed by the Army had any appreciable retarding effect on completing the atomic bombs. In the early stages, before atomic energy was of interest to the Army, it is probable that secrecy regarding the work on designing chain-reacting piles and the withholding, even from official reviewing committees, of information regarding explosive chain reactions may have delayed the development of the program by many months. This early secrecy was, however, self imposed by the scientists engaged in fission studies and those charged with promoting the research. After the summer of 1942, when the Army was placed in control, I know of no time when the program of producing the materials and building the bombs was appreciably delayed by lack of scientific or technical information. Military secrecy made necessary a greater scientific effort, and it occasionally caused some close approaches to serious errors; but it cannot fairly be charged with retarding the final preparation of the bomb.

## Gap between research and application

One of the unprecedented features of the atomic program was the large-scale cooperation of academic scientists, industrialists, and military men. The original ideas and their reduction to laboratory practice were primarily the contribution of men from the universities. The huge production program called for the strength of our best-organized industries. The transfer of academic knowledge to industrial production and military use could be coordinated in wartime only through the military.

The obstacles in the way of smooth cooperation were many. Many of the scientists, as is usually true of inventors, wanted to retain control of the design, the construction, and even the operation of the production plants. The ideas were theirs. None but they knew how to build and operate the new devices. Not only had they earned the right to control the first use of their inventions, but also they were confident that they could bring faster production results than could others who would have to learn the processes from the beginning. The industrial men started with little faith in the practical competence of the scientists; but that little faith grew to full reliance as the two groups worked together. The concern of the scientists with the objectives, the progress, and the consequences of their work was a worry to the Army men, who could not understand why a simple order was not an adequate basis for the scientists' action.

American education has never solved the problem of preparing men for research on the new developments required by industry. The traditional training received by an engineer has been in familiarizing himself with the accepted methods of performing important industrial processes. He is rarely introduced to the search for new methods of doing the old tasks, much less for methods of doing tasks such as have not been done before. The research scientist, on the other hand, has traditionally been led to consider fundamental science only as worthy of his attention, and the practical arts as of concern only to those in a lower stratum of intellectual society. He has been taught how to find all kinds of new facts and methods, but has not learned the value of concerning himself with the things of practical use.

The enforced wartime association of scientists and engineers has had at least some effect in giving each of these professions a greater appreciation of the task the other is performing. What is more, hundreds of young men have learned by practical experience the art of engineering research. It remains to be seen whether our universities and technical schools will be able to develop a postwar education that will supply the new men so urgently needed for solving the new technical problems of industry.*

## LASTING EFFECTS OF THE ATOMIC CRUSADE

The great human significance of the atomic crusade is its dramatic emphasis on the vital necessity of cooperation versus antagonism, of intelligent versus emotional or unconsidered living, and of great, commonly accepted objectives. These needs have become increasingly evident with every advance of science and technology. They are, in fact, essential to civilization. But the atomic bomb has written them before us in blazing letters.

The atomic bomb has made any future war between nations armed with such weapons so disastrous to both parties as to be irrational. The only way to avoid such disaster is that of international cooperation, intelligently planned, to prevent any nation from initiating a war. Only by progressive elimination of antagonisms and inculcation of a desire to cooperation can we hope to attain the great objective of a long enduring peace with freedom.

Science and technology have brought with them increasing specialization. Management and labor, the various trades and professions, government with its many branches, business and agriculture, school and church: each is developing toward doing a better job in a narrower field. This system greatly increases our strength and richness of life as long as we work effectively together. When antagonisms develop, however, as in a nationwide strike or an unwillingness to give justice to a minority group, the complex modern society becomes weakened so that all of us suffer.

## The value of cooperation

In this regard the atomic program is itself a notable example of the effectiveness of cooperation. Mention has already been made of the way in which the scientists, the industrialists, and the Army worked together. It should be noted that this cooperation was not based on any special friendship or understanding. It occurred rather because each group recognized that full cooperation with the others was necessary in order to perform its own task. Accordingly, each gave to the other the best help within its power. As a result of close working together over the years, there developed a much improved understanding of each other's attitudes and problems, an increased respect, and many friendships.

Within these three major groups, also, the differences were striking.

Under the officers of the regular Army were reserve officers, enlisted men and women with and without technical training, many civilians in various capacities, and even hundreds of naval personnel. The industries employed not only engineers, but specialists of all varieties, tough construction crews, skilled and unskilled labor of all kinds. It was remarkable to see thousands of newly recruited men and women learn to do new and unheard-of jobs as operators with skill equal to or better than that of their scientist teachers. Among the scientists were voluntary and compulsory exiles from Europe who brought a large share of the theoretical knowledge and earnest enthusiasm that made of the project a crusade. Noteworthy also were the dozen Negro scientists who worked in complete equality with their white colleagues. The men from all corners of the country, from England, and from other countries, worked together with no thought of differing interests.

To all concerned it was evident that this task called for more education and training than was usual for preparing our technical men. The physics and chemistry were of a highly advanced research type, which was understood at first only by those of the most extensive training. The organizational task performed by the Army was one requiring an acquaintance with the nation's industrial possibilities and a familiarity with Washington politics and with labor problems far beyond the ken of most engineers. Likewise, the engineering required to build a complex new plant, with not even a pilot plant as a pattern to follow, with small tolerances and details such as had never previously been heard of, called for the best skill the nation had available. The importance of the extra knowledge and skill in making sure that the right moves would be made was thus impressed upon all who shared the enterprise. Only by intelligent planning could such a task have a chance of success.

## Need for national goal

Above all, the atomic project is an example of the supreme value of a purpose. The war goal of the atomists was to build bombs that would bring victory and lasting peace. This was a part of the greater goal of defense and victory. The lesson one learns is that when people are working with a will to attain an objective, they will strive to learn how to do their part, and will willingly work with others as may be necessary for the desired result. With a goal established, training has a meaning and the will to cooperate is taken for granted. Here is the secret of coordinating the effort of free people.

In the success of the atomic bomb project the United States has perhaps caught a new view of its titanic strength. It is a strength that comes when a compelling objective draws the coordinated effort of trained and educated citizens. Those who have shared in the atomic crusade are now insisting that this titanic strength be turned toward insuring the world's peace and toward giving the world's people a chance to share more fully in making their lives of value. Toward this great task mobilization of the atomic strength of the nation was but a step.

# 33. The Moral Meaning of the Atomic Bomb

## 1946

Christianity Takes a Stand was an appeal to the Christian community to examine its social tasks and responsibilities and to demonstrate its Christian concern in approaching the issues of the day. Prepared at the request of the Joint Commission on Social Reconstruction of the Protestant Episcopal Church, under the chairmanship of Bishop William Scarlett, the volume contained statements by a dozen leaders. Among them was this discussion of the morality of atomic weapons.

## I

Perhaps never was a group of ordinary citizens so conscious of the responsibility that goes with power as was the small group of scientists who in 1941 awoke to the realization that in their hands lay the key to the atomic bomb. One troubled young pacifist would rather have met death than take the life of another. But he saw that the life or death of civilization could well depend upon whether he personally carried through his laboratory assignment. He had longed to keep his conscience free from the burden of causing death to his fellow man. But could he face the thought that by his failure to do the task that God had distinctively taught him the whole world might lose its freedom?

A brilliant young Methodist, after turning in a report showing that in all probability the atomic chain reaction was feasible, resigned his work on atomic science because he foresaw its destructiveness. A year later when the world's safety lay in the balance, he returned to the task with full determination.

Influential within this little group was the Jew who had felt the merciless hand of the Nazis and knew that their control of the world would mean death and slavery. In his heart was the interest of world humanity. He shuddered at the devastation that must come from his atomic bombs. But greater was his dread lest the Nazis, with a year's head start, should win the fearful race to control the energy of the atom, and with its power become masters of the world.

Now with the bomb a reality, the war won, and the danger of fearful destruction before us if another war should come, the evil of the bomb becomes appalling. "Modern man is obsolete," Norman Cousins warns us, as he and many others point out the need for man's rapid growth in moral stature if he is to survive in the atomic age. Science has given us great new powers. Among these is the power to destroy. There is also the power to build and live. More effectively than ever before, we can do what we want. To that extent our knowledge of scientific truth has made us free. Now with unprecedented urgency life demands that we learn the great truth, how can we live at peace? It is by love, not by bombs, that we shall conquer the hate that breeds wars. But how shall we learn to love one another in time to prevent world disaster?

Gradually the world is becoming aware that at all costs another major war must be prevented. Just because it is so effective a weapon no major war can be fought without the atomic bomb, unless it should be replaced by something yet more deadly. The scientists have worked with missionary zeal to impress our country with the urgent need to outlaw war. The military men carefully analyze our defenses and report that neither our nation nor any other can go through an atomic war without suffering heavy casualties and widespread destruction. Those who have studied the problem are unanimous that our only adequate defense lies in political agreements that will prevent war while existing hates and differences are given time to cool.

Our nation now has great power. With that power comes the responsibility to protect the world from suicidal war. Here perhaps is our greatest moral obligation of the present day.

As believers in government by the people, we should work diligently toward placing in the hands of all the world the power and responsibility for peace. Until that can be done, however, our refusal to do our proper share in protecting the world, even to the extent of acting as police, would be as indefensible as would have been the failure of my pacifist friend in 1941 to do his vital part in developing the atomic bomb.

## II

As a basis for a discussion of the morals of war and the bomb, it will help to review some of the reasons why we place such high value on human life. The first law of life is the survival of the species. It is perhaps the acceptance of this fundamental biological requirement of survival that gives universal assent to the commandment, "Thou shalt not kill," while at the same time condoning killing that is done for the protection of one's own life or that of others.

Since we are concerned with estimating value rather than physical quantity, we must think of beings who can make value judgments, for without such beings the concept of value ceases to have meaning. Thus those who are judges of value are themselves the basis of value and become consequently the objects of supreme worth. Other things have worth only because they are needed for supporting the existence of those who are judges of value or because they are valued by these judges. To the humanist, therefore, the highest good consists in the development of human beings who are alive to those true values that bring satisfaction and who are able to work effectively toward achieving these values. Such persons, aware of the things of worth and able to progress toward their attainment, are those whom we should describe as *free*. It is thus the free person who, in the eyes of the humanist, is the object of greatest value. The good act consists in promoting the development of such free human beings. The evil act consists in interfering with their development.

There is a variant of these biological and humanistic approaches to morals which, while contrary to the Christian and democratic view, is nevertheless frequently used as a basis of action. According to this argument the highest good will be attained by developing a group of superior persons who would reach their full growth at the expense of the freedom or even the lives of other persons. With a view toward encouraging the growth of this superior group one could justify the elimination of those who would retard their development, as weeds would be cut from a garden. Other persons would be used as tools (slaves) to enable the select group to attain full development. This old idea of the aristocracy has been revived in the Nazi doctrine of the superrace, and in the Russian justification of maintaining the Communist Party by eliminating those who oppose their principles. It is also the ever present temptation, even in the democracy, of using the nation's resources to strengthen the group that is in power.

Opposed to this variant of humanism is the basic principle of all monotheistic religions that the one God is concerned with the welfare of all mankind. While different stations in life are recognized, such religions agree that according to God's law all persons should live as responsible human beings who can work with hope and faith for the best they know.

As interpreted by Christianity, human life has its high value because man is a child of God, made in his image and beloved of him. Man shares with his Father the responsibility for shaping the world and the lives of his fellow men. God, not man, is the supreme judge of values, and is thus the object of supreme devotion. But because God considers man of so great worth, our highest duty to God is to serve our neighbors. The true child of God understands and appreciates the things that make a good life, and enjoys working toward such a life for himself and his fellows. Such a person is in the Christian sense free. Promoting for all men such freedom thus becomes to the Christian perhaps the supreme goal of his life.

It is clear that this responsibility for promoting freedom begins at home. Parents will do their best to protect their children from harm and to provide them with health, practical education, and understanding of the principles of right living. This Christian parents will do because their children can thus become worthy children of God. Having learned the things that are worth working for, and having the health, knowledge, and means needed to make their efforts effective, they can share fully the joy of working with their Heavenly Father in striving to shape a better world.

To the Roman world it came as a surprise that one's neighbor might be a Samaritan passing by on the road to Jericho. In the modern world our dependence on all nations for the articles of trade, no less than our ability with armadas of planes and atomic bombs to take decisive military action anywhere, means that the world is a single community and that everyone in it can be our neighbor.

It is such considerations that make it a matter of deep concern to Americans when a militaristic group usurps the government of Germany, murders the Jews who seem to be in their way, and starts a military campaign whose evident objective is reducing Europe and eventually perhaps the rest of the world to the status of vassal states whose citizens are to be denied the freedom familiar in civilized society. As freedom is lost, so also are the greatest values of life. In 1941 Europe needed our help to protect her from the tyrant threat. Where did our Christian duty lie?

There were those who said in all sincerity, "Thou shalt not kill." "If thine enemy smite thee upon one cheek, turn unto him the other." Let us do what we can by the power of persuasion and leave to our God the outcome. There were also those who remembered that when the Roman soldier asked what he should do, Jesus replied, "Exact from no one more than thy due," but said no word against his profession as a soldier. They remembered that he who would find his life must lose it in something worth more than life. Was not the freedom of the world worth more than one's own life?

Thus many Christians had made their choice or were ready to make it before the Japanese struck at Pearl Harbor. It was a choice that was as difficult for the clergy as for the laymen. After World War I many ministers felt that they had been misled into sponsoring a war of no basic moral significance. Were they being misled again by dispensers of propaganda? It was primarily the Christian laymen, many of them in high office, who saw clearly that their neighbors needed protection which only America could give, and that if we failed freedom was gone. The world was threatened with a life in which for many generations it would be impossible for most persons to grow to the full stature worthy of children of God.

When Pearl Harbor came, the nation saw that fighting to victory was the price we must pay if we were to remain a free nation. Some had questioned whether freedom was worth fighting for. These were those who felt that no tyranny would be worse than the "economic slavery" under which they felt they were laboring. But never did the freedom that our country enjoys seem so precious as when we were threatened with its loss. Perhaps never before in our nation's history did a war receive such general support. Young men were willingly giving their lives to a worthy cause. Loyally, if somewhat reluctantly, the churches of the nation heartened them with personal Godspeeds. Many church leaders, having weathered their own personal struggles, gave full support to those who were engaged upon their life's greatest venture in sacrificial service for their fellows.

### III

The morality of the atomic bomb is identical with the morality of war. War is nasty, brutal, and the inspirer of lasting fear and hate. It is an evil, whose elimination is a major goal of Christendom. Yet to avoid war should one sacrifice that which makes life itself of value, freedom to combat evil and to work for what one deems right, the opportunity of a world to seek after God? Should one, for fear of committing the sin of killing, permit one's neighbors to be enslaved or killed by a ruthless conqueror? Most Americans freely chose war with all its agony and evil rather than have their consciences bear the burden of refusing to share in protecting the world against greater disaster.

Having accepted war as the lesser evil, one seeks appropriate principles on which to base one's military actions. The primary objective of warfare among civilized nations is not, as is frequently supposed, to destroy the enemy. It is rather to destroy the enemy's will to resist, with minimum loss to one's own nation and no more damage to the enemy than necessary. No civilized army considers revenge as its function. Its task is to bring about the willingness of the enemy to accept the terms which the political heads of its nation wish to impose. Destruction of the enemy and his facilities beyond that necessary to destroy the will to resist only reduces the value of conquered territory and increases the difficulty of reorganization after the war is over. To the United States the prime national asset which our armed forces strove to preserve was American lives. We can properly be proud of our effort in this direction, of which a crude measure is the more than a million dollars spent in preparing for and conducting the war for each member of our armed forces who died.

Ordinarily the most effective way to destroy a warring enemy's will to resist is to destroy his fighting power. Experience indicates that a policy of frightfulness and wanton destruction, except as it disrupts internal operations, is more apt to strengthen than to weaken a nation's will to resist. It is noteworthy, however, that in modern warfare the source of fighting power is to a large extent located in the factories and railroads spread throughout the country. This means that the easiest way of destroying fighting power may be to destroy the cities and factories that produce the arms.

As an example, in large areas of Tokyo that were destroyed by fire from incendiary bombs, the chief monuments standing among the ashes of the wooden houses were the lathes, drill presses, and other machine tools that had been used for the phantom industry that supplied Japan's weapons. The loss of this industry was a significant factor in the weakening of her will to resist.

In previous wars much was made of the heinousness of waging war on noncombatants. Have our consciences merely become dulled as we, whose home territory has not been hit, found it good military strategy to bomb enemy cities? Perhaps we are too close to the war to answer that question fairly. The fact is, however, that the conditions of war have radically changed. No longer can an army, even when spread over a fighting front, protect the territory in its rear. Airplanes and rockets are not stopped by such lines. Moreover, the industrialization of modern war has made the territory in the rear vastly more significant as a military objective. Nor is it clear why the boy who is sent to the front to fight through no choice of his own should be considered a fair target while the political leaders and the voters who sent him remain inviolate.

The atomic bomb is simply a cheap and easy way of producing the destruction which had previously come from other weapons. The damage done to Tokyo by standard-type bombs was greater than that done to Hiroshima or Nagasaki, and the number of people killed was roughly the same. The difference is that one airplane armed with atomic bombs can inflict damage that required from a hundred to a thousand planes armed with the usual incendiary or explosive bombs. In the two cases where the atomic bomb was used there was also a somewhat greater ratio of casualties to material damage.

As contrasted with poison gas, the poisoning of water and food supply, and most forms of biological warfare, the atomic bomb is designed primarily toward effecting material rather than human destruction. It produces effects also which are of short duration and confined to the region of the target. It is the engineers' answer to the demand for a more destructive weapon that retains considerable discrimination in its area of destruction.

The very striking effect of the atomic bomb on our ideas regarding future war comes from its great destructiveness. If a prolonged war should arise, there can be no doubt that mutual suspicion will make it necessary for the antagonists to build and use atomic weapons. The amount of destruction resulting on any nation from an all-out attack by an enemy using atomic bombs would be far greater than that suffered by Germany and Japan in World War II. Military men advise that they find no means of protecting even the victor against such destruction.

A nation's leader will accordingly find difficulty in justifying such destruction in his own country by any possible advantage that may come from victory. In spite of Hiroshima and Nagasaki and Bikini, however, the world does not yet realize the full import of an atomic war. It is inconceivable that after a major war fought with atomic weapons people will permit war's recurrence as has happened in the past. Largely because of such enormously destructive weapons as the bomb, the world is already trying determinedly to find a way to prevent any more war. As never before in this world's history we are thus justified in looking ahead to the time when we can safely lay our plans on the assumption that wars will not come again. Would that this day of assurance were already here!

## IV

We thus arrive at the following conclusions, on the basis of which we may approach the questions raised by the birth of atomic energy.

> (a) The good world which the Christian should seek is that in which everyone can share in making the life of all worthwhile. This is the world of greatest freedom, freedom for people to become the children of God.

> (b) War, while itself an evil thing, must be accepted and waged with determination when the alternative is the loss of values which

one considers more important than the lives that will be lost. The Christian has always recognized the existence of such supreme values. Prominent among these is the right of all men to freedom as described above.

(c) The enormous destructiveness of the atomic bomb makes it doubtful whether an occasion will again arise in which even a defensive war will promote rather than retard the growth of human values. This gives greatly increased incentive to find a way by which war cannot again occur.

## V

Let us then review briefly the moral problems faced by the scientists who first knew the atomic bomb could be made. Their judgment was supported by those at Washington, including the President, into whose hands the nation had placed the responsibility for its defense. As long as they felt that the world's freedom depended on the speed of their development of the new atomic weapon, the scientists were unanimous in their determination to complete the task and thus if possible to bring victory. It is difficult to see any other attitude that they in good conscience could have taken.

After V-E Day it became evident that we should ourselves not be attacked by atomic weapons. In all probability victory over Japan was a straightforward matter of hard fighting and time, with the anticipated loss, however, of at least a half-million American lives. Development of the atomic bomb was now so far along also that unless work then in hand were stopped it would soon be ready for military use.

Now the scientists were of divided opinions. While the decisions were by this time out of their hands, President Truman sought their advice as well as that of the War Department before making his fateful decision to use the bomb against Japan. Some few endeavored earnestly to prevent the bomb's being used.* They felt our national honor demanded that we avoid the development of international fears and hates, and the responsibility for the killing of thousands of innocent people. The greater number, however, favored essentially the procedure that was followed. They hoped but could not be sure that the advent of the atomic bomb would retard rather than stimulate future wars. They knew it would help to win the present war quickly and with a great net saving of life both to ourselves and our enemies.

It is yet too early to say whether the moral historian, if there be one a thousand years hence, will record the use of the atomic bomb as the work of the world's guardian angel or as that of the devil bent on man's destruction. Under the cruel conditions imposed by war, recognition that withholding the bomb would mean in all probability the death of more millions of people and the extension of war's agony for perhaps another year made the choice to blot out two cities seem the lesser evil.

Now we are asked to destroy our atomic weapons and renounce atomic warfare. The Americans who make this demand believe that peace agreements can be maintained only in an atmosphere of confidence, and that possession of atomic weapons will prevent trust in us by other nations. It would be easy on the other hand to interpret the Russian demand for immediate destruction of all atomic arms as an attempt to bring about a unilateral disarmament. The fact is that our atomic bombs are the world's only balance to the tremendous military power of Russia.

Unfortunately, experience has shown that it requires generations for international hates to be removed even by true friendliness. In the meantime the world must find a way to survive in spite of antagonisms. While working toward international goodwill, we know of no way to avoid war in an unfriendly world other than by establishing police with authority and power to enforce the laws to which the nations express agreement.

It is notable that for the first time in history it is now possible to equip a world police with weapons by which war can be prevented and peace assured. An adequate air force equipped with atomic bombs, well dispersed over the earth, should suffice. No power would be likely to force a war if international police thus armed were prepared to punish their action. Thus it is possible that the atomic bomb may become the means whereby wars can now be prevented and peace with freedom be assured.

By virtue of its atomic bombs the United States can now control the peace of the world. This is true whether we wish it so or not. But with this power, we have a corresponding obligation. The real moral question is, do we have the right to divest ourselves of that power?

The answer seems clear. We should help the world set up a competent agency of its own choice with power and authority to prevent war. This we are now trying to do. Then, but not until then, can we in fairness to the world relieve ourselves of the burden of our own atomic weapons.

If we really believe that future wars must be prevented, we must work quickly. Our monopoly of atomic bombs and control of the world's peace is short-lived. It is our duty to do our utmost to effect the establishment of an adequate world police before peace can be threatened by others who will develop similarly destructive weapons. This is the obligation that goes with the power God has seen fit to give us.

## VI

The moral implications of atomic energy, however, go far beyond the problem of war. The wise use of this great new power in peace as well as in war requires corresponding advance in human justice, sympathy, and understanding. The power of the atom demands the moral growth of man in order that he shall survive. This is another way of saying that those who will survive will be of greater moral stature.

The development of atomic energy thus stimulates further the process of human development which science has long been encouraging. Science and technology are making of society a group of specialists, whose strength and survival depend upon cooperation. The society based on science demands technical knowledge and increased familiarity with human relations, that is, training and education. But above all, the society shaped by growing science requires formulating adequate objectives. Only as such objectives are understood and accepted as worthy of concerted effort can cooperation be secured among free people. But these are the human characteristics that we most cherish: the love of one's neighbor as expressed in the spirit of cooperation, increased knowledge and understanding, and the choice of worthy goals.

All of these trends are illustrated by the atomic program. Perhaps never has more extensive and complete cooperation been achieved among such widely varied groups as in the gigantic task of making the atomic bomb. Scientific specialists of a thousand types, engineers, managers, labor, skilled mechanics, construction crews, secretaries, Army and Navy, whites and Negroes, Americans and Europeans: all worked in harmony. Many differences arose, but the desire to work together was there. All were intent on completing the job, and differences were set aside in the interest of attaining the common goal. Thorough knowledge by many people also was needed. Only by the help of the best physicists, chemists, and biologists could the complex new problems be solved. Only the most experienced industrial organizations could be relied upon to build and operate the plants. Managers familiar with meeting human needs were required to set up and operate the mushroom villages. Our most competent administrators were called on to coordinate the various activities so as to bring a completed product ready to use on time.

It was the stimulus of a world struggle for freedom that called for the devotion of the hundreds of thousands of faithful toilers needed to build the bombs. The goal was a victory that would be the basis for a lasting peace. Now that the war is over, the first great goal is to prevent another war. The longer-distance objective of the atomic scientists is to use atomic energy to enrich the life of man. Thus already in the effort to find and use atomic energy we have learned better how to cooperate, we have seen the importance of technical and humanistic knowledge, and we have experienced the stimulus of a goal that is greater than selfish interests.

James Breasted, Chicago's late great Egyptologist, gave 3000 B.C. as the approximate date of the "dawn of conscience," when man first recognized that he was his brother's keeper. It may be doubted whether the occasion can be precisely dated. But at some period in his evolution man learned that he could shape his world to his needs, and he felt responsible for improving the lot of his fellows. Before that time the Creator of the universe held in his own hands the full burden of the development of the life on this planet. If there was any purpose in that marvelous development, that purpose was his alone. From then on his human creatures became his partners, sharing with him the great task of making life what they wanted it to be. Two thousand years ago the Son of Man could say, "My Father worketh to this end, and I work." With the gradual growth of knowledge and skills, more and more of the responsibility is being shifted to man's shoulders. The ability to use the cosmic energy of the atom for good or ill marks one further step in this transfer of authority to man.

When the man and the woman wished to return to the garden of innocence, an angel with a fiery sword blocked the way. They had eaten the fruit of the tree of knowledge, and as the serpent had promised, became "as gods, knowing good from evil." But this knowledge was a heavy burden. Their only peace lay in plowing the fields and in working to make their world as they felt it should be. Much as they longed to be free of the knowledge of good and evil, the way was blocked. Yet somehow, in their struggle to help each other in their common tasks, they found that God accepted them as his children.

If we long to return to a pre-Atomic Age, the same angel with the fiery sword blocks our path. Atomic power is ours, and who can deny that it was God's will that we should have it? As we struggle with the task of using this new power for the good of man, inevitably there must result a growth of the human spirit.

# 34. Nuclear Energy
## and the Growth of Man

## *1957*

The Atoms for Peace awards were established by the Ford Motor Company Fund to honor those judged to have contributed most to the peaceful uses of atomic energy. Niels Bohr, the noted Danish physicist, received the first award in a ceremony held at the National Academy of Sciences in Washington, D.C., on October 24, 1957. On that occasion the author was invited to discuss the human implications of nuclear energy. He stressed the necessity of formulating our national policy in a manner that will inspire worldwide cooperation in the cause of humanity.

In accord with the intent of the founders in establishing the Atoms for Peace award, I have been invited to speak about the broader human implications of the energy of the atomic nucleus. This I am pleased to do, especially before this distinguished and influential audience, and in the presence of our honored guest who has himself held this subject close to his heart.

It is appropriate that we should meet today in this building dedicated to science as it fosters man's human growth. Around the base of the dome that rises above us appear these words:

> *To science, pilot of industry, conqueror of disease, multiplier of the harvest, explorer of the universe, revealer of nature's laws, eternal guide to truth.*

Here is faithfully recorded the ardent hope of every man of science, that he may share in opening to all persons everywhere the way to more complete manhood.

My prime concern today is the urgency that nuclear energy gives to worldwide cooperation in the cause of humanity. It is toward such cooperation that we must now look for the growth of man.

In the program of "atoms for peace," emphasis has been laid on the usefulness of the energy of the nucleus. This is as it should be. We are using this energy, in the form of radiation, for diagnosis and for the healing of disease. We are using isotopes as tools in science and industry. With the important steps already made, we see electric power from nuclear furnaces ready to meet a great human need for a long time to come.

Consider as an example the use of nuclear radiations in the art of healing. Such use began with the discovery of X rays and radium about sixty years ago. Estimates have been made of the effectiveness of these rays in diagnosis and therapy. These estimates are necessarily only approximate. But they do show this—that by the use of these rays throughout the world some tens of millions of lives have been saved. This is roughly the number of lives destroyed in all the world's wars since the time of their discovery. In this way alone our concern with atoms and nuclei has opened to a vast multitude of men and women more complete physical health and life.

But, important as it is, here is not our prime point of emphasis when we think of nuclear energy and the growth of man.

The prime point is rather this: Science and technology have provided us with unprecedented new powers. We are acutely aware that these powers can bring us either greater opportunity or destruction and death. In this regard, nuclear energy is only one dramatic example of the new possibilities that science holds before us, possibilities for good or ill in truly startling measure. And the rate at which science is presenting man with these unprecedented powers is increasing at phenomenal speed. Furthermore, each such technical development multiplies the effectiveness of those that went before. This is a condition similar to that recognized in science as dynamic instability. We must expect the balance of world power to be continually shifting as new technical advances, occurring in different parts of the world, make more effective the use of the strength already in men's hands. The stability of civilization itself is at stake.

Immersed in the immediate task of protecting freedom, we must not fail to look to the future. For a limited period we may prevent war by keeping a strong and alert defense. And never was such defense needed more than today. But to bring stability among sovereign nations only one way is open. The nations must be united by some human goal worthy of their strength. There is no other hope for a peace that will endure.

A great vitality shows itself in the world's scientific and technological advances. Our danger is lest our technological rivalries be aimed toward destruction or toward establishment of tyrannical rule. Our safety and welfare lie in directing this rapidly developing strength toward the human growth of man. The time when we need the assurance of the human use of technical strength is now. We must not wait. Every day that we delay constitutes a statistically significant lessening of mankind's chance for survival.

I am not exaggerating. The seriousness of the dangers and the greatness of the corresponding opportunities are evident to all who have examined the changing situation of man.

What can be done that man's newfound strength will be used for building and strengthening our civilization? This is the all-important question.

As I see it, there is only one acceptable answer. If cooperation is to replace antagonism among nations, it will come only as they agree upon some common objective that will inspire the wholehearted support of their people. Such an objective cannot be one that places the interests of one nation above those of another. To be affirmed by all nations it must relate to the needs of all men and women.

There exists such an objective that during the past half century has arisen throughout the world as a hope in the hearts of men. In the United States we have known this hope since before our nation was founded. We call it the "American dream." Our vision is of a place where every man and every woman can grow to the best that is in them and where they are recognized for what they are and what they do to help others share this opportunity. Some years ago I showed to Mme. Pandit a description of this vision as written by our late historian James Truslow Adams.* "You call that the American dream!" she exclaimed. "It has become the dream of all the world."

Let us examine the answer to our central question that this dream suggests. To state that answer specifically, it is this. Let every nation affirm, as basic to its policy, the following principle:

> This nation will do all in its power toward opening the way for everyone under its jurisdiction to grow to his full human stature, and will cooperate with nations affirming and adhering to this principle in helping each other provide such opportunity for their people.
>
> In accord with this principle, each nation that thus commits itself will indeavor to direct its own actions so as not to interfere with those of other cooperating nations in their efforts on behalf of their people. It will consult in advance before taking action that might affect adversely the plans to this end of another cooperating nation. It will join

with other such nations in defense against threats to any of them regarding its internal actions on behalf of its citizens.

The intent of the proposal is to turn the world's resources toward enabling men and women to become competent and responsible citizens of their respective nations. Each nation sharing this objective retains the sovereign right to choose its own method for providing its citizens with increased opportunity. Each can also count on the help of the others in providing and defending these opportunities.

Can a government, whose prime responsibility is the safety and welfare of its citizens, agree to a policy that has in it so much of altruistic content?

In answer we note that every nation's safety and welfare requires assurance of cooperation by other nations. On no lesser objective than opening the way for all men and women to grow more fully can one nation expect to win the cooperation of other nations that are free. With acceptance of this objective as the alternative to national advantage, both the safety and the well-being of a nation's citizens will be as firmly assured as is possible under present world conditions.

Powerful support of such a policy can be counted on. Thus a nation's leaders must recognize that only as its citizens grow in health and understanding and have their heart in its objectives can the nation's strength be fully realized. Such growth is, however, at its best only through cooperation on an international as well as a national level.

Every organization to which men look for inspiration is concerned that each person shall have open to him a life of meaning. Whether one's first loyalty is to his eternal God, or to the principle of right dealing with his fellows, or to his system of government, the highest expression of that loyalty lies in promoting the health and human growth of men and women. Commitment to such a great human goal is precisely what is needed to give incentive to a person's best effort and meaning to his life.

To an increasing degree, society is giving its rewards to those who are opening new opportunities that all can enjoy. The Atoms for Peace award that is inaugurated today is an example of this trend in public acclaim. Both economic pressures and public opinion are encouraging every effort that would provide men and women with wider opportunities for growth as human beings.

In the autumn of 1945, Niels Bohr made an appointment to talk with me as we were journeying together toward Washington. Six months earlier, at Los Alamos, we had spent hours discussing how use of the atomic bomb, newly developed but not yet tried, might be turned toward establishing a harmonious and enduring peace. Following these discussions, one great question was now on his mind. "Is it not possible," he asked, "for the United States to perform some great moral act that will give hope to the world?" I suggested an action similar to what became the Marshall Plan, of economic help to the nations where help was needed. "Good," was his answer, "but this is not the basic thing we need." In our discussion we failed to pinpoint the "great moral act by our nation" that could accomplish what Bohr had in mind. Perhaps the time was not yet ripe.*

The experiences of the last decade have opened our eyes. The American dream has come to be recognized as the dream of the world. This dream must now take firm shape as the world's united, all-compelling purpose.

The era of nuclear power began fifteen years ago as a result of unprecedented international cooperation. Those whose efforts were responsible for the birth of the era were inspired by the hope that this newfound power would bring fuller life to all mankind. The Atoms for Peace award is a symbol that the citizens of our nation share and cherish this hope. Niels Bohr, whom we are honoring, has called on America to lead the world in another great cooperative venture. As I see it, this venture is that of committing the united efforts of the nations to the human growth of man. If in earnest we undertake to direct our own nation's prime efforts to this end, if we can bring the world to use thus the full powers of science and technology, the bright hopes inspired by nuclear energy will bear their full fruit.

Let us, the United States of America, proclaim boldly that what in our hearts has long been a cherished dream is henceforth the firmly established cornerstone of our national policy. Let us call on all nations to share this policy with us, that the world may work as one toward giving every man and every woman the opportunity to grow to their full human stature. Let us put our policy into practice by assuring all nations who will share this commitment that we will counsel with them regarding our proposed actions of international concern, and will cooperate with them in providing their people and ours with the means for healthy growth.

With such leadership, in our present anxious world, we can count confidently on a strong following. We may hope that our first steps will bring cooperation on an ever broader basis. It is a reasonable expectation that antagonisms will thus gradually be displaced by mutual confidence, and that peace based on harmony will grow.

No, competition and rivalry will not decline, but they will have a new spirit. As the dream of the world is transformed into one united purpose, men and nations will seek to outdo each other in advancing the human worth of man. Because life then takes on meaning our civilization itself will stir with new strength.

With such powers as nuclear energy in our hands, the need for affirming this united purpose is immediate, and is vital to man's welfare. Failure by the United States to make this commitment and to call on all nations to do likewise will leave the world in jeopardy. Acceptance of this leadership will give new hope. It will put new life into the world. If we are unwilling to take the lead, to whom shall we look?

# VIII

## The Struggle
## for Peace

Two contrary laws seem to be struggling with each other nowadays: the one a law of blood and death, ever imagining new means of destruction and forcing nations to be constantly ready for the battlefield; and the other, a law of peace, work, and health, ever evolving new means for delivering man from the scourges that beset him.

. . .

It is my invincible belief that science and peace will triumph over ignorance and war, that nations will eventually unite not to destroy but to build, and that the future will belong to those who will have done most for suffering humanity.

LOUIS PASTEUR

# 35. Science in the Program of Unesco

## *1947*

❧ A delegate to the first general session of Unesco, which opened in Paris in November 1946, the author was the only scientist in the United States delegation. Upon his return, he submitted a confidential report to the Secretary of State and later gave this address before the spring meeting of the American Philosophical Society, on March 25, 1947.

The United Nations Educational, Scientific, and Cultural Organization, whose opening session I had the privilege of attending as an American delegate, met last November and December at Paris. Its purpose had already been defined in its constitution written and ratified by the member nations during the previous year. This purpose is "to contribute to peace and security by promoting collaboration among the nations through education, science and culture in order to further universal respect for justice, for the rule of law and for the human rights and fundamental freedoms which are affirmed for the peoples of the world . . . by the Charter of the United Nations." More briefly, it is "to educate for peace." [1]

The first task before the assembly at Paris was to agree upon what they meant by the "peace" for which they were to work. An accurate and inspiring definition, drafted by the American delegation, was accepted and written into the organization's program. " 'Peace' in this context," so goes this statement, "means something more than a mere absence of overt hostilities. It means a condition of solidarity, harmony of purpose and coordination of activities in which free men and women can live a secure and satisfactory life—a condition in which war is affirmatively prevented by the dynamic and purposeful creation of a decent and human relationship between the peoples of the world—a condition in which the incentives

[1] Article I, Constitution of the United Nations Educational, Scientific, and Cultural Organization, adopted in London on November 16, 1945.

to war are neutralized by the social, spiritual and economic advances created and achieved." [2]

In bringing such peace into being, science can play a distinctive part. This is chiefly because a scientist is, as a scientist, essentially a citizen of the world and concerned with matters that affect not nations but the entire human race. A scientist uses ideas that have originated and have been developed in all parts of the world. His discoveries are not of distinctive interest to his own nation or race or creed. They are more likely to be the active subject of discussion by some colleague across the sea than by his next-door neighbor.

In this regard the scientist is sharply distinguished from the military man or the man of business. The businessman's interests are bounded by his market. Usually this is concentrated near his home. With the modern developments of technology and specialization, the markets for major industries extend more widely and become international, but usually the nearer markets are those of greater concern. The military man has taken an oath to defend his country. He is trained to consider its interests as his own interests. He would serve humanity through the agency of his own nation.

If it is thus true that the world of thought in which the scientist lives is international, it is likewise true that the contributions of the scientist's studies are welcome to all nations. In this regard, even among scholars he finds himself in a unique position. A British historian's version of the War of 1812 is hardly welcome to the board of education of an American city. The Frenchman is wary of accepting American educational techniques. But a discovery in the chemistry of synthetic rubber made by a Russian will be learned and used as readily by American chemists and industrialists as will a similar discovery made in an American university.

Thus it is that scientists have become in a distinctive sense citizens of the world. They are the first fruits of the social trend that is making all groups of people dependent upon other groups who live far away. They are those who understand best the thinking of their opposite numbers in other nations. They are thus in a good position to interpret reliably to their compatriots the thinking and attitudes of those in other nations.

This world consciousness of the scientist arises simply from the fact that the intellectual world in which he lives has no relation to political or racial boundaries. But there is the added fact that as a normal part of his professional activities the scientist is more accustomed to foreign travel than are most persons of comparable economic status. This is partly

[2] Unesco, General Conference, First Session, Document Unesco/C/ 30, p. 219.

because it usually happens that those with whom he can most profitably discuss his problems live in some other part of the world. It frequently occurs also that the scientific studies themselves can best be done in remote regions, as in the case of eclipse expeditions, or geological or cosmic-ray studies, or work with endemic diseases, or work in primitive anthropology. Frequently such studies also can most profitably be carried out in association with scientists of other nations.

The result of many such factors is that, to a degree difficult for many to understand, the scientist's interests are global. A national government appears to him of value only as it serves as a convenient administrative unit in the general task of coordinating and facilitating the common efforts of groups of people toward the good of all. It was in fact because they saw the United States as an effective administrative unit thus working for human welfare that so many foreign scientists were glad to work for us during the recent war.

Thus it is that science education is education for peace, and scientists can perform a unique service in establishing useful and friendly contacts between nations whose other citizens may be viewed with mutual suspicion.

Another powerful method whereby science is working toward peace is that of forcing the changes in world society that are making nations more dependent upon each other. The effect of this increasing interdependence is to make the preservation of peace more desirable and the outbreak of war more positively to be avoided. With the rapid march of science and technology, this trend is proceeding with great and increasing speed.

Many factors contribute to this ever widening interdependence. Among them are easy travel, rapid communication, large industries that demand immense plants and extensive organizations to do their work and require correspondingly widespread markets for their product, need for raw materials available in only a few locations, wider education, and more detailed specialization of skills. The growth of all these factors is a consequence of the advances of science.

It is only as the need for maintaining our worldwide ties becomes recognized that we can expect the world to want a planetary government that will ensure the peace. My point is that it is because of the powers that science is giving us that we are thus rapidly becoming a planetary community in which we see clearly the need for keeping a peaceful adjustment of our relationships.

There is also the negative side of this trend to be considered. Owing to scientific and technical developments, war has now become so dangerous that the provocation must indeed be great before a major war will be undertaken. No longer can military defense be assured against an enemy's armada of airplanes, rocket-propelled missiles, atomic bombs, and biological destruction of food supplies. The result, owing in large measure to the advance of science and its applications, is that war is becoming harmful even to the potentially victorious aggressor, and peaceful adjustment among nations is thus becoming more important to the welfare and survival of even the most powerful of their peoples.

I believe that careful consideration will show the correctness of the statement that the growth of science becomes perhaps the most potent force at work toward making men want to keep their activities in harmonious adjustment.

The obvious way to peace is thus to accelerate this trend toward the importance of peace and to encourage the growth of world-mindedness. Both results are accomplished by stimulating the worldwide growth of science.

On my way to Paris, I stopped at Oxford to visit Lord Lindsay, Master of Balliol College, philosopher-statesman, and leader of British educational thought. I asked him what Unesco could do. He gave me a copy of a carefully prepared address whose theme was: push science ahead with full vigor. It is our best hope to gain a stable world. The scientists are the natural world citizens, he said. They must be given a chance to shape both the thinking of mankind and the organization of society. If Unesco can encourage the strong development of science throughout the world, this will be its surest method of accomplishing its goal of peace. Coming from a thoughtful student of the Greek classics and of political principles, this was a strong word indeed.

This important place of science in the task of Unesco was recognized also by its representation in most of the major national delegations at Paris. Such influential countries as Britain, Brazil, China, France, India, and Mexico had a total of fourteen out of forty-one, or 34 per cent of their delegates representing science. Science is the one field in which Russia has shown a clear desire to cooperate.

Only in the United States delegation was the representation of science meager. Only one out of ten of our delegates represented science. That one delegate was given good support by his colleagues, and the American position regarding science fared well. But here is the part of Unesco's work in which American efforts can be of most distinctive effectiveness, and much stronger representation is needed.

Thanks in large measure to the excellent preparatory work of Joseph Needham, chairman of the Science Division of the Preparatory Commission, a strong program of science activities [3] by Unesco was agreed upon. The major items are: (a) rehabilitation of science education in devastated countries, (b) international interchange and conferences of scientists and technologists, and (c) promotion of research programs of international concern.

This science work is only a fraction of the total program of Unesco. Other major fields of activity include fundamental education, revision of teaching materials, use of methods of mass education such as radio, films, the press, public libraries, etc., also social science, the fine arts, and philosophy. Actually the budget for science activities represents about 20 per cent of that available for all such direct objectives.* Recent word from Paris indicates that the science program is in general off to a good start.

It is not difficult to understand why the concern with the international development of science and technology is so universal. Such knowledge is necessary in order that a nation may share the economic life of the modern world. This applies equally to the industrially backward and the industrially advanced nations. Russia's rise to power would not have been possible without her emphasis on technological growth, and her example is clearly seen by nations in which technology is as yet undeveloped. Industry in the United States is keenly aware of its need for more new scientific knowledge, for which for generations it has looked to Europe. Because science and its applications have thus become so important to the economy of all peoples, education and research in these fields are an immediate major concern of every nation. That the people of the nations are thinking of science and technology in international terms is shown by the roughly hundred thousand foreign students now wanting admission to American schools, and chiefly for studies in the field of science.

The United States will gain from the science program no less than other countries. First of all, we have an enormous stake in preserving the peace, and this program should contribute its share to that end. But also the revival of science in countries where it has previously flourished is perhaps our best method of raising the level of world science which supplies the new information that our own advancing industries must use. Recent illustrations of our demands on this world pool of scientific information are the American developments of radar, atomic energy, fluorescent lighting, penicillin, and DDT, in all of which the basic scientific work originated

[3] The science program is described in detail in literature prepared by the State Department and in an article by W. A. Noyes in a recent number of *Chemical and Engineering News*, XXV:294 (February 3, 1947). Roughly a hundred projects are included for attention.

mostly outside the United States. Scientists who come to our country for study or teaching can be counted on to develop more friendly attitudes and to carry with them active interest in using American products. Immediately their own countries become more interested in the advancing prosperity of our nation. Our scientists going abroad bring back ideas and skills which are useful in the development of our own science and technology. By working with scientists in other countries on problems of world concern with regard to health, nutrition, technology, or basic understanding of nature, there is developed the group of world-minded American citizens through whom valuable contacts with other nations can be maintained.

It is necessary for Unesco to start its work in fields which are welcomed by all nations and which lead demonstrably toward a peaceful adjustment of world society. This is the favored position of science and its applications. Other parts of Unesco's program present difficulties because the influence of one nation is unwelcome or subject to suspicion in others. This applies in greater or less degree to the moving pictures, radio programs, novel methods of education, censoring of information, religious and philosophical thought, and even some types of art. Such difficulties are rare in the field of science.

The world knows we stand foremost in the applications of science to human living. They see the pattern of life that is developing in America becoming the pattern for the world. They urgently want to fit themselves into this pattern. We may properly hope that our nation's great contribution to civilization will ultimately be as a guide to living the good life in a society based on technology. Just now, however, American science and technology are the most distinctive contributions we can make to world culture. Here is the need that the world at this time most universally feels. It is the need that the United States is in the leading position to meet.

Our national participation in world science does not need to be through Unesco. Spontaneous international scientific activities of many kinds exist and are effective. Unesco, however, offers the best medium that has yet appeared for intellectual cooperation with other nations. It offers a unique opportunity for the promotion of peace through the advancement of science. Science in Unesco deserves the best support our nation can give.

# 36. How Peace with the Hydrogen Bomb?

## 1954

Widespread anxiety and uncertainty resulted from the hydrogen weapons tests conducted in the Pacific during the spring of 1954 and the injuries to a group of Japanese fishermen caught in the test area.* Mr. Compton was traveling in Asia at the time and prepared this statement in response to a request from International News Service.

How can we win peace when nations are building hydrogen bombs?

As I see it, there are three things that are needed: (1) a reliable anti-war agreement; (2) interim military preparedness; and (3) education for mutual understanding.

I believe that the world situation is more favorable for meeting these conditions than at any previous time in history. If these conditions are met, we may expect hot competitive encounters and tough-minded struggle but ultimately enduring peace with freedom.

First, we must work as rapidly as possible toward a reliable agreement among the major powers. This agreement should limit military operations to police actions aimed toward preserving international order. Second, until such an agreement is reached, as many free nations as will unite must let others know that military action against their clearly defined vital interests will be met by appropriate military resistance. The third condition is the most important for bringing peace that will endure. It is that every nation shall actively educate its citizens to the vital need for cooperation among its component groups and between nation and nation.

That the hydrogen bomb would be built became evident when it was clear that no international agreement regarding atomic bombs would be reached.

Before the close of World War II the physicists of both the free world and the Soviet Union were aware that the basic principles of this device were known to each other. In the United States there was great reluctance to embark upon its development. The chief reason for this reluctance was the moral one: Would it not be better to accept conditions imposed by a foreign power than to perpetrate the holocaust that the use of such a bomb would imply?

There were other reasons. Already the atomic bomb was more widely destructive than military men wanted. The accepted objective of war is not to destroy but to overcome the enemy's will to resist. And a war waged with hydrogen bombs would create such destruction that even the victor would find himself in a chaotic shambles, probably in a worse position than with a negotiated peace that would amount to surrender.

And then there was the danger of a strongly unfavorable reaction from the rest of the world. Would anyone believe that a nation would develop such a weapon if its use were not contemplated? And could a nation be trusted that would contemplate its use? What about such a nation's attitude toward the value of human life? Would not development and testing of a hydrogen bomb be taken as adequate evidence that such a nation was preparing for ruthless domination of the world? Might not fears and distrust be aroused that would turn the entire world against such a nation, with results that in the end could only mean disaster?

Yet the experience of a century with technological invention has shown that nothing of importance that people know how to do can long be held back by mutual agreement. Someone, somewhere, always goes ahead with its development. And in this case the stakes were large, the rivalry intense. With the long tradition of Russian expansion and the recent examples of Poland and Czechoslovakia, could the free world afford to let the Soviet move into a position of military dominance?

The course of events had placed the United States in a position where only she could act in this regard on behalf of the free world. There had been real hope that some reliable agreement regarding atomic weapons could be reached with the Russians. By 1949 such hope had dwindled to the vanishing point. This could only mean that the Russians were themselves engaged in their atomic development with the hope of gaining superiority. In the autumn of 1949 this deduction was strikingly confirmed by the explosion of Russia's first atomic bomb. Could the free world permit them to achieve this dominance? The prevailing American opinion, reached after much heart searching, was no.

It was the responsibility of the only free nation that could match the weapons development of the Russians to see that an appropriate answer was ready. Otherwise the world would be at the mercy of the Soviet.

From what had happened to the nations that let themselves fall into that position, it was evident that such a possibility must be avoided. Hence the decision to proceed with the development of the hydrogen weapon, even though it was fully expected and ardently hoped that occasion would never arise when it would be used in war. I myself see no other conclusion to which men responsible for the world's safety could have come.

Yet the dangers foreseen by those who argued against the development of the hydrogen bomb are real. The shocked reaction of many people in every nation at the news of the effects of the hydrogen explosions in the Pacific has only emphasized these dangers.

I have recently been in Japan. Her people are sensitive to everything connected with atomic destruction. The conditions were ripe for the hysteria that followed the report of injuries to their fishermen from the recent H-bomb tests. It is not impossible that when the storm has blown over it will be found that no serious permanent damage was done to anyone.* Yet the sudden fear that was produced has dramatized the awful destructive power of the new weapon. The world is crying that the weapon itself and those responsible for its development and use be brought under control of those whose lives it endangers and at the same time protects. And this means everyone.

Is there then reasonable hope for peace? Can we ever live with confidence in a world where nations are making or can make hydrogen bombs?

My answer is yes. There have never been better grounds for hope.

I do not believe hydrogen or atomic weapons can or should be negotiated out of existence until all weapons of war are included in the agreement. A fleet of airplanes loaded with conventional bombs can deliver a blow as destructive as a single atomic bomb. The function of atomic weapons, just as of other war weapons, is to destroy military targets—not civilian lives. The chief military advantage of atomic weapons is to deliver heavy blows at a great distance from the home base. Those fighting close to home can deliver similarly destructive blows using tanks and infantry and planes armed with conventional weapons. The chief disadvantage of atomic weapons is their wide area of destructiveness, which prevents their use against small enemy targets surrounded by friendly or civilian areas. It is considerations such as these that must be the basis of any realistic negotiation toward disarmament.

It is thus evident that because of its wider destructiveness the military usefulness of the H-bomb is much more limited than that of the A-bomb. But if war develops it would be difficult to justify the prohibition of the use of the H-bomb against an enemy fleet of warships on the high seas while permitting the free use of submarines against unarmed shipping.

| 325 |

Nevertheless, the very existence of such highly destructive weapons is itself a hazard and a source of fear. How can we be assured that a ruthless man of power, in a tight situation, will not turn these weapons loose for mass destruction? How can we prevent the threat of such use as a means of extorting concessions or some form of tribute?

As I see it, there are three answers to these questions, which taken together are adequate. The first answer is to reach a reliable agreement among the major powers not to engage in war against each other or in any war that another of these nations may declare is against its vital interests. This would in effect mean an agreement to limit wars to international police actions such as may be necessary to keep order between nations. Within this agreement there would be ample room for orderly changes under international law.

The second answer is for immediate action while these negotiations are being carried through. A nation that feels the threat of the use against it of such highly destructive weapons can arm itself with comparable weapons or come to an agreement with another nation thus armed. It can then make clear that in case of attack appropriate countermeasures will be taken. Such a reply would make any ruler who cares for the welfare of his people pause long before initiating a war.

The third answer is to be found in the conditions for an enduring peace. Such peace depends upon internal national health and upon international friendliness and understanding. These conditions can be developed by appropriate education. Citizens of every nation can learn that their welfare depends upon cordial cooperation among their component groups. They can learn that their health and prosperity and vision are aided by friendly relations with their neighbor nations. And methods are available for making effective such education in good human relations.

It is the first of these answers on which our political leaders should now work—and work fast. For the risks of living without a no-war agreement are too great to tolerate. Until the agreement can be reached, it is the second answer that will of necessity be given. It is in the third answer, however, that our great hope lies, and it is to this that our every educational agency should turn.

Until this international point of view can be reached we shall be living in a world of fear and hot tension. But this does not mean war. It is more than a century since a war has been started under such intense motivation that severe and sure damage to the welfare of one's own country would be accepted as the price of victory. We may reasonably expect that those intent on the expansion of their hegemony will seek for other methods than war when they face its cost to themselves.

It is widely believed in responsible circles that war as an instrument of international policy is rapidly becoming obsolete. This is because of the increasing cost of military victory. The very destructiveness of modern weapons is one of the major factors that are making victory so expensive.

Another factor is the damage that war does to the smooth cooperation and coordination of our economic efforts. This cooperation is of rapidly growing importance in the technologically advanced societies that are capable of producing atomic weapons. The first effect of war's destruction is to interfere with a nation's coordinated economy. The consequence is that war now, to an unprecedented and rapidly growing extent, interferes with civilian life. The resulting human disaster from hunger, destitution, and disease outweighs even the great direct damage from military action. What has happened to Britain, victorious in two world wars, is only a minor foretaste of what any nation must expect if it fights World War III.

As I see it, therefore, the development of the hydrogen bomb has made it imperative that we reach as soon as possible an international agreement among the major military powers that they will not resort to war against each other's interests. The dramatic world response to the dangers of the hydrogen bomb has given new reason to believe that such an agreement may now be possible.

While these negotiations are under way, every step that we take toward increased cooperation between nations and among the various groups within nations will improve our chances for continued peace.

A major political step in this direction is now being taken in the development of international mutual defense agreements. It seems evident to me that these agreements should be extended to include international consultation regarding the development and the resources available in atomic weapons.

But such international agreements cannot insure lasting peace. This is possible only when people understand the conditions for peace. This understanding can be cultivated. Our religious organizations are powerful agencies for inspiring men to cast envy and hate aside and to work for each other's welfare in a spirit of companionship. Our universities can analyze the factors that are responsible for a nation's strength and health, resulting in clear evidence of the practical importance of cordial and enthusiastic cooperation. It will become evident also how important for progress the tensions of rivalry and competition can be when these tensions are kept within bounds and are directed toward the common good. The schools can teach the value of coexistence of varying cultures under rules that bar aggression. Teamwork based on understanding in human relations can be made as important an objective of education as are character-building, health, and good citizenship. All the agencies that form public attitudes can be called upon: the press, radio, television, women's clubs, business and social organizations, labor unions, political parties.

During the past three months, with two colleagues, I have been studying the group tensions that exist in Asia and what can be done about them. The responsible leaders of every one of the nine countries we visited are greatly concerned about establishing an effective program of education for friendly cooperation. They see in this cooperation the foundation of national strength and safety. In North America and in Europe such education is being carried on with increasing emphasis, but with far less vigor than the times demand.

Here lies, I believe, our hope for establishing an enduring peace with freedom. The opportunity is before us. Is there any task that is now more important?

# 37. World Tension and the
Approach to Peace

*1955*

In an effort to arouse public sentiment against the drift toward war, the *St. Louis Post-Dispatch* conducted in its editorial pages during the summer of 1955 a symposium on "The Struggle Toward Peace." This article was included among those by a number of prominent Americans who were invited to share in an examination of means of releasing world tensions.

The extraordinary state of tension in today's world should impel us to work the harder toward establishing a peace with freedom. There is sound basis for hope. But that hope will become a reality only if we do our part toward building a social order that is worthy to survive.

An open society, where men and women can grow to their best by sharing responsibly in the work of the world, is a dream of all persons everywhere. The inexorable forces of social evolution are compelling men to work together more fully and more widely. True, the powers of tyranny are mighty and are being used against us with cunning guile. Even our great nation cannot by itself prevent the spread of these powers throughout the earth. But we can do much. And we can take courage from the knowledge that other nations also desire to build a world where men can breathe in freedom. Working together, a harmonious peace with freedom can be achieved.

The requirements of living in a society based on science and technology are making it necessary for man to learn to work cordially with man. These forces are not confined by national boundaries. Ideologies as well as organizational patterns must work toward ever wider cooperation if they are to have survival value. Note the remarkably rapid rate of the social changes now going on. If we can prevent the current tensions from developing into catastrophic war, and I believe we can, it is reasonable to expect that within a generation we shall somehow have passed through the most critical period of our existence as a sharply divided world.

As I see it, it is highly unlikely that wars between the great military giants will be undertaken. For the next decade, at least, it would appear that the balance of power between the United States and Russia will remain so close that neither can be confident of the considerable degree of superiority required for victory. Without victory as a likely consequence a nation will not initiate a war. Over the longer period, if time should work in favor of the free nations and they gain a substantial superiority, the fear of major war will be absent. On the other hand, in the unlikely event that time should favor the Communists, whenever they shall have secured sufficient military superiority I should expect them to exert whatever pressure may be necessary to bring the world under their control. If the free world remains alert the power is available to us to prevent such a disaster.

Wars are not yet obsolete, but they are obsolescent. This is because they are becoming too costly for the gains that war may bring. Two factors are responsible for the greatly increasing human cost of modern war. The first is the development of new weapons, such as airplanes and atomic bombs, that open an entire nation to devastating attack by the enemy. The second is the increasing interdependence of individuals and groups within the social order, with the result that any breakdown of this order makes life extremely difficult.

The time scale of the obsolescence of war is essentially the rate of social change, the rate of growth of the interdependence among nations for their economic and cultural welfare. If by any means whatever major war can be held off for a few decades, it is entirely reasonable to hope that the growth of this interdependence will have gone so far that by common consent war will be ruled out as a means of settling disputes among nations.

There is concrete evidence that these social forces are becoming effective toward peace. It seems hazardous these days to talk of the hope for peace because of the way in which such talk has been exploited. Again and again the Communists have staged a peace offensive to prepare the ground for military aggression. Recognizing this as a fact, it would nevertheless appear that the present relaxation of pressure by the Soviet government reflects a true desire to reduce the military tensions, and that this desire arises from recognition of the conditions essential to the survival of their social order.

A possible reason for this is the growing importance to the Communist world of developing their internal economy. Their industry has been going strongly ahead, but agriculture in Russia and especially in China has lagged seriously behind. A program has recently been announced for the extensive development of trade within the Communist world. It is intended that each area will concentrate increasingly upon the products that it can best supply and will receive in return those from other provinces that will contribute most effectively to their strength and prosperity.

We see here an effort to demonstrate such a superiority of the Communist social system that they will gain the following of the world. Even if so conceived, we should nevertheless sincerely welcome such an economic development. A prosperous neighbor is not so much to be feared as one who is lean and hungry. There is a Chinese proverb that poverty dulls the wits. The converse is also true. Where health and prosperity reign, balanced thinking becomes possible. The conditions responsible for prosperity in a technological industrialized world are universal. They are not confined to either side of the Iron Curtain. We find that such conditions include, for example, honesty and reliability in business dealings, an aspect of morality which has developed enormously in the West during the past century. If this should develop extensively within the Soviet social structure, we may expect it to extend likewise to her conduct of international relations. In this case the free world could begin to do business with the Soviets with an increasing degree of confidence.

We have sound evidence also for the value of freedom itself as a source of strength. True, freedom becomes a source of strength only when those who are free commit themselves to a common purpose. But such a purpose the nations of the free world have before them, and on it they are agreed. That purpose is simply that their people shall live in a social order where all share freely the common responsibilities, a society where every person's dignity is recognized. Toward this end these nations, like our own, are shaping their courses.

It has become very evident that the United States alone cannot shape world conditions so that an era of peace will develop. But our nation is not alone. Powerful allies throughout the world are working with us. Because their methods may differ from ours, all too frequently we fail to recognize them as allies. But so they are, all nations inspired by the common purpose of achieving an increasing freedom for their people.

The resourcefulness and strength of free peoples thus committed to a common human cause is, as I see it, the power of God working in the world toward the establishment of an enduring peace with freedom. If indeed we have judged rightly that the great forces working in the world are on our side, in the long run our efforts cannot fail.

## THE REQUIREMENTS FOR PEACE

What then are the requirements for achieving an enduring peace with responsible freedom? The first requirement is a firm defense against the encroachment of those who would take our freedom from us. This defense is to be considered as a means of buying time. It cannot be of itself a permanent solution to our problems, for the hazards of the development of war are too great. But the defense must be maintained in order that a world of peace and opportunity may grow to impregnable strength.

The second requirement is supplying the most favorable possible conditions for the healthy growth of a free society. These conditions include economic opportunity, the improvement of health, and the development of a sound culture.

The third requirement, and this is the most vital of all, is that we shall find challenging goals toward whose achievement free men everywhere will agree. The importance of these goals lies in this, that only by their common acceptance can the strength of a free people show itself in united action. The nature of the goals is that they shall provide for men and women an increasing opportunity for their full personal development. The practical realization of the goals will come as they are made specific in terms of human needs and are achieved by appropriate action.

These then are the steps that need to be taken:

## 1. Defense

The free world's major problem of defense is that against the encroachment of Communism. As we have just indicated, there is no reason to believe that in the long run this problem may not yield to a peaceful solution. In the meantime, however, we must neither permit ourselves to fall into a position of relative weakness, nor should we take a belligerent attitude. We must make it completely evident to Russia that we are ready to share in the defense of those whose freedom is threatened, but that if she herself remains unaggressive she will have nothing to fear from us.

We must recognize that however falsely they may be based, the Russian fears of the social system represented by the United States are deeply ingrained. These fears will not be removed by an attitude of belligerence. A firmness based on a knowledge of our own strength combined with a willingness to cooperate where this is to our mutual advantage would seem to be the effective means of reducing these fears.

## 2. Economic and cultural development throughout the world

The really important task before the free world is the development of its economic and cultural strength. This is a problem for each nation itself, but it is also an international problem. Such strength depends on many factors. Important among these are industry, commerce, technology, science, and the understanding of human relations. It is important to note that in all of these aspects of human life, growth to our full strength requires extension of our activities beyond national boundaries. International cooperation is needed.

We are properly proud of the strength of our American industrial and commercial operations. We not only astounded the rest of the world by our productive achievement during the recent war; we also surprised ourselves. But we must remember that our business strength is in very large measure a consequence of the fact that we operate on a vast, almost continental, scale. Another factor is that through high wages the large majority of our people have been given a level of prosperity that has made them not only good consumers but more effective producers and more responsible citizens. The success of this method of developing our national strength by plowing into our citizenry a substantial part of the product of the national labors is what Frederick Lewis Allen has called "the great American discovery." [1] It is this great discovery that needs to be applied more fully on a worldwide scale. The investment will be large, but the returns will be immeasurably greater.

Many examples could be given of the importance of international cooperation in all fields of economic and cultural activity. The benefits go to everyone concerned. If we can hold off another major war, it is the development of strong international ties in the economic field which perhaps more than anything else will establish a firm peace for the society of free peoples.

Our nation needs to be needed. This is a truism with regard to individuals. We know that our lives take on meaning and that we have a place in society only so long as we perform some useful function. We make our livelihood by serving effectively the business of which we are a part. That business, in turn, thrives just insofar as it is of service to the community. In its turn the community becomes strong as it contributes to the life of the nation. What we have been too prone to forget is that a nation likewise is not sufficient unto itself. It is as it becomes a valued

[1] Frederick Lewis Allen: *The Big Change* (New York: Harper & Brothers; 1952), p. 286.

member of the society of nations that a nation can share the life of the world, and that in time of critical danger it will find that it has friends.

This statement is true not only of a little country such as Switzerland which makes its healthy way by fine manufactures and as host to the holiday world. It is equally true of the nation that would call itself great. In the words of Charles Burton Marshall, veteran student of the international scene, "The greatness of nations is measured not in glory and majesty but in the capacity to carry burdens." Among nations, as among individuals, "he that would be greatest among you shall be servant of all."

As a purely practical matter it is necessary to note that the differences among peoples in the free world are immense. They differ in historical tradition, in racial customs, in political and religious ideals, and in many other factors. If they are truly to be counted among the free nations, they will, however, have this in common—that their prime concern is with the welfare of their people.

If their basic interest is that the lives of their citizens shall have meaning, this is enough to give us confidence in their support of an enduring peace with freedom. This common aim may not be an adequate basis for a close political union. It will, however, strengthen the freed world if we develop such ties as are to our mutual benefit. This would mean agreement at least in the realms of mutual defense and of economic operations. The importance of such international agreements is greatly enhanced by the increasing interdependence that is a part of the atomic age.

## 3. The common purpose of achieving a greater freedom

If there is any one lesson of greatest human importance from the experience of releasing the atom's power, it is the effectiveness of free men who are agreed upon one common purpose. It is such a purpose that brings harmony to the choices that free people make. The harmony comes as each sees and chooses the part that he can do best toward the attainment of the desired end. It is only in terms of the purpose for which one lives that one can distinguish between good and evil and thus become a responsible citizen.

We have seen what that purpose is. It is nothing less than to create a social order in which every man and every woman has an opportunity to take a responsible share in the life of which they are a part. In the endeavor to do his part well, each will grow toward the best that is possible to him. He will be recognized and rewarded in his society for the way he does his part. Thus his life will take on dignity and meaning.

Such has been the dream of Americans throughout history. It has become the dream of many men and women throughout the world. Nor is it an idle dream. It was in the effort to achieve such a social order that our nation was born, and other nations also. It was the moving force back of the foundation of the United Nations. It has been crystallized in the Universal Declaration of Human Rights. I think of the president of the General Assembly of the United Nations telling a great St. Louis audience that it is this dream of an open opportunity for a worthy life that is the hope of all people everywhere. I hear a minor clerk on the island of Bali say, "We want to share the life of the world."

Truly the purpose is known and agreed upon; but it needs drafting into plans and the putting of these plans into action. Such steps require bold leadership. Our government showed such leadership as it undertook the Marshall Plan.

It is reflected again in Clarence Randall's proposals for opening the channels for more extensive international trade. Spaak and Schuman and Adenauer are pointing the way toward unified action in Europe. Pakistan and India and the Philippines and Japan all have among them men of vision who are laying plans for their nations' destinies that will mean greater opportunity for their citizens. Working together the task can be done.

Within us is the still, small voice—compelling, insistent. As we listen we know that the important thing is not the state, nor the power of the atom, nor the mighty machines of industry; it is the heart of man. To all persons everywhere the inner voice gives the same message. Because it speaks thus to all, we have a firm basis for hope.

# 38. Disarmament

## *1956*

**During** a two-year study of disarmament, a Subcommittee of the United States Senate charged with investigating all aspects of the problem conducted hearings in four cities. This testimony was presented before the Subcommittee on Disarmament of the Committee on Foreign Relations in its hearings in St. Louis on December 12, 1956.

I assume that the aim of the United States government is to achieve a condition of security where justice and freedom are assured. Our primary concern is the security of our own nation, but we recognize that our security is tied closely to that of the entire free world. We also share the concern and the responsibility for the well-being of all men everywhere.

To this end, as of 1956, American military strength must be great. Our weapons must include a versatile arsenal of atomic weapons. Our strength must be ready for use.

Protected by this military strength, we must work with urgent vigor on such political, economic, and ideological developments as will build the strength of the free world. Only as we make headway with such developments can we expect to achieve an enduring peace with justice and freedom.

As for myself, I have high hope that we shall reach such a peace. I see the great powers beyond man's control, including the advance of technology, the world's economic requirements, and the trends in education, as working rapidly toward the emergence of a stable, integrated world society where justice and freedom are dominant. The evidence indicates that each decade will show a substantial advance in this direction. But such advance can occur only as our guard is held firm against those forces that would create disorder and would subject free peoples to domination by tyrants.

In the present world situation, I do not consider it in the interest of the United States or of world peace that our government's military strength should be decreased. It should, rather, be enhanced.

There are, however, certain types of arms limitation that are feasible and should be carried through. These controls relate primarily to the various types of newly developed weapons regarding whose use no firm international agreement has been reached.

There are two proposals for such armament control, already presented before your committee, to which I should like to call particular attention. These are that of Senator Ralph E. Flanders of Vermont, presented on March 7, and that of Thomas E. Murray, member of the Atomic Energy Commission, presented on April 12. I find myself in general accord with the proposals made by these gentlemen. I should like, however, to note certain specific aspects of their proposals that seem worthy of particular comment.

(*a*) Of special timeliness and importance is Senator Flanders' proposal, "that we renounce unequivocally the use of hydrogen or atomic warheads for mass destruction in attacks on populations unless such attacks are made first by the Soviet on the populations of the nations outside the curtain. In that event we must retaliate in kind against the Soviet."

This proposal is closely similar to that of Dr. [Edward U.] Condon, that renounced first the use of the H-bomb, but is a somewhat wider principle on which it seems to me we can base a sounder and more practical action.

(*b*) It is almost a corollary to this proposal that we should prepare ourselves with a versatile assortment of atomic weapons and that we should be prepared to use them if occasion demands. This idea has been developed, in particular, by Commissioner Murray. Both he and Senator Flanders have emphasized that we should be prepared to use these weapons, as well as all conventional weapons, on a graduated scale. Each military attack should be met according to its intensity. The general military principle should be followed that destruction should be no greater than required to attain the military objective. Both gentlemen have argued, it seems to me correctly, that if we make known that we are ready to reply to any aggressive act with whatever strength and whatever weapons are necessary for our protection, this will be the best possible deterrent.

These proposals do not imply the elimination of hydrogen or superbombs. These should, in my opinion, be a part of our arsenal. But they should be available for use only in case their first use

| 337 |

by an enemy makes our employment of them necessary for the protection of ourselves and the free world.

(c) I would go along with Commissioner Murray when he argues that the size and number of these superweapons should be limited. His argument is based, however, solely on the economical provision of adequate armed strength. I would note also that there is the additional limitation that the use of any considerable number of such weapons would, because of radioactivity, endanger the lives of people all over the world. It is axiomatic that such action must be avoided.

Such limitation on account of radioactivity imparted to the atmosphere does not affect to any appreciable extent the tactical use of atomic weapons.

(d) A clear understanding should be reached with other nations, including Russia, as to what constitutes a military target as compared with an "open city." There is, in my view, no reason why areas devoted to the development and production of military weapons, or used for the housing and deployment of military personnel, should not be considered as military targets. To my mind, negotiations with regard to the distinction between civilian and military areas is an appropriate and rather urgent topic for international discussion.

(e) I am among those who believe it would be dangerous for the freedom of the world, and particularly for that of the United States, to deny ourselves the right to carry through any type of weapons test which does not endanger the lives and well-being of citizens of other nations. This means that I favor retaining our freedom to test tactical atomic weapons and ballistic missiles.

With regard to the continuation of tests of hydrogen or super-bombs, I would agree with Commissioner Murray that there is no need for attempting to develop larger superweapons than those already tested. As far as I am aware, there is no indication that larger weapons would have any important military value.

I can see, on the other hand, that there may be need for occasional tests of these superweapons as the military technologists proceed with their development. Extensive technical advance is necessary in order that a large and clumsy bomb shall be transformed into a compact, relatively simple weapon that can be relied upon if or when it is needed.

It is my own impression, and I have studied the matter with some care, that the health hazards resulting from tests of superbombs have frequently been exaggerated. These hazards are nevertheless real. Based on a recent report by Atomic Energy Commissioner Willard F. Libby, combined with reports during the past year by the National Academy of Sciences and the British Medical Research Council, I see no reason to fear for the health of people throughout the world as a result of tests that have so far been made. It would seem possible, however, that a continuation of such tests, especially if at an increased tempo, might lead to dangerous concentrations of radioactive material.

With this in mind, I would urge strongly that some scientific body, independent of the government, be requested to prepare annually objective reports with regard to radioactive hazards. These reports should be aimed not only at the danger from nuclear weapons but also at dangers from the increasing use of nuclear power, and especially at the hazards from medical and industrial uses of ionizing radiations. Knowledge of these hazards is important for the peace of mind as well as the health of men and women everywhere.

Excellent work is being done in this direction by the Atomic Energy Commission itself. In some respects, however, the commission may be considered as an interested party. This is the reason for suggesting that such reports be prepared independently under the auspices of some nongovernmental agency. During the past year such a report was, in fact, prepared by the National Academy of Sciences. It would seem to me appropriate that this academy should be asked to publish such reports on an annual basis.

I have no doubt that if information with regard to such hazards is thus made generally available, the government will control the testing and use of atomic weapons with full consideration for the health of peoples throughout the world.

(f) This brings me to one further point, brought out in the testimony of Commissioner Murray. It is this. It seems to me of vital importance as a matter of democratic principle that ultimate decisions with regard to the policy of the testing and use of weapons, whether conventional or nuclear, should reside in civilian hands. It seemed to be Mr. Murray's thought that this policy should be ultimately in the hands of the military general staff. This would seem to me to violate a very fundamental principle. Is it not correct that on such a matter of policy our military men should be the advisers to the civilian government, and that the policy should be

determined on a civilian level? If this is true, it should be the responsibility of Congress to see that this matter is placed in the
hands of the appropriate civilian agency of the government.

So much with regard to steps in the development and control and the
use of weapons. Is there nothing more that we can do?

I have indicated that it does not seem to me now feasible to reduce
the armed strength of our nation. There are, however, steps that can be
taken which would make such reduction of armament appropriate. These
steps have to do with reducing the tensions that tend toward war, with
developing the ties that demand a stable peace, and with the development
of a supernational body competent to keep the peace. In all three of these
directions it is now possible to take significant steps.

For example, problems of colonialism are now inciting warlike action
in North Africa and the Middle East. These dissatisfactions are being
played upon by Russia to weaken the strength of the free world. It should
be possible at some level to discuss objectively what steps can be taken
to bring about peacefully and smoothly the transitions from colonial status
that need to be made in the interest of greater freedom.

As another example, we are coming to realize that the large majority
of the peoples of the world see eye to eye with us in the United States that
the great human task is to promote the well-being of all men and women
everywhere. In this great undertaking of building a world where justice
and freedom are secure, all who thus take man's well-being as the ultimate
measure of value are working on our side. If we confidently keep this
fact foremost in our dealing with other nations—that we are sharing with
them in the effort to promote freedom and justice for all concerned—we
can build up rapidly the morale and strength of the free world.

# 39. On Nuclear Testing

## 1958

Lively public controversy over the continuation of nuclear weapons tests prompted the author to state his views in this letter of May 8, 1958, to Senator Stuart Symington of Missouri. It was published in full in the *St. Louis Globe-Democrat* and in slightly abbreviated form in the *Congressional Record*.

May 8, 1958

The Honorable Stuart Symington
United States Senator from Missouri
Washington, D. C.

Dear Senator Symington:

The point of this letter is twofold. First, I want to express my congratulations for your recent (April 22) testimony before the Senate favoring a continuation of the testing of nuclear weapons. Your testimony showed careful study, mature balance of judgment, and a high degree of moral courage. I hope your recommendations prevail.

Second, because the question of what should be done about nuclear tests comes to me repeatedly from many quarters, I want to summarize for the record my present views on this matter. At your invitation I presented testimony before the Subcommittee on Disarmament of the Senate Committee on Foreign Relations, meeting here in St. Louis on December 12, 1956.* This letter may be considered as an extension of this earlier statement. Such further testimony seems appropriate at this time because of the sharply divided views regarding the value of nuclear weapons tests as expressed recently by various scientists, and particularly in view of the vigorous opposition to such tests currently publicized by certain of my esteemed colleagues at Washington University.

I favor a vigorous extension of the American work needed to enable our nation to use nuclear explosives effectually for either military or peaceful purposes. To the best of my knowledge this agrees with your own views.

## PROFESSIONAL BACKGROUND

The study of physical properties of X rays, cosmic rays, and other ionizing radiations was my primary professional task from 1913 until 1942. Recognition of my work in these fields has included many medals and honorary citations by scientific organizations in this country and abroad, including the Nobel prize in 1927 for work with X rays. I served as president of the American Physical Society in 1934 and as president of the American Association for the Advancement of Science in 1942.

The physiological effects of ionizing rays have also been a matter of active concern for me. I was a member of the National Cancer Advisory Council from 1937 to 1944, and served as its representative in supporting the construction of a cyclotron at Berkeley, California, for the study of the biological effects of neutrons, and in the building of a cyclotron at St. Louis designed especially for producing artificial isotopes for medical purposes. I also helped to organize the Chicago Tumor Institute and served on its Scientific Committee from 1937–49.

I had the responsibility for initiating and organizing (in 1942) the health and safety program for the use of radioactive materials in connection with the American nuclear reactors. I worked closely with the officers of the Manhattan District in setting up the procedures for health and safety and also the radiobiology research for the entire atomic energy program. This program of safety precautions has resulted in an exceptional record for safety among those working with nuclear reactions. The research we began on the biological effects of radioactive materials continues to be carried on, with extensions and improvements, by the United States Atomic Energy Commission.

I personally made the first estimates of the hazards from radioactive fallout from the nuclear reactors at Oak Ridge and Hanford, recommended precautions for their safe operation, and assisted in developing an organization to give this matter continued competent and responsible study. I consulted regarding the fallout dangers with those responsible for the postwar nuclear tests at Bikini. I have also discussed cases of radiation damage with radiologists and geneticists in both Japan and the United States.

## MAJOR WORLD ISSUES

It will be widely agreed that two world issues are today of greater importance than any others. The most immediate is the avoidance of major war. More fundamental is the concentration of the efforts of civilization on the full personal development of all men and women. The United States will meet its great responsibilities of leadership to the extent that it helps the world achieve these two great goals.

A major source of our present confusion is the announced and demonstrated goal of Russian Communism, namely, to bring the world under a kind of imperial domination that in the view of the great majority of men would make impossible for most men and women a satisfactory human development. As long as such is the Russian objective, the rest of the world has no alternative but to protect itself against falling under Russian domination. While such protection is a world problem, today's realities mean that without the effective cooperation of the United States the defense of the world's freedom for encouraging the full development of persons would be impossible. Thus it becomes a prime human responsibility of American citizens to maintain a defensive strength adequate to meet the aggressive power of the Russian empire.

In order that such defensive strength shall be maintained, effective atomic armament is essential. This follows from the fact that Russia's first objective is to bring and keep its immediate neighbors within its political orbit. In order to be effective in defense, the United States must therefore be prepared to fight at a long distance from home. But nuclear weapons are now the engineers' best answer to delivering heavy blows at a distance. If by any means, as through world political pressure, the United States could be induced to make her nuclear arms ineffective, there would remain nothing to prevent the massed armies, tanks, and planes of the Russian empire from taking over complete control of Europe, Asia, and nearer Africa. Reduction of American nuclear strength is thus to Russia of critical importance. By the same token, American nuclear weapons are the key to the strength of NATO, and in fact to the defense of the world.

As you are well aware, this critical importance of nuclear weapons is fully recognized in all military circles, including not only the United States and Russia but also such traditionally neutral areas as Switzerland and Scandinavia. The reason that nuclear weapons are more important to the United States than to Russia is because, as all the world knows, it is Russia, not the United States, that is a military threat to its neighbors. It is the United States, not Russia, that is concerned with protecting the interests of nations that are far from its borders.

| 343 |

It would thus be a tragedy for the world and a major hazard for America if our nation should reduce the effectiveness of its nuclear armament without firm assurance that Russia is not left in a position to exercise military dominance over its neighbors.

There are those, however, who believe that by arming our nation with the most effective weapons we are exciting the world toward war. My own appraisal of history is the reverse. I believe lack of adequate preparedness for defense has proved itself an invitation to aggression, and that the reactions induced by aggression would be such as to make war inevitable even though the outcome would be disaster.

Thus my basic reason for advocating a continuation of tests of nuclear explosives is because I do not see how we can be confident that our weapons are adequate for defense unless tests continue to be made.

## FALLOUT HAZARDS

Consideration must be given, however, to the dangers that inhere in the tests themselves. As I stated in my testimony before your committee a year ago, these hazards are real, and must be carefully guarded against. Yet in my judgment the magnitude of the hazard has in certain quarters been grossly exaggerated. To my mind, the danger that would surely be done in case war should occur is so much greater that to hesitate in making important tests because of the relatively small damage they may do would be a tragic error of judgment.

This is not the place to present the technical arguments; but I note this contrast: On the one hand Professor Pauling and others have stated that each nuclear explosion introduces radioactive materials into the atmosphere that will shorten the lives of thousands of people through such effects as genetic mutations, leukemia, and bone cancer. On the other hand, as of this date, there is only one case (that of a Japanese fisherman) where good evidence exists that a person's life was shortened by fallout. Statistical evidence on populations living in areas where they are exposed to substantially greater differences in ionization than are induced by the usual radioactive fallout shows no significant genetic or cancerous effects. Considering the evidence that I have seen, it is my own expectation that when really thorough tests shall have been made, it will be seen that the worldwide effects on people's health of nuclear tests continued at the level of the past few years are small as compared with many other hazards to which we are exposed.

To set the record straight, may I pause to note two points. The first is that the attention recently called to the hidden hazards of radiation has stimulated radiologists to improve greatly their techniques of use of X rays and radium in diagnosis and therapy. These improvements have already resulted in a reduction in the exposure of the average American to ionizing rays by an amount several times greater than the increased exposure resulting from fallout. That is, the net result of our work with ionizing rays during recent years has been to reduce substantially rather than to increase our chance of being injured by such rays.

The second point is the very great debt we owe to these ionizing rays in terms of health and human life. Radiologists working independently in the United States and Germany have estimated "roughly but reliably" that the use of X rays and radioactive materials in diagnosis and therapy has saved the lives of as many persons as have been killed in all the wars fought since 1895 when these agencies were discovered. While it has been salutary to have our attention called to the very real dangers in the peaceful as well as military uses of nuclear rays, we should remember that when properly used such rays are of great human value.

## WEIGHING THE HAZARD

On the one hand, we recognize the likelihood that some persons will be injured, perhaps even fatally, by the longtime effects of nuclear explosions. On the other hand, we see the chance that a slackening in our work on nuclear weapons may so weaken our defensive strength that the world may be baited into the fatal trap of a major war. In my own judgment, the possibility of drifting into war is by far the greater danger.

If this judgment is correct, we should continue to exert every effort to maintain our defenses. This means that we should continue the development of the nuclear weapons needed to insure the success of the aims of the free world in case war should be thrust upon us. In such work, however, continued care should be taken to avoid endangering people, whether citizens of our own or other nations.

Unfortunately, there exists today no responsible body that can say what experiments are in the interests or contrary to the interests of mankind. This is one of the more obvious duties that the United Nations should be authorized to perform. Until, however, it has a police force of adequate strength, putting such a judgment into effect is beyond the power of the United Nations. Until the United Nations develops such power, the responsibility for conducting nuclear experiments in the best interest of mankind must be accepted individually by every sovereign nation and carried through in accord with its own best judgment.

The policy that guides the United States Atomic Energy Commission is obviously to carry on the experiments that it finds necessary for both military and peaceful purposes, while keeping human risks to a minimum. The responsibility for the broader national and international implications of this work cannot, however, be avoided by the Congress. It is at this point where I should be glad for assurance that the Joint Congressional Committee on Atomic Energy is fully alert to the issues involved.

As a matter of military judgment, it would seem to me wise for emphasis now to be laid on the development of nuclear explosives of lower caliber. It seems evident that if war should come again it is the smaller nuclear bombs that will be most useful as tactical weapons. The relatively limited area of destruction by such weapons would raise far fewer political problems than the use of larger bombs. Superbombs, of over one megaton rating, will always be difficult to use in war without raising serious political issues.

We cannot afford to be caught unprepared with the most powerful weapons in case of a real power showdown. Yet we may hope that only an occasional test of such huge weapons may be adequate for the very unlikely event that their use may be called for. It is thus in the area of superbombs * that we may advantageously negotiate regarding reduction of bomb tests. For example, it would probably be within the bounds of prudence to state unilaterally that we will not be the first to use in war a bomb more powerful than a certain specified size. As you are aware, the fallout hazards are thousands of times less for the small caliber bombs, so that their tests are of relatively little international concern.

It is probably fortunate for the world's peace of mind that it is American citizens, rather than those of any other nation, who are exposed most strongly to the radioactive effects of the nuclear explosions that have so far been made. It is this fact also, however, that gives especial point to our taking every possible safety measure as we proceed with our own crucially important experiments.

## THE DIRECTION OF PEACE

I am by no means hopeless with regard to avoiding another major war. For the immediate future I believe the likelihood that such a war would bring atomic weapons into use is recognized by all concerned. No nation would expect such a war to end without itself suffering more damage than its possible gains would be worth. Establishing an enduring peace thus would seem to require most careful and prudent negotiations during the next decade or two. By this time one may hope that the growing strength of new nations, the increasing need for economic and cultural cooperation, and the rapid strengthening of other international ties will prevent the revival of a will to war.

As I see it, our best means of promoting such an atmosphere in which peace will develop and endure is for us to accept as our firm national policy what we have recognized for generations as the "American dream"; that is, that we shall make it possible for all of our citizens to grow to their fullest stature as men and women, and that we will cooperate with other nations in their efforts to do the same for their citizens. To this end, we would do well, I believe, to negotiate with Russia, intensively and with full determination, working preferably through the United Nations, regarding means of advancing cooperatively with the nations involved the health, economic condition, and cultural status of men and women everywhere. As this becomes recognized as our consistent and sincere intention, we shall gain the support and confidence of the world. In such world confidence lies finally our only safety.

This, as I see it, is the direction in which we must move—but with every sense alert, lest eager on the way toward peace we fall into some trap that we must expect to find carefully laid for us.

Yours sincerely,
*Arthur H. Compton*

# IX

## Science and the Growth of Man

The past is but the beginning of a beginning, and all that is and has been is but the twilight of the dawn. . . . A day will come when beings who are now latent in our thoughts and hidden in our loins shall stand upon this earth as one stands upon a footstool, and shall laugh and reach out their hands amid the stars.

H. G. WELLS

# 40. We Must Shape Our New World

## 1936

𝕮𝕽 Mr. Compton took a year's leave of absence from his position as professor of physics at the University of Chicago to serve as George Eastman Visiting Professor at Oxford University during 1934-5. He was the first scientist to be invited to fill this distinguished professorship, which was endowed by the American inventor to encourage Anglo-American understanding. Upon his return from England he contrasted the intellectual climate of the two communities and stressed the distinctive task of American education in identifying and developing human values in a world of rapid technological advance.*

An English friend, after a brief visit in Chicago, remarked that he found its life unbearably superficial. The total lack of tradition, the complete absorption of effort in the machinery of life! How could people endure an existence so empty of human values?

A week earlier my wife and I had dined in Oxford with a leader of British education. The question arose regarding the place of science in life. It has proved itself as a method for arriving at reliable knowledge, and for supplying us with certain necessities of life—but the inhumanness of it all! The discipline of thought inculcated by science was already embodied in Plato's mathematics. The predominant trend of modern science is toward replacing the human interests embodied in literature, art, and music with technological developments in which the human factor becomes less and less significant. The most fundamental bases of morality and religion have been ruthlessly shaken, with the implication that their value is insignificant. In place of a quiet ramble over the varied English countryside, we have a powerful motorcar tearing down the broad, hard highway. In Oxford, fortunately, there survives the tradition of emphasis on human values.

In Oxford, science and technology form a dark cloud, threatening the

| 351 |

very existence of the traditional mode of life which has proved its value through the ages. In Chicago, life is based upon technology and science, which have become an accepted part of life as fundamental as agriculture, and no more to be feared.

With but brief history, Chicago shows a spirit of youthful enthusiasm. The powerful methods of technology are used to build what it considers a beautiful type of architecture adapted to modern needs. Its university devoted to the advancement of knowledge in the spirit of science has won its spurs. Its grand opera, though financially unfortunate, marked a notable effort to enrich art by the gifts of technology. Though unquestionably more crude in these early stages than the highly refined culture developed through the ages upon the classical background of Greece, no one who has lived in the Midwest of the United States can doubt that it has a spirit that goes far beyond the superficial machinery of life as observed by the casual visitor. Men and women with interests as high as heaven and as deep as the heart of man arise in all communities. I find them among my friends in Chicago as well as among those in Oxford. But their backgrounds are widely different. For the Oxonian the love of history and literature is the starting point with which an effort is being made to reconcile the facts of science and the changing society based on technology. The Chicagoan postulates the world of science and gropes for a more complete understanding of life, using ancient tradition only as an occasional guide.

I have chosen Chicago and Oxford because they represent opposite extremes in the attitude toward science and its application. Oxford with her scorn of central heating but her mellow old buildings and beautiful gardens and her gentlemen of culture and leisure, shows a very different sense of values from Chicago with her innocence of tradition but her eagerness to try experiments in architecture or education and her rating of citizens according to their accomplishment for the common weal.

Chicago, as the metropolis of the Middle West, represents urban Americanism in its purest form, remote from the foreign influences that enrich life near the borders of the country. In a new community new ideas are readily absorbed, and newness becomes a virtue. Oxford, more than any other city, represents to my mind the legacy of the ages of Western culture, and the studied effort to incorporate the most valuable parts of this legacy into the lives of the young men who are to guide the development of the growing world. Thus I am taking Chicago to represent the extreme, and in certain respects the best, development of American culture, just as Oxford represents the fine traditions of Europe. They are approaching by different routes the more satisfactory adjustment of life to a world in which man, using the tools of science, is empowered to shape his world as he will.

In India it is possible for Gandhi to persuade his followers that the works of technology are harmful and should be kept out of their lives. The Oxford don may decry the dehumanizing influence of science, prefer a pen (though a fountain pen) to a typewriter, and walk rather than ride behind a petrol motor. The American, however, cannot question the value of science and technology. They are his very life. Railroads, automobiles, airplanes; agricultural machinery, mechanized meat packing, pasteurized milk; telephones, radios, movies; electric power . . . if these were gone he could not live. One might as well ask the farmer whether there is any value in planting crops. These things are the basis of existence. The rapid growth of the community gives evidence that many find life in such a world worthwhile.

None but a hasty consideration can result in a judgment that the achievements of science and technology are of only passing interest. With the present worldwide spread of knowledge it is almost unthinkable that those technological developments that have been found of fundamental human value should be lost. Among such basic crafts we must include modern methods of transportation, communication, heating and lighting, and sanitation. These by themselves would make necessary continued knowledge of the fundamental sciences. It was possible during an earlier stage of history for men to lose their interest in science because it had not proved its practical worth, and in philosophical thought the incomplete form of science led to difficulties that no longer appear. I can envisage nothing short of a worldwide catastrophe almost completely destroying mankind that could now do more than make a temporary pause in man's interest in science and technology. If this view is correct, the "mechanized world" which some already feel so oppressive is destined to be the world of the future. Blessed are those who can find in such a world the outlets which their spirits require.

It would be false to conclude that the major interests of mankind will dwell more and more upon technology; rather the reverse. When men first found agriculture profitable, it became the great center of interest, for it was the new basis of civilization. In time, however, agriculture became so much a matter of routine that it ceased to hold this pre-eminent position. As a result of agricultural development, man's world has been completely changed. Who has not sighed for the lonely peace of the primeval forest or failed to be inspired by the vast expanse of desert sands or the untouched rugged mountains? Yet we no longer live in these surroundings. Our fields are cultivated; our trees are for the most part planted. In place

| 353 |

of the primitive beauties of nature, we shape nature to our desires in flowerbeds and hedgerows. Who would say that the Japanese does not find as great satisfaction in his cultivated garden as the American Indian in the forests through which he used to roam? Likewise we find ourselves developing new tastes for beauty in our machines. I confess a thrill of pleasure from the lines and performance of a well-made automobile quite comparable with that from watching a deer spring lightly through the forest. The fact that the car was built to fit my needs adds to my appreciation. Similarly, with new forms of illuminants, a new art of home lighting arises. New technics lead to new possibilities of expression, and man becomes more of a creator. Gradually we may anticipate less attention being given to the technical methods and their scientific basis, and more emphasis on those refinements which enable us to express our personalities.

Science and technology are thus placing in our hands new and more mighty powers. Inevitably there comes a change in our mode of life comparable with that which accompanied the development of growing grain as a source of food. With increased population, changed social habits, and new codes of morals, human life is being formed anew.

In this new world where we depend more and more upon science and its consequences, it becomes education's primary responsibility to help men find a satisfying way of life in their new surroundings. That spiritual needs exist and are not being satisfied becomes evident from the multiplication of faddist cults, from the frequent outcries against science as the despoiler of religion, or against technology as molding us into machines. It is not only in the Oxfords that such needs are felt. Men of spiritual aspiration live also in our Chicagos.

Fortunately, the human species is extraordinarily adaptable. Under changed conditions evolutionary changes proceed at an accelerated rate. In the present case this means social evolution. If men are to reach a satisfying life as masters of machines, it cannot be by fighting against a "brave new world" that is thrust upon them, but by finding themselves a part of this world and adapting their lives to it. Those on whom this world merely thrusts itself with irritating frequency may retreat behind walls of tradition and consider academically what adjustments should be made. Those, however, who are a part of the mechanized world must adapt themselves to it or perish. Clearly it is toward the mechanized communities that we must look to find the most rapid adaptation of our thought and customs.

For this reason, as I see it, the educational institutions in our Chicagos are those toward which men must look for leadership in meeting the spiritual as well as the more mundane problems of life in the changing world. Here are communities of scholars schooled in the scientific method. In Oxford, with its "classics" and "modern greats," science plays a minor role. In the University of Chicago, which in this regard is typical of American education, three of the four main divisions are sciences: physical, biological, and social; and even in the humanities the scientific approach is close to the surface. At the same time, with four affiliated theological schools, a great Oriental Institute for studying man's growth through the ages, and extensive development in art, we find a conscious effort to find how those things of tested worth can be incorporated into our modern society. To a greater or less extent any one of the large universities of the Middle West presents a similar picture. Nor is it confined to our Midwest. If the severity of the demands of mechanized life is not felt quite so strongly along the Atlantic Coast, the great educational institutions located there have the advantage of a closer contact with Europe, which must serve as a most valuable guide. Using the powerful methods of science, and sharing the life of the mechanized community, our educational leaders are making every effort to find and develop the true values present in the new world. This search is naturally most urgent and the changes most rapid where science and technology are most essential to life.

In the senior fellows' common room of one of the Oxford colleges, I was seated between two classics dons. Trying to find what was included in a well-rounded course in classics, I inquired whether their students looked into the question of the influence of Oriental mysticism in changing Greek thought after Alexander's Eastern conquests. "That is the kind of subject a research student might investigate as a specialty," was the reply, "but it would be out of place in our classics courses. For, you see, we have carefully worked over the ancient writings, and we mean by the classics those writings that have been found of greatest value. It would waste the time of our students to divert their attention toward other works." Tradition—yesterday, today, forever; conservator of ancient values, without a glimpse of changing conditions!

One of the finest products of civilization is the well-organized life found in Oxford, mellowed by the appreciation of human values as revealed by the thought of centuries of scholars and as cultivated by many generations of men of leisure. The legacy of past ages is used in such communities to enrich the life of today. In many ways the life of Oxford has a completeness that is not approached in our more modern and supposedly more sophisticated cities. Our world could ill afford to lose the leaven supplied by these centers of culture.

Yet in the industrial communities where technological civilization is at its height, the life of Oxford cannot be lived. It is only by setting itself apart from the world both physically and intellectually that this charming community has retained its traditional values. What the world needs is the building of these values or their modern equivalent into the structure of twentieth-century life. It is this objective which has been seen perhaps more clearly by the leading universities of our central United States than by any other important educational group. Our Chicagos must look for spiritual leadership to universities whose men are themselves a part of the machine age, but who have learned to take into their own lives the legacies transmitted from old cultures.

Nor do I believe this hope of leadership is vain. Almost unconsciously perhaps a philosophy of life appropriate to modern needs is formulating itself on the campuses of our American universities. Science and the freedom to study all subjects by the scientific method are assumed without question. We thus have more effective tools for the interpretation of life. The astronomer opens to us a new and mightier universe. The physicist finds unsuspected limits to our knowledge which promise to simplify the problems of the philosophers. The chemist applies his powerful methods to the problems of life, while the professor of physiology makes a religion of his science. The sociologist studies the development of human life in our mechanized community, while the theologian aspires to express his ideas so as to be acceptable to his scientific colleagues. Over the round table at the club these various points of view are matched to throw into clearer perspective the human problems of the day. Every man in the group is engaged in reformulating his own world view. Perhaps such thinking is unorthodox; but in a very real sense I believe it is the most vital and concentrated "religious" thinking that has been done since the Reformation.

Those who have watched developments since the war [i.e., 1914–18] cannot fail to be impressed by the way in which the leadership in almost all branches of science has passed to the United States. Germany has lost her one-time pre-eminence. France, Italy, Sweden, and other European countries continue to do good work, but on a relatively small scale. Per capita I suppose England at least matches our efforts; but the many research institutions in our country easily outstrip her in the value of their total output. Russia's intense interest in technology and science has not yet carried her to the stage of great achievement. The mantle of leadership in science rests upon our shoulders.

Where then if not toward American education must a scientifically minded world look for spiritual leadership? Education even more than technology is passing through a formative period. Though technology has yet far to go before its task is complete, the direction it will follow, of making the world a social and economic unit in which the physical needs of man are satisfied in a more abundant manner, seems evident. The molding of our lives to make the best of such a world has, however, hardly begun. Science is giving us clearer vision with which to see and appreciate the world of which we are part. We can begin to see more clearly outlined the great plan according to which that world is developing. We cannot yet discern the goal. But in some mysterious way we find ourselves able to take part in shaping this world. More and more the responsibility for the life upon this planet, and even for the direction of our own evolution, is being transferred to us. Considering the many obvious errors we are making, we may be thankful that we do not yet have complete control. Yet who can fail to respond to the opportunity and challenge before us?

Of the world's vast multitudes, it is thus those whose civilization is based upon science and technology who seem to hold the keys to the future. We find ourselves in the heart of that civilization. Of this limited part of humanity, it is the educated group who are in a position to understand what is going on. Only those educated men and women who will concern themselves with the more fundamental values of life can act as leaders in shaping the new world. In a day when freedom for effective thinking regarding the objectives of life is denied to large portions of educated mankind, it is those of us who retain this cherished freedom who must carry this task. I do not want to be sensational; but if we carry the thought we have been developing to its logical conclusion, we are led to see that a surprisingly large share of the responsibility for carrying through the program of the God of the universe rests upon our shoulders.

Even though one may hesitate to accept so bold a view, the conclusion is inescapable that we have here in the United States an opportunity that is unparalleled for finding and developing the distinctive values of the new civilization. Here is one of history's greatest opportunities for social pioneering—the discovery and development of human objectives that will enable us to use to their full value the new powers with which science has gifted us. To make these values evident will require all the science, education, and religion of our community. We form a natural world focus; and if we can point the way to higher human values, the world will follow our leadership. We must shape our new world.

# 41. Science Makes Us Grow

## 1941

The following article, which represents a prewar summation of Mr. Compton's views on the role of science in society, appeared in the April 1941 issue of the quarterly journal of *Sigma Xi*, the national honorary science fraternity. During the same month that the article appeared, he was asked by the president of the National Academy of Sciences to direct his attention to an evaluation of the military implications of atomic energy.

In no other part of the world and at no previous time in history has life been so greatly influenced by science and technology as in the United States today. This influence extends not only to the means of living, but likewise to our amusements, our thinking, and our religion.

The uniqueness of American technological society was impressed upon me when recently I was speaking on the human effects of science to a group of students in India. I was about to remark upon the applications of science in everyday life, such as the electric light, motor transportation, mechanically woven cloth, scientifically selected seed, inoculation against disease, pasteurized milk, and conversations over the telephone, when I realized that these things were no part of the experience of my listeners. Even in England I found my colleagues dreading the approach of the world of technology which we have come to take as a part of life. East or west or north or south, the American sees a life less dependent upon technology than his own.

There is no doubt that science and its applications have supplied real needs. Through their help our average life span has been nearly doubled. We enjoy better food, housing, and clothing. We are freed from long hours of physical drudgery. New opportunities for education, amusement, and cultural development abound. "Yesterday my son was married," remarked the foreman of our shop. "With a wife, a car, and a radio, what more does a man want?" Thus the American rates high the contributions of science.

In our recreation we may try to lead a primitive life. Having motored hundreds of miles over hard highways, we arrive at a cabin in the wildwood, cook Chicago bacon on a stove using oil from Texas refined in New Jersey, and go fishing with an outboard motor made in Michigan. Or it may be that we go so completely native as to canoe down the river, relying only on our Pittsburgh steel ax, matches made in Ohio from Louisiana sulphur to light our fires, fruit canned in California for our food, and mosquito netting woven in New England to keep off the pests. Though we want to be free from the ring of the telephone and to use the sun as our clock, we must take care that the milk we drink is pasteurized. Thus the American frees himself from technology!

Upon our social organization and our cultural life the effect of this technology has been revolutionary. The men and women who live in our cities and on our farms have become completely dependent upon each other. Each contributes his own share with the efficiency of a specialist and receives from many others most of the things with which he lives. In prosperous days the resulting life in America is more abundant in material goods than has been the life of any large social group in history. Yet when times are hard, as in older, less technical civilizations from time immemorial, unemployed laborers, dispossessed sharecroppers, and bankrupt businessmen live on the verge of starvation, and curse the technology that has built a world in which their own efforts cannot bring forth the necessities of life.

In factory and in home are those whose monotonous tasks make them feel as cogs in a great machine. Yet the average level of public education by our schools and colleges is rapidly rising. Through magazines, radio, moving pictures, and unprecedented travel by rich and poor, our contacts with the world are greatly multiplied. New professions arise that are based upon science. It becomes profitable as well as satisfying to search for new knowledge, and scientific research becomes our great intellectual quest.

Science gives to man three Promethean gifts. First, it supplies more adequate means of living, giving longer, healthier life, and a richer variety of experience. Second, by placing a high premium on expert knowledge and by rewarding more abundantly cooperative effort, it stimulates man's social development. Third, science serves as a vehicle for cultural expression and forces further moral and religious growth.

The gift of fire was a mixed blessing to man. So also are the gifts of modern science. With new powers war becomes more fearful. Rapid social changes bring maladjustment and misery. Even the anchor of religion is found to drag as the storm of science blows. One is reminded of the legend in which the people complain to Daedalus that the steel sword he has given to King Minos will bring not happiness but strife. Daedalus replies "It is not my purpose to make man happy, but to make him great." For those who have courage, the new powers thus given by science present a challenge to shape the life of man on a more heroic scale. Here is a vision of a new world which only the brave may enter.

## SCIENCE STIMULATES SOCIAL GROWTH

George Sarton, in his recent book *Science and the New Humanism*,[1] shows how through the ages man's increasing knowledge of the world has made him develop a distinctive life. Science and its application, he points out, have made man human.

Note how technology in American society places an unprecedented emphasis upon the value of increased education. The use of steam and electric power has decreased the need for common labor, while growing specialization has increased the need for those who coordinate our activities. Thus the slave has been freed, and unskilled labor is to a large extent unemployed. Skilled labor, however, remains vital to American society for building and operating our machines, and is rewarded with shortened hours and higher pay. Business requires middlemen to handle its varied commerce. Vastly increased numbers of professional men and women have been absorbed in occupations of responsibility which before the era of technology were hardly known. Here we find the engineer, the secretary, the economist, the patent lawyer, the research scientist, and many others. The citizens responsible for planning the work of society have never been so driven by ceaseless demands as in today's America. Reflections of this pressure are to be seen in the multiplication of governmental offices, in the rise of schools of business and public administration, and in the frequency of nervous breakdown among professional men driven beyond endurance. The masters of society have indeed become the servants of all, in an unresting labor that knows no freedom. By emphasizing the need for intelligent direction, and reducing the need for unskilled labor, technology is thus spurring Americans of all levels toward an ever higher standard of training and education.

Our European contemporaries have presented cogent arguments to show

[1] George Sarton: *The History of Science and the New Humanism* (New York: Holt, Rinehart and Winston; 1931).

that the American system of universally available higher education must lead to severe unrest as men and women trained for a life of the intellect find that they must live by their hands. In large areas of our country twenty-five per cent of the total population of college age are now attending college. Two generations ago the figure was two per cent. It is amazing that these vastly increased numbers are finding the white-color jobs they seek. In spite of our mass education, unemployment is less frequent in the professions than in common labor. The prophets of doom had not counted on the growth of the specialized society based on technology, which has demanded increasing numbers of highly trained men and women as rapidly as our universities have been able to supply them. The result instead of being tragic has been the happy one of giving our citizens an unparalleled opportunity for intellectual growth. Through their more extended education, millions of our citizens are awakening to a new understanding of life's values. Such is the humanizing action of science.

To visualize how our gradually growing knowledge has from the beginning stimulated man's growth, let us imagine the last million years of his history to be compressed into the lifetime of a middle-aged man of fifty. Let us suppose that he is reading this article on a Saturday evening. It was then as a child that he learned the use of certain odd-shaped sticks and stones as tools. The meaning of sounds became definite as he learned to talk, and as his vocabulary increased so likewise did the clarity of his thought. By the time he was forty, he had developed the art of skillfully shaping stones to fit his needs. Last year he became an artist, and a few months ago learned to use simplified pictures as symbolic writing. Less than two months ago the Phoenicians introduced to him the alphabet, and after a fortnight came the brilliant art and science of ancient Greece. Five weeks ago was the dawn of Christianity and the start of the Roman Empire, and he recalls how a week later Rome fell, hiding for some weeks the values of civilized life. Last Sunday morning, so the report has it, Galileo dropped the heavy and the light cannon balls from the leaning tower of Pisa, refuting a proposition of Aristotle and starting the period of modern science. By Wednesday afternoon this had led to building the first practical steam engine, and it was at about this time that the United States came into being. On Thursday the major laws of electromagnetism were being discovered, which by last evening had given us the telegraph, the telephone, and incandescent electric light. Only last night X rays were discovered, followed quickly by radium and wireless telegraphy. It was this morning that automobiles came into general use. Airmail began to be carried only at noon today. Popular shortwave broadcasts, practical color photography, and fluorescent lighting were unknown until this afternoon.

We were discussing recently the problems faced by the rising generation. My dinner partner remarked that she saw no need for worry on their behalf. With the introduction of the automobile, the moving picture, and the radio it has been during our generation that the great changes have occurred. The rising generation can now use our experience as a reliable guide. This is comparable with the view of those economists who, noting that no further geographic frontiers exist, are basing their predictions on the hypothesis that our nation has reached a stable economic maturity.

A survey of present technical publications and patent office records shows, on the contrary, that the rate of growth of our scientific knowledge and of useful inventions is at an all-time high. It is these advances that are responsible for the accelerated social changes exhibited by our quick review of history. If our experience can reliably tell the rising generation anything, it is that they may anticipate an even greater development of technology and corresponding change of social customs.

The knowledge of nature, which from the beginning had been man's gradually but accidentally increasing heritage, has now become the conscious objective of alert minds. In the time of Benjamin Franklin, science was the hobby of a few amateurs. Now there are in the United States nearly two thousand research laboratories, equipped with refined apparatus, where men of the highest training are striving to enlarge our understanding of the world. It is their newfound knowledge which changes our lives.

## THE TRENDS OF SOCIAL EVOLUTION

We may think of these changes in man's mode of living as an aspect of adaptation to environment. It is in fact social evolution. In a short thousand generations, man has changed from an individualistic to a social animal, and that change is continuing at an increasing rate. It is thus important to consider what the directions may be along which this evolution will proceed.

It is clear that we may expect those modifications in our way of life to survive which give strength to the social group. Prominent among these strengthening factors are knowledge and cooperation. Enough has been said regarding the strength that comes through science and technology. The continuous growth of scientific knowledge which Sarton observes throughout human history is thus to be expected from the fundamental principles of evolution. In a highly competitive, warlike world, that society cannot long survive which neglects the truths of science.

Advances in technology enhance the value of specialization and cooperation. Without cooperation, knowledge cannot be made effective. If men divide into antagonistic groups, it becomes terribly destructive. Experience as well as theory has shown the superior strength of those social groups which work together. Thus a more closely coordinated and cooperative society is likewise to be considered an inevitable evolutionary trend.

It is noteworthy also that the conditions have now become such that the larger economic, social, and political units are the stronger. Before the period of rapid communication and transportation large units became unstable. As a result of geographic exploration, steam and motor transportation, telegraph and telephone, the press, moving pictures, and radio, we already share each other's lives and obtain our needed supplies from far corners of the globe. Intellectually, science has already made man a citizen of the world. The present turmoil is at least in part ascribable to the need by a technological world for the development of larger economic and political units. We are rapidly moving toward the condition under which the only stable life is that in which the whole planet is a unified community. With continued growth of science and technology some kind of world government now seems inevitable, and in the not distant future.

## DOES SCIENCE THREATEN HUMAN VALUES?

It is not surprising that those who have known and loved the tradition of classic culture should dread the approach of a technology which threatens the values they have cherished. They see science replacing the human interests present in literature, art, and music with technological developments in which the human factor becomes less and less significant. The most fundamental values of morality and religion are ruthlessly shaken, with the implication that their value is negligible. It is just because so many scientific men seem blind to these human difficulties that one feels the greater concern lest in following science mankind may lose its soul.

There is a passage in Plato's *Phaedo* [2] in which Socrates describes his early interest in physics and how he had found that physics fails to account for the important things in life. Thus, he explains, Anaxagoras would say that Socrates sits on his cot waiting to drink the hemlock

[2] B. Jowett, trans.: *The Dialogues of Plato* (Oxford: Clarendon Press; 1871; 4th edn., 1953), pp. 453-6.

because of certain tensions of tendons acting on his bones. The true reason is rather because he has been condemned by the people of Athens, and as a man of honor he cannot creep stealthily away. Such moral forces as honor are not to be explained by science; yet these are forces that shape men's acts. Since it did not meet their human needs, the followers of Socrates and Plato abandoned science, and the study of the truths of nature was forgotten for a thousand years.

For those who know science, its inhumanness is a fiction. We have noted how science is making man develop into a social being. We can now begin to see the cultural expression of this social growth. We look to science to satisfy the human hunger for a better understanding of the world. The civilizaton which is being built with the tools of science is one which requires man's moral growth. We must recognize with Plato that without a central objective life has lost its meaning. Yet in this age when men throughout the world are trying to formulate a philosophy by which they can live, it is to science that they are turning with confidence in its truth.

## CULTURAL LIFE IN A CHANGING WORLD

"Johnny, is that your cello?" Kenneth, who asked the question, was the first playmate our son had found on coming to the new city. "One of the cellists in our junior orchestra has graduated to senior high, and we need someone to take his place." Thus Johnny found that after all he wasn't going to miss playing with the school orchestra which he had so enjoyed at home.

Ten years ago we were noting with alarm the elimination of the professional musician by the radio. The musical public was, we were told, degenerating from players to listeners. Now we find millions of Americans for the first time aware of orchestral music. In the shops the demand for violins and flutes and cornets and drums has multiplied. Most of these instruments have gone to the tens of thousands of school orchestras and bands which are giving boys and girls the chance to share in producing harmony. Throughout the country the musical standard is rising. College glee clubs sing better songs. Sound movies and radio programs find they must continually improve their variety. A hundred professional symphony orchestras now play where there were a score.

The example of the school orchestras is typical of the way in which a broader base for the fine arts is being developed among millions in our country. It is not impossible that use of the radio may mask the birth of a new era in American music. In a similar way good color reproductions of the best (and perhaps the worst) paintings have recently become widely available. One might have feared that the opportunity thus afforded for the vicarious enjoyment of great pictures would discourage the amateur painter who sees that he cannot compete with the masters. The director of the Metropolitan Museum of Art tells me, however, that sixty thousand professional artists are now listed in New York City, and that the interest in amateur painting is rapidly increasing. Over the country are to be found, likewise, camera clubs and photographic exhibits where amateurs vie with each other in finding the most pleasing effects. Thus artistic America as well as musical America is finding its soul in individual expression.

The culture of our scientific era is, it is true, that of a rapidly changing society whose customs and ideas are only partly adapted to the new conditions. For example, I have been living recently in an apartment by which a streetcar clangs its noisy course. The installation of these cars gave the rapid transportation that made the city possible. Now, however, the demand is insistent that the streetcars be replaced by quieter, streamlined buses that will permit conversation by day and sleep by night. Thus the first application of technology was to meet the primary need of transportation, but eventually the refinements come that add to life's enjoyment. As long as growing science brings such rapid changes in our life, it is futile to hope to attain an adjustment of the art of living that can compare in refinement with the classic culture initiated by the Greeks and developed in Europe and England through centuries of slow social change. As our knowledge grows, however, we seek to build a greater culture upon a broader, firmer base.

## SCIENCE IN AMERICAN THOUGHT

It is but natural that in a society so profoundly affected by science our intellectual life should likewise be focused in that direction. At Oxford it remains doubtful whether science has yet earned a true place in education. At Chicago, on the other hand, three of the four main divisions of the University are called sciences. A part of this emphasis is indeed ascribable to the need for at least a passing knowledge of science in every profession; but it nevertheless represents truly our educators' judgment of the value of science in enriching life.

To the man of science himself, it is primarily as a method of developing the human spirit that he values his work. In this regard science is to him a truly cultural pursuit. His study affords exercise of imagination and broadening of perspective. Whereas to Plotinus it appeared that "It is through intuition rather than through reason that we may approach our highest aspirations," the scientist finds that in the discipline of unprejudiced search for truth lies the beginning of wisdom. Thus, in the words of Thomas Huxley:

> Science seems to me to teach in the highest and strongest manner the great truth which is embodied in the Christian conception of entire surrender to the will of God. Sit down before a fact as a little child, be prepared to give up every preconceived notion, follow humbly wherever and to whatever abysses nature leads, or you shall learn nothing.[3]

To a certain degree this humanizing aspect of science is esoteric, since it can be fully appreciated only by those who have themselves submitted to the discipline required to share in the effort to widen the horizons of knowledge. Certain fields of science, notably astronomy, have enabled amateurs to take part in their enterprise, however, and anyone can learn to practice a scientific approach to the everyday facts which shape his acts. It is hard to suggest any method more effective in bringing about a widely spread regard for impartial truth than by the growth of such active participation in scientific endeavor. Herbert Hoover speaks for American science when he would "strengthen the fiber of national life by the inculcation of that veracity of thought which springs alone from the search for truth."

This direct encouragement toward reliance upon tested truth is but one of the moral implications of science. Perhaps more evident in historical perspective is its indirect consequence in the moral growth required by the socialization of man. Just as the automobile demands sobriety, or congested life makes necessary careful sanitation, so the mutual dependence of people in a technological civilization implies consideration of the rights of others. James Breasted has shown how the growth of community life along the Nile stimulated among the Egyptians the "dawn of conscience." Professor Cheney, in his retiring presidential address before the American Historical Association, lists prominently among his "laws" of history the trend toward a greater consideration of one's fellows as society grows more complex. In our American technological society when each contributes his expert part our needs are fully met, while hardship comes to all if any fails his share. Thus science and industry are emphasizing as never before the need of the will toward cooperation. This is simply the Christian doctrine of the love of our neighbors as expressed in service.

## SCIENCE DEMANDS RELIGIOUS GROWTH

Both directly and indirectly science affects also religious attitudes. The effect of the impact of modern science on Christian doctrine is an exam-

[3] See Chapter 1, fn. 4.

ple of a long historical development of religion as influenced by man's growing understanding. Among the more thoughtful members of the American community there appears no longer any serious intellectual threat by science against an adequately formulated religion. Saint Paul described the religious man as one who "is alive to all true values." By enabling men to see more clearly what these values are and to work for them more effectively, science has, as Dean Inge recently remarked, become an ally of religion.

The world of science and technology is one in which an adequate religion is most urgently needed. We have noted above that the great demand of modern life is for adequate guidance in directing the mighty forces at our disposal. Such guidance implies knowledge of the road toward the best. Thus attention to the fundamental problem of ethics is the supreme demand of an age of science. Technology supplies the motive power. Organized industry and government constitute the control and steering mechanism. But who will tell us where to go? In America it is only our religious leaders who have seriously attempted to answer this question.

Most significant of the factors that give strength to man is the vision of a goal which he recognizes as worthy of his supreme effort. On this basis Lenin rallies all the Russians to support a Communistic world revolution. Hitler makes a sick Germany throb with vitality by the sacrificial call to every man to devote himself to the welfare of the state. Here are unifying religions in action. If there is a fatal weakness in American society it is in our lack of objective. With our divided counsels, an efficient social evolution will not let us survive in competition with nations or social groups that know where they want to go. Our formal religious organizations offer just such divided counsels. As one who has been actively concerned with efforts to bring amity and understanding among Catholics, Protestants, and Jews,* I find it easy to become discouraged. These are those who know best that to glorify their God they must seek the welfare of all mankind. Yet among them are suspicions and jealousies, deeply based upon historical conflicts, which roughen the road of friendly cooperation. If the counsels of our spiritual leaders divide us, where is our hope? We must look to them for vision. "Art thou the Christ, or look we for another?" "To whom shall we go?"

Science presents to religion the greatest challenge of a millennium, that of presenting modern man with an objective adequate to his needs. We cannot be satisfied with the cold, godless, nationalistic doctrines of Europe. Untold strength and comfort lie in the ancient teachings; but we find no life in much of the diluted, supine, and self-interested dogma that is now being taught in the name of religion. Yet religion we must have.

Never were men more eager to work for the best. Without the unifying religion that can show us that best, our lives are purposeless and our society cannot long endure.

Science itself is not that religion. Nevertheless, though the student of science may not feel qualified to choose for others that which gives life dignity and worth, he does supply the data from which that choice must be made. How can we correctly orient ourselves without learning the facts about the world and dispassionately considering their implications? Thus the Christian's great need is, as Paul says, "that your love may grow richer in knowledge and perfect insight, so that you may have a sense of what is vital." It is, I believe, in just this direction that science must ultimately make its greatest human contribution. Science must clarify the vision of the seers who would point out to us the goal of life.

Of the three Promethean gifts of science, it was the greater variety of life that Francis Bacon described in his *New Atlantis*. It was its responsibility for man's social evolution that led George Sarton to describe the growth of science as the central thread along which may be traced the biography of mankind. To the scientist himself comes the satisfaction that with his new knowledge an addition has been made to man's heritage which not only is permanent but is a seed that will grow from more to more.

Having eaten of the fruit of the tree of knowledge we have in a new sense become as gods, with greater power for good and evil. We have been cast once more from the paradise of a well-established, traditional life. Punishment for our errors is by an angel with a keener, more flaming sword as we live the hard life of new responsibilities. And so we are forced to search for greater wisdom to govern our greater powers. If a brighter paradise is to be regained, it is that of the joy of the struggle toward greater manhood.

# 42. Science and the Supernatural

## 1946

In 1931 Professor A. J. Carlson, a noted physiologist, delivered a lecture that Mr. Compton interpreted as denying significance to anything other than physical events and implying that religion is inconsistent with science. Upon Carlson's election as president of the American Association for the Advancement of Science, in 1944, the *Scientific Monthly* published his address * as indicative of a distinguished scientist's outlook on science and on life. Concerned lest Carlson's views on religion be considered representative of those held by most scientists, Mr. Compton, himself a past president of the AAAS, prepared this article as a reply.* In it he states his own belief that a world that has science needs religion as never before.

Those whose thinking is disciplined by science, like all others, need a basis for the good life, for aspiration, for courage to do great deeds. They need a faith to live by. The hope of the world lies in those who have such faith and who use the methods of science to make their visions become real. Such visions and hope and faith are not a part of science. Physics, chemistry, and biology are not concerned with them. They are known by an individual only as he himself experiences them. Though stimulated by the outside world, they are not of it. They are beyond the nature that science knows. Of such is the true "supernatural" that gives meaning to life. This supernatural is as real as the natural world of science and is consistent with the most rigorous application of the scientific method.

It is important for those who are concerned with finding adequate objectives for living in a scientific world to understand the danger that comes from basing our greatest values on evidence that science cannot accept. Science requires of religion that the language in which its great truths have been stated by prophets who lived in an age of magic, miracles, and mysticism be translated into a language of verifiable fact. This lesson our religious leaders must learn, or inevitably with the growth of public reliance on science the effectiveness of their teaching will decline.

Let me give one scientist's view of the fundamentals of religion. The following ideas are taken almost wholly from religious sources whose traditional authenticity is unquestionable. Yet I find no way in which they conflict with the spirit of science.

I take it that religion is concerned with the worship of God. God, however, is a word with many meanings. I shall consider three meanings that are of special religious significance: God as the ruler of the universe, God as a hero to be admired and emulated, and God as the spirit of the highest good which serves as the guiding principle of one's life.

Better than at any earlier time, we who live in a scientific world can recognize the grandeur of the universe of which we are a part. We have learned many of the laws by which it works, of the motions of stars and atoms, and something of the evolution of galaxies and of life. What will be our attitude toward this world? Shall we fear what may happen to us, be impassive, or have confidence in what the future will bring? Can our efforts adapt our world to our needs, or must we suppose that an irrevocable fate approaches over which we have no control, so that effort is meaningless?

Science tells us that a well-adapted organism thrives and an ill-adapted one declines and eventually disappears. This may be summarized by saying that on the whole the world is kind to all that live and is especially so to those that learn nature's laws and follow them. Experience shows that we can use the forces of nature to shape our world and that our lives are better or worse according to what type of changes we make.

Jesus has summarized such common experience with the great powers that shape our destinies by the phrase "Our Father which art in heaven," or "Heavenly Father." By this he implies that these great powers help those who work in accord with their laws. As children in our father's home, we have a proper place in the world. We also can share in shaping the world: "My Father worketh to this end, and I work."

It is helpful to compare such a religious concept with a typical scientific theory; for example, the physicist's theory of the ether. When we pray to our fatherly God it is common experience that we receive courage and strength to do deeds of friendliness toward his children. It is hard to think of receiving strength without imagining a being that gives us the strength. Similarly, by performing certain optical experiments, we find that light has the properties of waves, and it is hard to think of waves without imagining a medium in which the waves can occur. Hence the concept of the "luminiferous ether."

Both the fatherly God and the luminiferous ether are hypotheses that are fruitful of useful consequences. If God is our father, we are his children and other persons become our brothers. We thus have an understandable basis for loving our fellows. When we examine the properties that the ether must have to transmit waves with the speed of light, we find that these properties also fit it to transmit electric and magnetic forces and we have a basis for understanding the relation between electricity and light. If the Ruler of the Universe is as a father, we can rest assured and he will provide for our basic needs. If space is filled with a medium that has the properties needed for it to transmit electrical waves of light, then we can predict interesting effects produced on light by electrical and magnetic fields, predictions which when tested by Faraday and Kerr are found to be correct.

A scientist gauges the value of a theory by the fruitfulness of its consequences. In judging the worth of religious teachings our highest authority says, "By their fruits ye shall know them." By this test both the theory of the ether and the concept of God as a father are fruitful of valuable results and hence good.

The rationalist can correctly claim that in neither case do the tests supply valid evidence for the truth of the hypothesis. Is it God that gives us strength or is it our faith that there is a God? Is there indeed a medium that transmits the waves, or is the medium merely an intellectual device for interpreting an observed pattern of optical effects? Physicists recognize that the ether is a convenient name for certain properties of space and that calling it a "medium" gives inaccurate connotations because of our familiarity with solid, liquid, and gaseous media; yet because in terms of this ethereal medium it is possible to explain what actually happens, we continue to use the concept. An "ethereal medium" is the best brief description of these properties of space that has been invented. It helps our constructive imagination to think of an ether in dealing with light and electricity. Similarly, theologians recognize that the use of the term God is only a convenient name for certain great powers that operate in nature and particularly in man and that speaking of God as a father gives inaccurate connotations because of our tendency to think of all the physiological characteristics of the human fathers that we know. Yet, because in terms of this fatherly God we can so accurately describe what actually happens in the normal life of an individual living in a world to which he is adapted, the concept remains very useful and no other brief description of these powers has proved to be so adequate. Thinking of a fatherly God thus helps in giving us a correct attitude toward our world.

"Is there a fatherly God?" is a question precisely similar to "Is there an ethereal medium?" In both cases the answer is yes and no. If by ethereal you mean something mystical or to be found only outside the earth, if by medium you mean a solid or a liquid or a gas, there is no ethereal medium that transmits waves of light. But if by ethereal you mean the dialectric constant and magnetic permeability appropriate to empty space, and if by medium you mean that which transmits electromagnetic waves, there is in truth an ethereal medium.

Likewise, if by father you mean the physiological sire of a child, if by God you mean a manlike entity that dwells in the space between the stars, there is no fatherly God. But if by fatherly you refer to the friendly, yet disciplinary, aspects of the world that teach you how best to act to meet whatever happens and to be pleased that your experiences make you more of a man, if by God you mean the creative and controlling forces at work in the world, then there is indeed a fatherly God for all who want to find him.

So much for the concept of God as ruler of the universe. Now let us think of God as a hero to be admired and emulated. Our heroes have always been our gods who have helped us in shaping our attitudes and actions. We see in our great men the embodiment of some spirit we admire and want to share. I remember how my father reasoned out his own Christian philosophy and used it to fortify and stabilize his life; and, trying to follow his footsteps, I became an ancestor worshiper. I have an older brother whose interest and achievement in science have inspired me to do likewise, and I have sought and carefully weighed his counsel when facing crucial decisions. The General with whom I was most intimately associated in the effort to win the war has become to me the personification of complete patriotism. He helps me understand the values and the dangers of that great virtue. Anton Carlson I admire because of his devotion to rigorous scientific truth. "Honest Anton," we call him and love him for his courage, though we may deplore his inability to recognize the limitations of science. From earliest childhood I have learned to see in Jesus the supreme example of one who loves his neighbors and expresses that love in actions that count, who knows that people can find their souls by losing themselves in something of great value, who will die rather than deny the truth in favor of the popular view held by his most respected contemporaries. That Jesus' spirit lives so vitally in men today makes me hope that by following in his footsteps in my small way I also may live forever.

It would do violence to common usage to say, except in the extreme case of the One whom I hold as my supreme example, that these men are my gods. But it is correct to say that for me they all represent certain aspects of the Divine Spirit, and by knowing them I come to know my God. In particular, Jesus becomes the central figure in exemplifying the ideals that I would like to live by. I admire him, emulate him, and become loyal to him. He becomes my Hero-God.

Yet from the religious point of view, the most fundamental meaning of God is neither the ruler of the universe nor the hero after whom one patterns one's life. It is rather the "highest good" which one takes as the guiding principle of one's life.

I am reminded of the day when Jesus paused to chat with the woman at the well. You recall the setting. "Our fathers worshiped in this mountain," was the woman's comment; "and ye say that in Jerusalem is the place where men ought to worship." "Believe me," replied Jesus, "the hour cometh, and now is, when the true worshipers shall worship the Father in spirit and in truth. God is a spirit; and they that worship him must worship him in spirit and in truth."

If God is what we worship, God is that which we value most highly, to which we would devote our lives. We may worship that God by prayer or by action. Prayer consists in trying to find what our God would have us do. The action is determined on the basis of the answer to that prayer.

Take, for example, the man whose god is money. The gaining of riches becomes the objective of his life. His sordid prayer becomes the scheming to gain more wealth, and his acquisitiveness is reflected in his every act. Or take the man whose god is the state. He puts its welfare above all other values. He is the patriot who sees the supreme good in the glory of his nation, even at the expense of the rest of the world. The Christian's God is the God of love. "God is love; and he who ever continues in love keeps in union with God, and God wth him." Perhaps one should explain that by Christian love is meant not a physical passion nor a sentiment of adoration and admiration, but a friendliness that expresses itself in doing good to one's neighbors. Prayer to the God of love means a thoughtful consideration of how such good can best be done. The action resulting from such a prayer is the highest worship of the God of love. "A religious observance that is pure and stainless in the sight of God the Father is this: to look after orphans and widows in their trouble, and keep oneself unstained by the world."

Jesus is vehement in his insistence that concern with the true worth of things is the one essential without which life really has no value: "Whoever speaks against the Son of Man will be forgiven for it; but whoever speaks against the Holy Spirit cannot be forgiven for it, either in this world or in the world to come." St. Paul in a positive way is equally outspoken: "The spiritual man is alive to all true values, but his own true value no unspiritual man can see."

There is an immense difference between a good religion and a bad religion in the satisfactions and disappointments to which they lead. The main difference is the nature of the values or the kind of spirit that the religion inspires. The true God is the spirit that is found to be of lasting value, so that when the test comes one can feel that whatever may happen he has spent his life for the best that he knows. The false God is the desire that when attained does not bring satisfaction but makes one feel that he has betrayed or lost something of greater value.

Here is the essence of religion, the pearl of great price for which one sells everything that he has in order that he may own the pearl. One's God is in truth the spirit that inspires his actions, that which gives him the aspiration and purpose—the will—to lose himself in something of value. What is that spirit? The Christian answer is love that shows itself in deeds that help one's fellows.

It remains only to point out that the God of the highest good is indeed effective in our lives. During the recent war, as we saw the value of freedom, our nation became inspired to the great achievement that brought us victory. Freedom was the great good, the aspect of God, that we sought. I saw one group, determined to stop the Nazi threat against the world's freedom, catch the vision of the new weapon of atomic energy. With faith in that vision and driven by devotion to freedom, they performed the miracle of the atomic bomb. I have seen my friends, worshiping the God of love, catch the vison of a richer life for all mankind and by heroic self-sacrifice bring new hope to people whose lives had held little meaning. I have seen young men and women in college catch the spirit of service for their fellows and do a job far greater than that of their companions who had failed to catch that spirit. And the lives of the latter have been drab, whereas those that have been driven by the spirit of service have had the glowing faces that come with the rich life that money cannot buy. Do we want magic and mysticism, an Aladdin's lamp that will change a peasant's hut into a prince's palace? Here in worship of the God of the spirit of the highest good such magic is truly to be found.

Without saying so, I have outlined here an interpretation of that most abstruse of Christian teachings, the doctrine of the Trinity: God the Father, God the Hero-Son, and God the Spirit. In their essence there can be no conflict between science and religion. Science is a reliable method of finding truth. Religion is the search for a satisfying basis for life.

Every religion builds for itself a structure that goes far beyond the foundation that I have just sketched. It develops its guiding principles using the best thought of the time. Jesus taught in stories of daily life. The later Christian writings were shaped in the combined atmosphere of later Greek philosophy and of Oriental magic and mysticism. It was an intellectual atmosphere to which present-day thought is ill adapted. It is of most vital importance that the eternal spirit of religion for which our century cries shall break out of the sarcophagus of the magic formulas in which it is buried and come to vigorous life in our lives.

The breaking of idols is a necessary and recurring process. This is done not only in religion. Science also has its Gideons, its John the Baptists, and its Luthers. It was not long ago that Werner Heisenberg told the scientific world:

> The resolution of the paradoxes of atomic physics can be accomplished only by renunciation of old and cherished ideas. Most important of these is the idea that natural phenomena obey exact laws—the principle of causality.[1]

No principle had seemed more precious in science than that of exact laws, and it has gone hard with many old heroes in the field to see the younger men quit the faith that to them seemed the very foundation of their thinking. Yet the worshipers of this idol are rapidly growing less, and in its place is a spirit of faith in the simplest interpretation of scientific evidence that has given to physics a vigorous new life.

For many centuries concepts of the supernatural have served as focusing points for the thought and meditation of millions of faithful religious souls. These concepts have served as our icons and idols; but some of them are now as anachronistic as the golden calf. If our religious leaders are to bring to the present day the vital, living spirit of their faith, they must take science seriously. Science is growing. Yet a world that has science needs as never before the inspiration that religion has to offer. In a strict, literal sense it is true that the supernatural of magic and miracles and mysticism is of an outlived era. But the other half of the picture is far more important. Beyond the nature taught by science is the spirit that gives meaning to life.

"So faith, hope, and love endure, these three; but the greatest of them is love." This is not science, or nature. It is the true supernatural.

[1] Heisenberg: *The Physical Principles of the Quantum Theory,* p. 62.

# X

## Science and
## Man's Destiny

The *American dream* . . . is not a dream of motor
cars and high wages merely, but a dream of a social
order in which each man and each woman shall be
able to attain to the fullest stature of which they are
innately capable, and be recognized by others for
what they are, regardless of the fortuitous circumstances of birth or position.

JAMES TRUSLOW ADAMS

# 43.  Man's Hopes and the New Need
for Human Responsibility

*1954*

&#x269C; At Mr. Compton's invitation, leaders of thought from
many fields in the United States and abroad assembled at Washington
University in October 1954 for the first of a series of private conferences on Science and Human Responsibility.* The participants * considered in detail how the powers of science might be used to combat
destitution, disease, and degrading ignorance in order that mankind
might achieve a humanly satisfying destiny. In his opening address
Mr. Compton discussed the rapidity of social change and called for a
cooperative effort to utilize the opportunities provided by science to
enable men and women to fulfill their potentialities.

## INTRODUCTION

The time has come to consider human responsibility in light of science.
The hard, straight thinking that is typified by science has profoundly
altered man's view of himself and his world. The unprecedented powers
that technology has placed in man's hands have increased greatly his
capacity for shaping his life for either good or evil. Both dangers and
opportunities appear before us demanding urgent attention. It is a time
requiring great decisions.

At such a time it is of utmost importance that we review the possibilities
that lie before us, that we appraise our sources of strength, above all that
we consider with care the direction in which we wish to move. Powers
beyond human control are forcing us into rapid change. We can, however,
control in substantial measure the direction of the change. Here lies our
great opportunity, our human responsibility.

In what direction does man want to go? What is possible for us? What
is our economic and physical potential? What sources of knowledge, what

deep wells of courage and inspiration are available to us, in order that we may work effectively toward the goals we select? What are the practical steps that need to be taken now in order that the way toward these goals may be kept open, in order that the changes that are taking place may build and not destroy what we value most highly?

It is to consider such questons that we have come together. This conference has been called by scientists. In our work we have known the excitement of the search for new truth. We have shared in placing new and powerful tools in the hands of those who are shaping the world. The full urgency of the decisions that the existence of these tools demands stands sharply before us.

One is reminded of an old legend of Daedalus. He had discovered the art of making steel. Working long with forge and hammer he fashioned a steel sword and presented it to King Minos of Crete. His friends came to him in dismay saying, "Daedalus, why did you give the king a sword of steel? This will not bring us happiness; it will bring us strife."

"It is not my purpose to make you happy," was Daedalus' reply. "I want to make you great."

It is evident that science plays much the same role as the steel of Daedalus. With the new strength that it gives science is forcing man to make decisions that will either ruin him or educate him to greatness.

It is our faith and our ardent hope that knowledge of scientific truth will ultimately ennoble human life. It is to ensure such use of our precious truth that we have invited here men and women who are active in shaping the new world. Among us are scholars of history and philosophy and religion, technologists in the fields of engineering, medicine, business and public administration. Industry is represented; education in its formal and in its informal aspects; thinkers and governors from East and West. We who are scientists appreciate your response to our call for your counsel. We are united in the hope that our newly formed strength may be used that men and women shall grow to greater stature.

There are those who will question the usefulness of such a gathering as this. Too much needs to be done now, they say, to spend time in thought! It is true that man is embarking on a jet plane rather than on a leisurely sailing ship; but this is the greater reason to pause before we take off on our journey. We must first make sure of our destination. We must locate the refueling stops, the dangerous mountains, and the emergency landing fields en route.

There are some who believe that today the defense of our freedom is so urgently important that here is where our full attention should be concentrated. Others see in the problem of economic sufficiency in a world of rapidly growing population the crucial question, now and for generations to come.

The truth is that the problems we face, urgent and difficult though they are, can be solved. There is only one condition. That condition lies in the spirit of man. How important is it to man that destitution and disease and ignorance shall decline? How important is it to man that he shall be free to work toward the best he knows? Science and technology supply the means to advance in these directions. Whether we do advance depends upon what is in the hearts of men. This is why the prime concern of the present conference is with the values of life and how we can best work toward their attainment.

Many years ago Nehemiah told how he and his men rebuilt the walls of Jerusalem. In one hand they held a sword, in the other a trowel. "And so," he said, "the wall was built, for the men had a mind to work."

Thus it is today. Unfortunately, one hand must still hold the sword, for once again there are those who want us to fail in our effort to build the wall. But what is of prime importance is that men shall see the importance of the wall itself and of building the city that the wall will protect. For it is when they feel the vital value to them of this noble city that men have a mind to work.

There are at this conference those who have spent many of their best years at war, defending man's freedom. The scientists among us can hardly be blind to the urgent military and political problems posed by the dread power of the atom. It was, after all, their fate to be responsible for the release of this power. Now, however, we are concerned with the noble city of man that we want to build. May we not hope that when the vision of this city becomes clear, it will appear so desirable to all men everywhere that they will have a mind to work together in its construction? If this hope can be achieved, the hands that hold the sword will be freed, and progress in building the city will be greatly advanced.

## RAPID GROWTH OF HUMAN RESPONSIBILITY

Whence then does the new need for human responsibility arise? To this question there are two answers that supplement each other. The first is that science and technology are changing the way we live. We are being rapidly transformed from one condition of life to another. This calls for many new choices, for drastic decisions. The question of what is good and what is evil cannot be avoided. The responsibilities of freedom are upon us. The very power of science has made our decisions vital to all mankind. We must do our best to choose wisely.

The second answer is that with our growing knowledge we see ourselves in new perspective. What are we? Whence have we come? Whither are we going? In what respects is our life determined by conditions beyond our control? To what degree are we free? What new possibilities does science open before us? What sources of strength of spirit are open to us? What are the goals toward which men may reasonably aspire? Faced by such questions as these, we must review the old answers and search for new insght in light of the expanding vistas and clearer vision that science supplies. It is on the basis of our answers to these questions that we must make the choices required by our rapidly changing pattern of life.

## 1. Social changes now in progress

What are these changes to which we refer? One fundamental change in our mode of life is that the contacts of person with person are becoming more frequent and more extensive. This growing interdependence is a part of the process of becoming more civilized. From an individual as a member of a family, man finds himself becoming in turn a villager, a citizen of a city-state, and now of a nation. We are in the process of becoming members of a world community. Thus the community to which one belongs is extending more and more widely until already in many of its aspects it embraces all of mankind.

Another significant change is that in the part of the world that has been most strongly affected by technology, health and prosperity have been increasing. Thus in the United States, between 1900 and 1950, while the population approximately doubled, the life expectancy has increased from forty-six to sixty-nine years and the real wages have risen threefold. These figures are not typical of what is happening over the world, first because this nation is far above the average in the use of technology, and second because it was not as seriously damaged as was most of the industrialized world by the two great wars. For these very reasons, however, the changes in the United States show the more clearly the characteristic effects of advancing technology.

But the changes extend also to other aspects of life. Thus in 1900 in the United States about four per cent of the young people of college age were attending college, while in 1950 about 20 per cent were enrolled. Church membership has increased over this fifty-year period from less than 30 per cent of the population to about 56 per cent.

These favorable changes in the pattern of our normal way of life seem to me much more significant than the troubles that have been so greatly dramatized—troubles such as those resulting from the drastic advances in the art of war, and the painful by-products of rapid social change. It is true that the existence of airplanes, long-range guided missiles, and atomic bombs has altered our whole attitude toward war as a means of settling disputes. Appeal to arms has become so dangerous that major war is henceforth a matter of desperation rather than of political judgment. Similarly, with rapidly changing conditions, new conflicts arise among groups differing in race, religion, occupation, or culture as they are thrown into closer competition or are compelled to work more closely together. Painful alterations of marriage customs are occurring, together with feelings of insecurity, anxiety, and tensions of many kinds. It is because of such developments that effort toward mutual understanding has become increasingly so important.

To me it seems evident, however, that the constructive achievements of this era are vastly more significant. Where technology has been used for the service of man, there is in broad total a healthy growth not only in man's biological life but also in his intellectual and spiritual life.

## 2. The role of science in effecting social change

Though these changes are occurring most obviously in communities where technology has been highly developed, it would be a mistake, as I see it, to suppose that science and technology are their primary source. Science has indeed given us a new and clearer view of ourselves. Technology has enabled us to live longer and to meet our needs more fully. But these constitute only the means whereby we work toward what we wish to attain. The motivation for these changes is to be found rather in the recognition of the value of man as a human being and in the desire to improve our own lot and that of those around us.

This recognition of the inherent value and importance of man came first perhaps through religious sources. It has become incorporated in our political organization, especially in what we call our democratic society. The religions of Judaic origin have taught that since man is a child of God, each person should recognize the value of every other. Such emphasis on the value of every person is to some degree an essential aspect of all important living religions.

The political development of this idea of man's value began with Greek democracy. Here the view of democracy was limited: only the free man might aspire to achieve his best development. That such high aspiration is the proper heritage of all persons, while recognized by Stoic Rome, did not become essential to any major political structure until the eighteenth century. One of the striking observations that I made on a recent trip through Asia and Europe is that the ideal of human dignity as ascribed to every individual is now a concept of worldwide influence. This concept has, as a matter of fact, become the keystone of the political structure of the free world.

What science and technology have added is the all-important practical possibility of achieving this universal dignity and freedom for man of which we have dreamed. Until the present century, the only practical possibility for the good life in most parts of the world has been that recognized by the Greeks: that certain select individuals through the efforts of others might hope to free themselves from the limitations of poverty, ignorance, and disease and develop toward the best that they know. The introduction of technology based on science [1] has altered this situation in two ways. It has made possible a growing abundance such that every person may hope for a better life. It has also created a situation in which the most promising approach for an individual toward his own welfare is through wide cooperation with others toward fuller life as a common goal. It is thus that the attainment of a better life has in fact become a vision toward which men and women throughout the world now aspire.

## 3. The increasing tempo of history

It is significant that the changes of which we have been speaking have been occurring at a rapidly increasing rate. For the first time in history, changes in man's way of life that modify his whole future outlook are now happening in the span of one generation. This is why we say that the choices made now are crucial.

This appraisal is supported by a review of man's long growth. Let us turn for a moment toward the picture that science gives us of whence we have come.

According to the most generally accepted thinking of astronomers and

---

[1] Let me pause to clarify the sense in which I am using the terms "science" and "technology." Strictly speaking, we mean by science the body of knowledge that has arisen from observation of the world and that is subject to verification by any who will make the appropriate tests. By technology we refer to all systematized arts that make use of scientific knowledge. Thus science includes not only the physical and biological sciences but also the sciences of society and of psychology insofar as these represent objective knowledge that can be verified. Similarly, I am using technology to include not only the mechanical arts as they depend on physical science, but also agriculture, medicine, education, and the administration of business and public affairs insofar as these arts make use of their related sciences. In a less strict sense we frequently use the word science also to include both science and technology. I trust that the gain in simplicity of wording that comes from such rather loose usage will justify the lack of precision that will sometimes be apparent.

physicists, the beginning of the physical universe dates from about four or five billion years ago. Before this time it seems that not only were there no stars and atoms but that time itself was something of only indefinite meaning. It may be that this concept will need revision, but at least it will serve as the starting point for our present review of man's history.*

Roughly three billion years ago the earth was formed. Our earliest evidences of life date back a billion years. Then came in succession the appearance of the vertebrates, the mammals, and, a million or so years ago, primitive man. It is some fifty thousand years since *Homo sapiens*, man of the kind we know, first appeared on the scene. Six thousand years ago we find the beginnings of civilized life, and as my late colleague James Breasted described it, the dawn of social conscience. In the following millennia came the introduction of writing, the foundations of logic and of Greek science, the growth of the great religions, the development of the technology first of the precious metals, then of bronze, and later of iron and steel. Some five hundred years ago occurred the European Renaissance, the printing of books, the discoveries of the great geographic explorers, and the establishment of the testing of hypotheses as the foundation for the firm growth of modern science. It is within the last two generations that so many of the great developments of science and technology have occurred. These include the establishment of the germ theory of disease, proof of the existence of atoms, the discovery of the electron and of radioactivity, the knowledge of the age of the rocks, the measurement of the distance of the stars and galaxies, the development of organic chemistry, the discovery of antibiotics, and the extensive applications of many forms of technology.

If we should liken the five billion years of the world's existence to a year, the last two generations are but a third of a second, the time required to take a quick step. The remarkable fact is that during the time required for this step there has been added to the heritage of man something that is substantial in relation to that of all the long year of his previous history. This is what we mean by saying that we are changing rapidly. It is this striking fact that impels us to ask with new urgency: Where are we going? Toward what destiny should we aspire?

### THE HUMAN SITUATION

## 1. Man's nature

As we look at ourselves through the eyes of science, what do we find? Briefly, it is this. We are a part of nature, comparable with all that we see around us. In every act we obey the same natural laws. We are, neverthe-less, a most remarkable part. We are aware of what goes on. We can exchange ideas with each other. Within certain limits we can shape the world about us. We are free to create new structures, new ideas, that have not existed before.

Last autumn I heard Sir Lawrence Bragg, the distinguished British physicist, present a lecture on the arrangement of the atoms in protein molecules. Proteins are chemical compounds that constitute an essential part of living matter. Bragg was concerned with the particular protein molecule that had recently been identified as the gene that plays a funda-mental part in heredity.* Its structure he described as being in the form of a twin spiral, each twin having a relation to the other similar to that of a template and its corresponding pattern. Such a structure affords a means of precise reproduction from one molecule to the next. The spirals them-selves are composed of hundreds of thousands of atoms, arranged in clusters called "radicals" by the chemists. Just as letters grouped into words can give complicated and precise instructions, so atoms grouped into such radicals that are in turn arranged in complicated but definite molecules may determine the structure of an organism. Thus though we do not know the details, we see the possibility that heredity has its expla-nation in purely physical terms.

I mention this one recent development of physical chemistry to empha-size the fact that what the scientist finds gives us good reason to suppose that man in his physical structure is in no essential way different from the rest of the world of nature: he is composed of the same atoms, obeys the same laws of conservation of energy, or thermodynamics, and so on. All that we know in science seems to confirm this conclusion.

## 2. Awareness

Nevertheless, men and women have this remarkable characteristic: we are aware of what happens to us; we think, we feel, we have emotions.

There has long been a tendency to suppose that these conscious aspects of man are in some way to be explained in terms of our physical nature. Such effects as those of coffee and alcohol on our thought processes have shown a connection between the state of our consciousness and the chemi-cal balance in our blood. When it became recognized also that our tem-perament was strongly affected by the hormones secreted by various glands, the materialistic interpretation of consciousness seemed strongly supported. Surprisingly, however, it was when the engineers began to develop what they called "thinking" machines that the inability to approach an understanding of thought by physical methods became most obvious.

A simple form of thinking machine is a thermostat, which notes when the temperature is too high or too low and makes the appropriate response.

A more complicated thinking machine is the antiaircraft gun control. Such a device has its radar for detecting danger. Its electronic brain judges how to aim the gun and when the shell shall be fired; or if the plane does not come within range it will refuse to fire. No wonder we call it a thinking machine. Yet to suppose that this device is aware of what is happening would be a completely gratuitous assumption. While it responds to stimuli as does a thinking man, all of its processes follow a plan set by its builder and act in accord with well-tested physical principles. There is no evidence whatever of awareness.

But this raises another far-reaching question. You may suppose a speaker addressing an audience has ideas going through his mind and that he is aware of what he is saying. But what evidence is available to you that he has any such awareness? The fact is that if you were to examine him with the best instruments that science knows, you would find a mechanism that is merely acting according to well-known laws of physics and chemistry. Nothing more. Is he more conscious than a phonograph speaking what it is made to say? What makes you think that he has ideas and emotions? Is not the answer that you see in him something that is similar to yourself and you know that if you were speaking similar words, your words would be related to your own thoughts and emotions?

The only reliable evidence we have of awareness and thoughts and emotions is that which each of us has within himself, as a matter of his own firsthand knowledge. Insofar as we recognize similar ideas and awareness in someone or something else, it is through a sense of kinship. We see in the other person something that acts so like ourselves that we ascribe to him that of which we are ourselves aware. This knowledge of our own awareness—our acquaintance with thoughts, sensations, and emotions—is something that is much more immediate than objective scientific knowledge.

This is a point that needs special emphasis. We do not arrive at information about our state of mind through observation and analysis of data. Such knowledge is much more immediate to us than in our observation of something external, not to mention our logical analysis of the meaning of such observations. Here is information that we have about ourselves that also goes behind and beyond anything that can be deduced from scientific data. It is a matter of firsthand knowledge within ourselves.

My reason for emphasizing this point is that, in the effort to obtain a more adequate view of ourselves through science, we have found that an important area of our knowledge goes beyond the realm of scientific observation. Certain things are discoverable by precise observation and logical analysis. Some of these facts we have learned, and these form the basis of our picture of man's physical nature. But we learn further that the realm of consciousness, feeling, emotion, and awareness, is one about which physical observation by itself gives us no information whatever.

The fact is rather this: the physical object that we call man acts according to certain physical laws that are more or less well understood. These acts and laws do not of themselves imply anything with regard to the conscious aspects of man. Nevertheless, they are obviously consistent with the fact that man is a conscious being. This is evident from the very fact that each of us knows within himself the presence of his consciousness while, if he examines himself as a physical mechanism, he finds that he obeys the same laws of nature as do the objects in the world around him.

Thus it is that we must recognize the two distinct sources of information with regard to man. The first of these is that of our immediate awareness regarding our own thoughts and feelings. The second is that of our scientific knowledge that comes through physical observations.

## 3. The experience of freedom

There is another significant realm in which man's actions go beyond the province of science. This is our experience of freedom. We mean by our experience of freedom that within certain limits we find that we can shape the world to our desires. Typical is the fact that, if I wish, I can raise my arm. As a matter of external observation, if you can see my arm rise, you can note merely that in this action such laws as those of Newton, the conservation of energy, the second law of thermodynamics, etc., are observed. You may perhaps find the physical causes of which the motion is a consequence. It is only I who can authoritatively say that my arm moved as I willed. Nor can anyone else properly question whether this is the fact. This is a matter of my firsthand experience.

Over a considerable part of the history of science it has been thought that the world is a physically determined system, so that the experience of freedom must have little connection with physical events. With the advent of quantum mechanics some thirty years ago, the thought of physicists in this regard has undergone a significant revolution. Attending this conference are those who have taken a most active part in this revolution. It is fair to say that the laws of science as we now know them describe physical events in such a way as to leave open the possibility of human freedom.

Our scientific knowledge does not, however, of itself give any indication that such freedom exists. That we do in fact shape the world to our desires, just as the fact that we are aware of what is happening, is known only from our firsthand experience. These facts are not obtainable through scientific observation, but they are nevertheless consistent with our scientific knowledge of the physical world.

## 4. Man's growth as a person

It is significant that the aspects of life that are of human meaning are those that go beyond scientific observation. I have in mind such matters as emotion and feeling and thought, the excitement of the search for truth, the love of beauty, the aspiration for goodness. These things that give meaning to life have reality because we know them as a part of our immediate consciousness. They are, however, things about which scientific observation gives no indication whatever.

Thus as we view man through the eye of science we find much valuable information regarding his origin, his structure, and the physical basis of his life. But in the broader view we find that he is much more than the sum of all these things. He is a being of spiritual aspiration, of human feeling and emotion. It is these aspects of man that demand for him an increasing destiny.

I recall as a college student reading a book by the eminent American psychologist William James. He was discussing what we mean by the "self." He pointed out that the boundary of what I consider as my self is not my skin; it includes, for example, the clothes that I wear. Thus it is important to my state of mind that in addressing this audience I shall be properly clad for the occasion. The self, he adds, extends to the family. What my wife, my brothers, my parents, my children may think and do affects my confidence in myself, my status in society, my ability to meet the demands of life. They are in this sense a part of my own life.

What technology is doing is to extend this "selfhood" to include an ever widening circle. It includes, to a greater or lesser degree, all of mankind.

Thus during recent months I flew away from the United States and back again by way of the Pacific and India and Europe. I take some pride in the fact that I am one who can fly. And yet is it true to say that *I* can fly? It would be more correct to say not that I can fly, but that *man* can fly. I identify myself with those who are capable of this achievement.

This is what I mean by saying that the individual self extends to all mankind.

This is true also in another sense. My mind is as it is because of many experiences. These experiences have come from contact with parents and friends and people of all sorts, also from the reading of books. Ideas from all over the world have influenced me. Some of these have become impressed on my memory. They form the background of what I am saying now. The very physical condition of my brain has presumably been modified by what has happened in the world over the ages and in many places.

In a similar way my own actions and thoughts have to a certain degree extended throughout the world. I have affected, more or less, the lives of many persons who have never heard of me. I am living in them.

As one's self is thus extended more and more widely his individual personality is not becoming submerged as a mere part of a society. The contrary is true. It is not even enough to say that each person is the center of his world. As I see it, a person knows himself only as he sees himself related to the world of other persons and things. Similarly, the world takes on reality for him only in its relationship to himself. It is in the interdependence between a person and his world that his existence takes on meaning. It is strictly correct to say that the existence of one's self, in any recognizable sense, depends upon the presence of these relationships with the world. His life ceases to have meaning when these relationships to the world are broken.

What is actually happening is that each person's relationships to the world around him are becoming both closer and more extensive. As a man accepts these growing relationships, he himself grows, and his life takes on richer meaning.

Here then is the unfolding view of man as a person that develops under the stimulus of science: the life of each person is in rapidly increasing degree becoming identified with the life of mankind. To an ever increasing extent we are living in each other. It is as one grows in the lives of those about him that he approaches his fullest stature. Such growth is being stimulated by the advances of science and technology.

## ON WHAT GOALS CAN MAN UNITE?

### 1. Man's new possibilities

In a recent article Arnold Toynbee expressed the view that the first half of the twentieth century would be known in history not so much because of two great world wars as because it was during this period that mankind became aware of the possibility of a new freedom. He meant the freedom for all mankind from destitution and disease. He called attention to the fact that during this half century, in certain major portions of the world, in particular Western Europe and North America, the peoples confined within definitely limited areas have steadily improved in health and have attained continually increasing abundance of means of living. Men all over the world, as they have become aware of what is happening here, have caught a new vision. This vision is that for themselves also the specters of destitution and disease can be conquered.

I would add that of comparable significance is the aspiration that has arisen throughout the world toward freedom from ignorance.

How has this increasing freedom come about? First of all, it is because of the advance of medicine and engineering, making use of new knowledge obtained through science. It likewise involves improved techniques in the organization of our life in industry and government. But most of all it is concerned with holding before ourselves as a desirable goal that every person should have the health, the physical means, and the necessary education with which to take his part in the life of society. An unexpected lesson that has been learned during this period is that in the effort to secure such health and competence for everyone, each individual who shares in this effort is finding for himself a better opportunity for health and the abundant life.

## 2. The problem presented by increasing population

As a kind of footnote I should comment that there are those who doubt whether it is within the power of science to ensure over a prolonged period freedom from destitution and famine for mankind. The argument is the old one of Malthus, that in the race between increasing population and increasing production, population must eventually win. Those of us who decline to accept this pessimistic view recognize the difficulty of the practical problem of meeting the needs of an ever expanding population. We have, however, greater faith in human resourcefulness. We note that it is not only in the technology of production and medicine that the present generation differs so greatly from the one before. A similar rapid change is likewise occurring in the thinking of masses of people. This change is brought about partly by experience with technology and partly by more widespread education. Here lies a new realm in which dramatic advance is being made.

The hope for the longer future lies in a growing understanding of the conditions for the good life of man in a world of science and technology, and the acceptance of a morality that is consistent with these conditions. With the widespread thought now being given to such problems by persons whose thinking is schooled to rely on reason and tested fact, it is evident that advance from this angle also will appear. You may, for example, consider these remarks as an effort to see in truer perspective the type of ideals that are appropriate to the age of science. Many are those who are now sharing in this exploration of human values.

The great question is whether such understanding of human goals and the corresponding development of morals can be achieved before the forces seen by Malthus, and emphasized so forcefully by recent writers, overwhelm the efforts of the pioneers in this new and critical field. I do not believe that this is inevitable. I am confident of man's ability to meet and solve this ethical problem that is so vital to the success of his effort to achieve physical and spiritual freedom.

It is relevant that as I analyze the reasons for my faith in man's eventual ability to meet this critical problem, I find that prominent in my mind is the confidence that the God who made us holds for us an increasing destiny, to be achieved through our own efforts in the world setting that he supplies. This observation is significant in the present setting because it is my strong impression that most of those who have the firm faith in man's future that gives them courage to work strongly toward man's advancement likewise have a religious basis for their faith. If this impression is valid, its consequence is clear. It means that it is men and women of religious faith on whom we must primarily rely to work strongly toward achieving a favorable world society. It means also that those of religious faith have because of their faith a better chance for survival, a fact that has bearing on the attitudes that may be expected in the society of the future.

## 3. The problem of war

Let me make a second footnote: How is man's growing hope for a world in which all may live freely to be fitted with the ugly fact of more destructive wars? The hope of this situation lies, as I see it, in the world's rapidly changing attitude toward war.

Probably the greatest incentive toward war has been the desire of one group to prey upon another to its own advantage. We have just noted that men are learning with new emphasis that health and abundance are best achieved by cooperative effort. That in unity lies strength is nothing new. But the effectiveness of mass production, of widespread markets, and of the sharp specialization possible only in a large coordinated society has become tremendously impressive during the last century. That control of disease is a worldwide problem in which everyone shares has become evident to all. On the other hand, the failure of Germany to promote her economic welfare through two great wars, while she was enjoying rapid economic growth through the peaceful development of her organized science and industry, is a sharp deterrent to any nation looking toward war as a means of promoting her own economic welfare.

That aggression for economic advantage remains a motive for war is, however, undeniable. Here it seems was the prime idea that stimulated the action of all the Axis powers in World War II. But the balance is turning rapidly. Already it is recognized that major war must be economically damaging even to the victor. This is not only because of the impossibility of protection against highly destructive long-range weapons. It is also because major war involves the disruption of highly organized means of production, which now constitute in new measure the means of people's livelihood. It is for such reasons that more and more clearly war is becoming recognized as a crime against humanity.

In the actuality of the present, however, war remains not only a threat but a fact that, like an epidemic disease, must be kept under control until such time as we learn how it can be eliminated.

## 4. Adjustment to widening human responsibility

Let me turn back to the central thread of our discussion. As we have noted, one of the dominant features of today's existence is the speed of the changes now occurring. In my travels this winter through Asia I have seen agricultural and industrial methods that I can dimly recall as a youth disappearing from the life of our own country: the oxcart, the use of the sickle for harvesting, hand-planting of seeds, foot-driven bellows for the forge, the mouth-operated blowpipe for soldering. The changes that have occurred in such matters in the last half century in our society are greater than those of the previous two thousand years. Added also are the motor car, the movies, and the radio that have so greatly altered the pattern of our family life. These changes are not complete. They have only begun. With the hundreds of thousands of research men now engaged in developing technological improvements, new ideas and new inventions are the order of the day. It is these that are altering our world.

A biologist views these changes with trepidation. He knows the maxim that most changes are damaging to an organism. This reflects the fact that a living thing is adjusted to the conditions that prevailed during previous generations. Only occasionally does a modification arise that opens new

| 393 |

and greater possibilities for life. It is thus not surprising that the by-products of changes brought by technology are frequently found troublesome. And yet if we refuse to adapt ourselves as our environment changes we cannot hope to survive. We can only endeavor to accept those changes in our way of life that, for the most part, are constructive.

One worldwide change is worthy of particular emphasis. This is the growing concern that the walfare of *every* individual shall be considered important. We have noted how during the last half century men have become aware of the possibility that every person may reasonably hope for such a degree of freedom from disease, destitution, and ignorance that he can take a responsible share in the great human enterprise. Man's new vision is that every person is important, and that we should turn our great new powers toward giving every person his proper chance.

Such a concept has long been a part of the world's religious heritage. But the growth of this vision, which during the past two centuries has gradually become a part of our democratic system of government, is itself one of the most significant changes in modern society. It has become a practically feasible goal only with the advent of a technology and industry based on science.

We see here a broadening of the principle of democracy. Like the other changes ushered in by advancing technology, this one also, while in itself good, has its troublesome side effects. Social patterns become dislocated as new responsibilities fall onto unaccustomed shoulders. Mistakes are made, and new injustices and sources of weakness arise. Yet here is one of those progressive changes that we must accept as essential to the life of which we are a part.

It would take us too far afield to consider the many ways in which modern industry, as it becomes more mature, is widening the responsibility for the means of living. Related to this development is the fact that mass production implies that many people shall be financially able to buy. But I must emphasize the fact that in political life—at least in the free countries—those in responsible positions are realizing more and more that the interests of all citizens must be taken into account.

The effect of these economic and political developments is to reduce class distinctions. In our more mature technological societies the economic differences between the upper and lower levels of society are becoming less. More people are demanding and receiving education. The concept is spreading that everyone should share in the responsibility for government and for the business that means their livelihood.

These changes are, I believe, an essential aspect of the maturing of technological society. If this is true, it becomes necessary for our adaptation to the modern environment that we shall welcome these changes and adjust ourselves to them.

Let me put this in another way. If we really want our society to be strong and to survive, we must avoid obstruction to the changes and adjust the lives of people to the new conditions. We recognize that order and stability are needed for the cooperation that is so vital to a technological civilization. If changes are to occur with order and stability, they must happen in a gradual manner. This is not possible when barriers are placed in the way of change. For these barriers will be broken down by disastrous strikes or revolutions when the social pressures become too great. We thus have the paradox that it is necessary to encourage social changes of a gradual sort if we are to retain the really important values of the life we know.

## 5. The great goal

This brings us to the question of the goals toward which man should aspire.

When one raises this question, one thinks at once of the old Greek ideals of the understanding of truth, the appreciation of beauty, the striving for perfection. These goals are as significant today as they were twenty-five hundred years ago. What is new is that in our effort to attain the true, the beautiful, and the good, we find that now to greater degree this can best be done when we endeavor to attain these same objectives for others as well as for ourselves.

Thus no one by himself can discover the truths of science. The search for scientific truth becomes a worldwide enterprise in which a multitude of people throughout the world are engaged. The efforts of each strengthen and enrich those of the others. As Aristotle said:

> The search for truth is in one way hard and in another way easy, for it is evident that no one can master it fully nor miss it wholly. But each adds a little to our knowledge of nature; and from all the facts assembled there arises a certain grandeur.[2]

The same is true in our effort to achieve the beautiful in art and music, and in our endeavor to approach perfection whether in health or in our spiritual aspirations. In every case we find that the task is a cooperative one.

Is not this, then, the distinctive feature of man's aspiration that is characteristic of the age of science? This approach to the great values of life

[2] *Metaphysica*, Bk. 2, Chap. 1.

shall be a cooperative effort, an effort in which every man and every woman may do their share toward enabling all to live more fully, an effort in which every person will be respected for the way in which he plays his part. It is thus that we see ourselves living increasingly in the lives of each other.

Not long ago I was discussing with one of India's great leaders * what it is that gives meaning to life. He suggested that it is such things as truth and beauty and freedom. I asked him, what about service for one's fellows? Is not such service a source of meaning for life?

He paused a moment; then he replied: "Yes. Service can be a great factor in giving meaning, but only in case it is given freely, for persons you love. Not if it is given for pay. But if it is given freely, then the service becomes an aspect of freedom."

So he returned to his original triad, of truth and beauty and freedom.

He had here a point that is vital to the present discussion. Where is the motive that will inspire us to cooperative effort, to work freely for each other?

The only answer that seems to me adequate is the ancient doctrine of the love of one's neighbor, the heart of Jesus' teaching and prominent in every religion that is now of major influence. Here is precisely what is needed to fit man to life in the world that science is shaping, that he shall love his neighbor with the kind of love that inspires one to help his neighbor live. Having such love, a person will learn the techniques needed for service. He will endeavor to understand what is required to attain the good life. He will gladly cooperate in tasks toward the common good. It is the presence of persons with such a spirit that gives strength and health to a modern social order. For a person whose heart is in enabling others to live, science and technology present a great opportunity. He finds in their use the joy of life.

## PRACTICAL STEPS TOWARD THE HUMAN GOAL

We have noted how rapidly new responsibilities are falling upon us for choices that have far-reaching human effects. Toward what ends should these choices be made? We have drawn attention to the increasing specialization and the widespread cooperation in attaining our ends that are characteristic of a maturing technological culture. We have seen how closely the growth of personality is related to the development of a person's contacts, and that thanks to technology each individual is sharing increasingly the life of every other. We have found that throughout the world the inherent dignity of man is taking on new importance. An urgent demand is thus arising that our great new powers shall be turned toward human ends in which all may share.

The growing worldwide resolution, as I understand it, is simply this: *Let us work together that everyone may have a chance to do his part. Let us respect and reward each person according as he uses his chance.*

An attempt to state more accurately what it seems to me the world is wanting takes this form: *a situation in which every person has the opportunity and the encouragement to grow by taking a responsible part in the common task of enabling all to live as fully and freely as possible.*

We can think of this as the dream that is in the hearts of free men everywhere. It describes the kind of social order that men and women want. Toward its attainment they would turn the full power of science and technology. They want to share in bringing this order into being.

What does such a dream mean in practical action? This is a major problem for our conference.

In approaching this question it may be of some help for me to suggest a partial answer, as I see it, for a particular case that is close to my own professional interest. What is the practical meaning and usefulness of this goal regarding the direction that education should take?

Many aspects of education crowd to mind. But there is one particular aspect of education that impresses me as of especial importance in a technological world. It is that of rallying to the achievement of our great human goal the wholehearted strength of the many diverse elements that comprise our society. We have seen the rapidly growing importance of cooperation. This implies that the success of our social order depends upon its ability to win the full and devoted participation of its component groups in doing its tasks.

There are obstacles in the road. Many prejudices exist that make cooperation difficult. Sometimes mutual distrust and antagonisms block completely the performance of essential work. There are prejudices based on race, religious affiliations, national origins; cultural, occupational, economic, political, social differences. In a specialized society it is possible for these differences to become sources of strength rather than weakness, since each of these groups can contribute its own distinctive part to our total life.

Agreement upon a common goal can afford the basis for wholehearted and powerful cooperation. In wartime the will to freedom has rallied the versatile strength of diverse nations, races, and religions. In such time of stress they have risen above their differences. They have pooled their resources, and they have thus become more than a match for their monolithic enemies. Similarly, in peacetime it should be possible to place before these groups a human goal whose importance to them will rally their united strength toward its achievement.

Here is a task worthy of education's best. It requires, however, not only the formal education of the schools and colleges. It needs the participation of all the agencies that form attitudes and spread information. The churches, the press and radio and film, writers and artists, civic organizations, labor and management groups: all of these must share in the educational task if we are to rally the many elements in our society to a wholehearted effort toward achieving man's great goal.

If we accept such a goal as we have described, what must our united educational program seek to accomplish? First, it must make men and women everywhere aware that we, the free people of the world, want a social order where everyone has a chance to do his proper part. Second, we must explain that rapid progress can be made toward such a social order if we will do certain things. Each group must then be encouraged to find what it can do most effectively toward achieving this goal. Each must have in mind how its contribution will fit with that of the others. Such an effort, in which all are sharing, will go far toward creating mutual understanding.

Can our schools be more effective in training for such cooperative effort? Can our labor and management groups find ways of meeting each other's needs to their mutual advantage? Can our religious organizations cooperate toward inspiring men and women to work toward the achievement of such freedom for everyone?

Already enough preliminary work along these lines has been done to show that when our educational agencies unite in such a task the results can be very effective. But the surface of what may be done by such an effort has hardly been scratched. The vision can thus be made to shine bright before us. When it does so shine we shall have the courage, if need be, to hold the sword with one hand while with the other we eagerly ply the trowel. And so we shall build the wall, for the men will have a mind to work.

Here then is where our deliberations begin.* I have tried to indicate, as I see it, the general direction of the journey on which we are embarking. I have tried to locate some of the mountain ranges that must be avoided as well as the refueling stops, so that we may start the flight with confidence in safe and happy landings.

The way is open for practical steps that should now be taken in order that men may live fully and freely in the new era that we are entering. Like the steel of Daedalus, science carries with it great human responsibility. We have accepted the gift. We shall endeavor to find the wisdom to use it well, so that man may grow to greater stature.

# 44. Give Us Vision!

## *1959*

In an address at the National Book Awards ceremony in New York City on March 3, 1959, the author renewed his plea for a national policy directed toward enabling men and women throughout the world to achieve full health and human dignity.

Two summers ago Pearl Buck came to talk with me at our summer home beside a beautiful lake in northern Michigan.

"What was the most critical decision that you had to make as you were working on the atomic project?" was the question on her mind.

"Should we try the experiment of exploding an atomic bomb?" I replied. "This was a decision made right here at Otsego Lake."

Robert Oppenheimer had phoned that he must see me at once about something that had emerged from the calculations of his team engaged in designing the bomb. I met him at the early morning train and drove him down to the beach of the quiet lake, where the sun had just risen. There we could talk quietly, without fear of interruption or of listening ears.

"We have just found that there is a possibility of an enormous catastrophe if we explode a nuclear bomb," Oppie began. "Of course, the temperature produced by such an explosion will be hundreds of millions of degrees. May that not be enough to start a fusion reaction of the hydrogen nuclei in the ocean or of the nitrogen nuclei in the atmosphere? If it should, this would be the ultimate calamity—the earth would be no more."

"Go into this in more detail. How do you estimate the probability of such an explosion of the atmosphere?" I asked.

Oppenheimer rapidly outlined to me the theory on which they were working, and how one might predict the likelihood that such a catastrophe would occur. At this stage of their calculations it was evident that some of the conditions for such an explosion would be met, and Oppenheimer's men were as yet unable to say firmly that the event was impossible. It did not take us long to agree upon our immediate course of action. Oppenheimer's theoretical team should make every effort to arrive promptly at a reliable conclusion. If there were even a remote chance of such a catastrophe, the test of the atomic explosion would of course not be tried. Pending the outcome of his calculations, work on the development of the bomb would, however, go ahead with full vigor, with the intention of testing the nuclear explosion as soon as the equipment could be prepared. In the meantime, Vannevar Bush, who was then responsible to the government for the progress of the project, must be told of the possibility that the project might have to be called off. Having reached this agreement, Oppenheimer and I adjourned our conversation to join the family for breakfast, and Oppie then took the next train for Washington.

Within some weeks Oppenheimer was able to give a well-documented report that an atomic explosion would *not* set off the earth as a huge fusion bomb. So the atomic project drove ahead to its rapid and dramatic conclusion. But from that time on we had to live with the realization that with the initiation of the first nuclear explosion the possibility of making the vastly more powerful hydrogen bomb was just over the horizon.

Eventually, three years later, the critical test came, as the trial nuclear explosion was set off at Alamogordo, New Mexico, on July 16, 1945. It was an explosion of unprecedented violence. But, as we were by that time able to predict with confidence, the earth itself did not explode. In this sense, mankind was safe.

But of another danger of world explosion presented by that first nuclear bomb, Pearl Buck and I talked only briefly; and this is a danger that is not yet past. In fact, we are now in the midst of this second type of exploding chain reaction.

From the day that the discovery of nuclear fission was announced by Professor Hahn and Doctor Strassmann, in Germany in January 1939, it seemed inevitable that somewhere within a few years a nuclear explosion would be produced. For scientists the world over recognized this possibility at once, and they knew the general procedures that would be necessary to achieve the result. It fell to the lot of the United States to carry through first the immense task of building this first nuclear bomb, prodded on by the intense pressures of war. But with this achievement, the overwhelming effectiveness of the bomb as a weapon made it imperative for every nation that could do so to develop its own nuclear weapons, and to devise new, more effective means for their delivery at remote targets. The result you all know. We are in an arms race of unprecedented vigor. Its vigor was enhanced by the military effectiveness of the first use of the bombs in bringing World War II to a quick end.

After the fission bomb came the hydrogen fusion bomb, and now the race for operational intercontinental missiles is on. Thus the military chain reaction is developing. Each advance in this international race for more powerful arms makes it necessary for other nations to move that much the faster. The conditions are thus like those of a chemical reaction in which each stage of the reaction releases more energy than the previous stage, building up until either the fuel is exhausted or the container is burst by the growing violence of the reaction—in other words, an explosion. This is a realistic description of the present state of human society as viewed by a scientist.

Does this mean that we are *inevitably* approaching either a military explosion or a state of complete economic exhaustion? I do not believe so. The alternative, though difficult in practice, is in principle simple. It is, I believe, to divert the energy of the social reaction into useful instead of destructive channels. The young and vigorous Russian nation is challenging the West, and the West is responding with a vigor that demonstrates a high level of vitality. It seems clear that such a situation calls for channeling the energies of both groups of nations into objectives on the need for whose achievement both are agreed. What are such objectives, and how can we orient the flow of energy in the desired direction?

The Greek philosophers, in their discussions of how mind induces matter to act as it desires, explained that the mind sets up an image of the desired condition, whereupon the body, in accord with its nature, proceeds to fit itself as closely as possible to this idealized image. Modern science has done no better toward explaining how mind acts on matter.

Following this suggestion, what is now urgently needed is for our minds to set up the image of the condition of man and society that we need to attain. This is certainly the starting point in redirecting human energies into desired channels.

To this end much has been done, but to all too great an extent Americans have lost sight of the inspiring possibilities that at other times we have seen more clearly. Thus, in his *Epic of America,* the late James Truslow Adams had much to say of the importance of the "American dream" as an effective force in stimulating the growth of our nation. In this historical study Adams was concerned to find the factors that have affected our development.

"If," he wrote, "the things already listed were all we had had to contribute, America would have made no distinctive and unique gift to mankind. But there has been also the *American dream. . . .* It is not a dream of motor cars and high wages merely, but a dream of a social order in which each man and each woman shall be able to attain the fullest stature of which they are innately capable, and be recognized by others for what they are, regardless of the fortuitous circumstances of birth or position." [1]

Adams recognized that this dream has not always been uppermost in the minds of our citizens. At times, with a Washington or a Jefferson or a Lincoln, it has burned bright before us and has inspired us to great achievements. At other times the dream has been all but forgotten, as we have immersed ourselves in partisan conflicts and in attaining selfish goals. But never has the dream been completely lost.

We began our nation by declaring in 1776 that "all men are created equal," that their Creator gave them the right to "life, liberty, and the pursuit of happiness," and in 1787 we committed our government to "provide for the common welfare," and secure for all our citizens "the blessings of liberty." During the 1860's we fought a great war to the end that our nation "dedicated to the proposition that all men are created equal," might endure; in 1945 we shared with other nations of the world in expressing the determination "to save succeeding generations from the scourge of war, which . . . has brought untold sorrow to mankind," in reaffirming officially our faith "in the dignity and worth of the human person"; and in 1947 we gave body to our dream through the Marshall Plan, in which we set our financial strength to work with that of other nations "toward the social and economic advancement of all people."

And yet, how lightly on our minds rest these noble commitments. I have to recall the lines in *South Pacific*,[2] where the American officers are asking Emile de Becque to join them in a dangerous mission during the Japanese war. They say:

"We're asking you to help us lick the Japs. It's as simple as that. We're against the Japs."

"I know what you're against," returns Emile. "What are you for?" And he waits in vain for an answer.

As Emile leaves, the officers are shaken. Harbison says to the others: "He's an honest man, but he's wrong. Of course, we can't guarantee him a better world if we win. Point is, we can be damned sure it'll be worse if we lose. Can't we? . . . Well, can't we?"

And the real tragedy here is that the audience listening to these lines agrees that no one knows what we're for. Is there no longer an American dream? No vision? Well, is there?

One recalls the words of King Solomon: "Where there is no vision, the

---

[1] James Truslow Adams: *The Epic of America* (Boston: Little, Brown and Company; 1932), p. 404.
[2] Oscar Hammerstein II and Joshua Logan: *South Pacific* (New York: Random House; 1949), pp. 85-6.

people perish." Great God, grant us renewed vision lest *our* people perish!

There are those who seek the needed vision, and are trying to show it to us, but our eyes were dimmed.

I recall an occasion a little more than a year ago that left me shaken. It was the occasion of the first Atoms for Peace award given in 1957 to Niels Bohr, Denmark's most famous citizen, the world's number one atomic physicist, and over many years an ardent seeker for a road to peace. The auditorium of the National Academy of Sciences at Washington was packed by an audience including ambassadors of friendly nations, newsmen, and scientists from over the world.

Niels Bohr was introduced as the exemplar of the scientist working in all countries for an open world, a leaven that has been shaping the foreign policy of many nations. He responded in his typically humble way, "The rapid advance of science and technology in our age, which involves such bright promises and grave dangers, presents civilization with a most serious challenge." Bohr told us that to meet this challenge, "the road is indicated by *that world-wide cooperation which has manifested itself* through the ages *in the development of science.*"

President Eisenhower, in saluting Doctor Bohr as "one whose mind has explored the mysteries of the inner structure of the atom," remarked that "it will be only the Almighty who will delve deeply enough into the hearts and minds of men . . . to develop in us the compassion, the sympathy, the understanding, the consideration for other points of view that will eventually bring . . . a just peace to the world."

It fell to my lot to make the concluding remarks.* I reminded the audience that Doctor Bohr, whom we were honoring that day, was appealing to the nations for cooperation in building a humane world as they were already cooperating in scientific research. I told how some years earlier I had shown to Mme. Pandit, then President of the United Nations General Assembly, the description of the American dream as written by James Truslow Adams. "You call that the *American* dream," she exclaimed. "It has become the dream of all the world!"

If Mme. Pandit is right that our great dream has now become the world's dream, I said, do we not have here the signpost that marks the road to peace? Let every nation, starting with the United States, affirm this dream as its basic national policy. The hope seems reasonable that with the widespread acceptance of the American dream, such a commitment by this nation accompanied by appropriate action of the kind we have from time to time shown ourselves prepared to take, will displace by a growing mutual confidence the mutual international antagonisms that have arisen, so that a peace based on confidence will grow. International rivalry will then develop a new spirit. As the dream of the world is transformed into one united purpose, men and nations will vie with each other in advancing the human worth of man. Life will thus take on new meaning and our civilization itself will stir with new strength.

Such was our appeal. The response: A London journal presented to its readers in full the proceedings of the award ceremony. I sought in vain for any reference in the American press to the ideas that were brought forward on this occasion. There was some attention paid to the modest drama of the presentation. But neither news item nor editorial comment in any American paper that I could find indicated that on the occasion of the presentation of the Atoms for Peace award the participants had been concerned with how the nations might be set on the road to peace. If any of the speakers was trying to transmit a hopeful vision, those who represented the nation's eyes and ears were unconcerned with that vision.

It is not unlikely that the unwillingness of our tough-minded newsmen to note the suggestions that came from such visionaries as the nuclear scientists and the President, as they were searching for promising paths toward peace through peaceful use of the atom, was because hard experience had taught them to believe that rescue from our present apparently inevitable fate of annihilation in World War III can come only through a miracle—and they refused to believe in miracles.

It is precisely at this point that the hard-boiled newsmen, who will deal only with known facts, differ with the simple-minded scientists. The scientists—and I am one of them—*do* believe in miracles. We have lived miracles, and we know how miracles work. The miracle of the atomic bomb came precisely because someone saw a vision. It was a vision of a nuclear chain reaction, and he saw that this could mean either triumph for the tyranny of the Nazis or a quickened end to World War II with victory in the hands of the free world. This vision quickly became shared by a few hundred other scientists whose hearts and minds' eyes were attuned to what people such as Einstein, Fermi, Lawrence, and Szilard were trying to show them. In due time, this clear vision of the scientists became shared also by heads of government, by leaders of industry, and eventually by the military; and a determination to achieve the impossible developed that could not be defeated. Thus it was that the miracle occurred. Don't tell me that such a miracle can't happen again!

But today it is not the vision of the scientists that is needed. It is the vision of you authors. You are the seers whose concern is first of all with what is in the hearts and minds of men. How can we open the way for the fullest growth of the spirit of man? This is the question that is on our hearts.

There are those who are seriously engaged in searching for the right answers, and it is to them we should look.

Thus, for example, in Berne, Switzerland, last August there met a small group of dedicated and experienced men from America, Europe, Asia, and Africa to search for effective and feasible steps toward peace.[3] They recognized the urgent need for a change in the direction in which the world is heading. They saw that, while the central responsibility for progress toward peace clearly rests with governments, there is much that private citizens should, can, and must do. They thus set themselves to finding long-range goals that must serve as guides toward a durable peace and also to listing certain specific projects that should be feasible for the near future and would contribute to achieving these goals.

This little working party, under the chairmanship of Ambassador G. L. Mehta of India, included such persons as Adlai Stevenson, Paul Hoffman, and Henry Wriston from the United States, Paul Reynaud of France, David Astor from London, Axel Springer from Germany, and persons of similar standing from Japan, Iran, Sudan, Belgium, and Ghana. They agreed upon four long-range goals which should guide efforts toward peace: (1) an enforceable body of world law; (2) social and economic well-being of all peoples; (3) an open world, with freedom of travel and communication; (4) a strengthened United Nations. And they proceeded to outline appropriate steps toward achieving these goals.

Ideas such as these need to be worked over by all who are concerned for the future of man. Only thus can the ideas take root and grow. They need to be discussed. Perhaps some of the ideas are wrong or inadequate to the need. If they are, let's say so. Some of the ideas may inspire in us new and better thoughts.

You may remember that twenty-five hundred years ago Zoroaster extracted from his disciples the following pledge:

I will praise out loud the thought well thought, the word well spoken, the deed well done.

And he might well have added, "the book well written." Here is a pledge of great significance, indeed.

Assuming then the role of Zoroaster, I would make this request of you,

---

[3] This conference, convened to consider "Steps Toward Peace," was held under the auspices of World Brotherhood. The working papers and conclusions were published and distributed by the sponsoring organization.

writers of books, molders of attitudes and opinions. If you find inspiring vision anywhere, tell us about it. Interpret it to us through your own medium, so that we may share it with you. Thus you will give new life to the American dream as it becomes the dream of the world. Give us *your* vision, that our people may not perish but live!

# 45. Science and Man's Destiny

## 1962

In one of his last public appearances, a lecture at the University of Alabama on January 16, 1962, the author summarized his views on the vastly increased opportunities for human growth implicit in the advance of science.

We are now well into the second half of the twentieth century. If I am not mistaken, the first half of this century will be remembered in the long view of history as epochal in the effect that the advance of science has had on man's view of himself. We have come to understand more clearly our place in space and time. We have learned that we are an integral part of the great cosmic event that we call nature, but with certain distinctive characteristics: We are aware of our world; we are able within expanding limits to shape the world to our needs; and, reaffirming that we are indeed our brothers' keepers, we find in this fact real meaning for the life of which we are a part. For the first time in man's history, we have a sound basis for aspiring to a social order in which the great tragedies of destitution and premature death shall be the exception rather than the rule, in which education that brings understanding of truth and appreciation of beauty shall be generally available, and in which the dominant social force will be the desire to work with one's fellows toward achieving a worthy life.

Half a century ago, with far-seeing vision, H. G. Wells wrote:

> The past is but the beginning of a beginning, and all that is and has been is but the twilight of the dawn. . . . A day will come when beings who are now latent in our thoughts and hidden in our loins shall stand upon the earth as one stands upon a footstool, and shall laugh and reach out their hands amid the stars.[1]

[1] H. G. Wells: "The Discovery of the Future," *Nature*, LXV: 1683 (February 6, 1902), p. 331.

It is to enable us to plan realistically for the greater possibilities that lie ahead that we shall attempt a rather comprehensive review of what the science of the last two generations has shown us about what we are and what we may reasonably hope to become.

Over the archway of Brookings Hall, in which for many years I had my office, is carved the seal of Washington University with the words, *Per Veritatem Vis* [Strength Through Truth]. The fact that truth is a source of power has long been recognized. It has remained, however, for the last century to set aside major groups of men, our scientific research men, whose primary occupation is to find useful knowledge. During the present century the product of their studies has so greatly increased our ability to do the things that we want to do that man today finds himself in a new sense responsible for guiding wisely his own development and the development of all life on this planet. We recognize also, however, that great powers beyond our control, working not only in the outside world, but also within ourselves, are shaping our destiny along lines that may be at sharp variance with our intentions.

As the knowledge of science and the strength that goes with it have increased, the way in which man's powers are a part of these great world forces and are limited by them has become increasingly evident. Yet to an ever greater degree we find ourselves able to harmonize our efforts with the requirements of cosmic law. It is both by turning nature to meet our needs and by adjusting our desires to the possibilities of nature that we are making for ourselves a better life.

We have come to see nature as a great event moving with an increasing tempo from certain beginnings toward what would appear to be a long drawn out conclusion. In this great event we do our part with the powers that have been given us. By increased understanding of our physical nature and of the biological and psychological laws of the individual and of society, we hope to avoid the pitfalls that have resulted in disasters to former civilizations, and to chart our course toward the noblest destiny that is possible to us.


## WE SEE OURSELVES AS A PART OF NATURE

That we may appreciate what the last sixty or seventy years of science have done to our view of ourselves as a part of nature, it will be useful to gain perspective by taking seven-league steps backward in time.

Look first at what has happened to man during the brief years since World War II. The cost of that epic struggle has left us aware in a totally new degree that mankind has a single, united destiny. Among the earth's billions of men, women, and children are many varieties of race, religion, and political doctrine, and diverse forms of social and economic life; but we all depend on each other. An effort by North Koreans in 1950 to subjugate their South Korean neighbors brought on in that remote land a turmoil that caused the death of thousands of Americans, Chinese, and Turks. The application of methods of malaria control, developed largely in the United States, brought new health and vigor to Indian peasants, resulting in an increase in food production that raises new hope among Asia's millions. Trouble in any part of the world affects us all. Strength and vision anywhere can be turned to the benefit of all. Our economy is a world economy, limited by the planet's resources. The thinking of every person and of every group affects the attitudes and destiny of mankind. With radio, television, jet airplanes, artificial satellites, atomic energy, and other facilities that require vast nationwide organizations to produce and use, our thinking has of necessity become to a new degree global.

Technical development and man's growing world consciousness are but limited aspects of what two short decades since the war have done to our thinking about ourselves. We must remember that every comparable period in the life of each person has been filled with similar soul-stirring events. While it is true that social changes are increasingly rapid, it is primarily because they are more remote that we do not see the active drama in the lives of our forebears. As we think back in history to the problems faced by our ancestors, we see that the same elements of vision, bold decision, and courageous adventure in a difficult world that we are now experiencing were likewise present to them.

We have just noted our growth in outlook during the last two decades and our increasing sense of world unity. Let us now move backward in time with increasingly larger steps.

Our next step backward will take us to the year 1895, which is the date of the discovery of X rays, one of the historic landmarks of science. It was during the half century after 1895 that man learned the bounds of the universe as to its smallest and largest dimensions, made a reasonable estimate of its age, and found the elemental parts of which it is made and the sources of physical energy that keep it going. The world became aware of the immense practical usefulness of science in giving health and longer life, in supplying our needs, and in defending us against our enemies. During this period there occurred history's first wars of worldwide scope. These vast conflicts reflected the failure of rival governments to adjust themselves to the growing powers from advancing technology.

Our next backward step will be ten times greater, to A.D. 1450, the beginning of the Renaissance. During this period arose an invigorated culture, including a reformation of Christianity, an increase in the appreciation of art, and the birth of modern science. This was the period of the great geographic and scientific explorers, who found the New World, revealed the solar system, established the laws of motion, and developed the theory of evolution. The recognition of the unique value of man in the sight of God culminated heroically during this period in the establishment of nations governed by the people and for the people.

Another tenfold step backward in times takes us to the fifth millennium before Christ, the dawn of written history. Early in this period we find the beginnings of medical science in Egypt and of astronomical records in Babylonia. We find also the dawn of social conscience, a man's first awareness that he is inescapably his brother's keeper, and the development of the world's great religions. The Greeks set for themselves a high task of scholarship, to find "of what and how the world is made" in order that they might know a better way of life. Empires and civilizations rose and fell. At the crossroads of East and West emerged the great discovery of the one reliable basis for the good life, the love of one's God and of one's fellows.

A further step backward of perhaps tenfold takes us to the first appearance of *Homo sapiens,* estimated by anthropologists to have come on the scene about fifty thousand years ago. Though these forebears of ours were endowed with the same native capacities as ourselves, it required the many intervening millennia of struggle, with nature and with each other, for them to develop the tribal patterns from which civilization was to emerge.

Another step, this time some twentyfold, takes us back a million years to the primitive ape-man. As an animal who could talk and use tools effectively, he was fitted to grow in wisdom and to survive in competition with his physically more powerful animal cousins.

Our next step backward in time we shall make a hundredfold, to the period when the great mammals flourished most abundantly—the mammoth, the horse, the ape, the cat. Another fivefold step goes back through the period of the dinosaurs to the beginnings of vertebrate life. Another two or threefold step to a billion years ago, and we are at the origin of the most primitive life that appears in the record of the rocks. Thence a final step backward of five or tenfold, and, according to the dominant view of astronomers, we go beyond the beginnings of our earth to the origin of the universe itself. Beyond this date it would seem that neither stars nor planets, and perhaps not even atoms, were in existence. The universe was indeed a chaos.

I have presented this perspective of how we have come to our present state to emphasize two points. The first is that what has happened to man during the lifetime of one person has been possible only because of the long periods of development that have gone before. Just as the leaves of a great tree in the forest are this year's expression of the growth that during the years has built the tree's trunk and limbs, so what has happened to mankind in the lifetime of people now living is our generation's experience of the great human adventure. This adventure has included three hundred years of American pioneering, two thousand years of the development of the spirit of brotherly love in the hearts of men, and hundreds of millions of years of ceaseless struggle by living creatures to achieve the best that nature has made possible for them.

My second point is that while seventy years is indeed only a thousandth of a second at the end of the long day that the world has existed, that moment has given a very substantial addition to the heritage of the future. In terms of man's awareness of his relation to the world of nature, and in terms of the ability of living creatures to bend nature to their needs, the advance during the lifetime of men now living has been comparable with that during all the previous history of the earth. For their opportunity to share in these heroic contributions to man's enduring heritage, our men of science may properly be humbly thankful.

## WHAT SCIENCE HAS SHOWN US
## ABOUT OURSELVES

From the active research of the present century, two facts regarding man's own nature have emerged that even in this brief summary are worthy of special note. The first is that while according to the accepted science of the last century man's every act was completely determined in advance by the inevitable motions and forces between the elemental atoms, today's science recognizes that there is no complete predetermination of man's actions by physical law. After taking into account all the physical factors introduced through the external world and the physiology of the nervous system, there still remains an area within which man's actions are in principle unpredictable. This means that in terms of physical science, while a century ago one saw no possible counterpart in man's actions to his feeling of free choice, the physical possibility of such a counterpart is now recognized. That is, physics now accepts the possibility of the self-determination of human action, and thus man's moral responsibility, which earlier it could not with consistency admit.

This development is of no small significance in this day of conflict between the authoritarian and the free world. It is no accident that in Communist Russia the physical principle of uncertainty, on which this change from physical determinism depends, was widely rejected as inconsistent with the principles of the Marxian materialism that arose during the nineteenth century. Thus is emphasized the human importance of science's carefully tested finding that the responsible freedom of man is consistent with physical law.

A second notable fact about man that emerges is that science seems incapable of giving any clue as to how man's awareness is related to what happens in the world of matter. Our studies of physical science have given us no clue whatever of how it is that we feel and think and choose.

The development of so-called "thinking" machines has brought sharply to our attention the fact that considered responses to stimuli do not imply awareness. Awareness, or consciousness, is in a category distinct from our objective science. It is something that each of us experiences subjectively, and hence knows more immediately than he does the external world. We can find by experiment how our own conscious life may be affected by internal and external physical conditions. But as to how this consciousness comes to be, or as to how widely awareness may occur throughout the universe, science gives us little guide.

Man knows himself as an observer of the world about him. He can influence that world to work, within certain limits, in accord with his own desires. With all that science has done, however, man remains separated by an impenetrable barrier from sharing any awareness that other portions of the world may have of the drama that is happening in the universe. No avenue has appeared whereby we may gain reliable knowledge from observing the world around us as to whether consciousness exists anywhere outside ourselves.

By some intuition, nevertheless, man learned a million years ago that certain sounds and gestures made by his fellows meant that they too had thoughts and feelings like his own. Since our actions are, to the best of our knowledge, completely consistent with physical laws that are themselves rigorously independent of any consideration of thought or emotion, this understanding of the meaning of language goes beyond any purely physical explanation. Nevertheless, the fact is that by the help of the spoken and written word, by gestures and other means, we do share each other's thoughts. In fact, it is largely through the use of language that our own thoughts develop in richness and precision. During our own lifetime, by such devices as the press, the moving pictures, the radio, and television, our sharing of ideas has extended rapidly on a worldwide scale.

It is possible that physical science may in principle describe completely the structure and actions of man as a part of the material world. From what we have just seen, however, it is clear that man is not thus completely accounted for. Left wholly out of consideration in this description is the realm of sensation, of ideas and ideals, of understanding and emotion that gives life its human significance. Just as these things reveal themselves in our own immediate consciousness, so we likewise recognize them as the factors that give inherent value to other persons. This value of our fellows is not proved by science, but the way is left open by physical science for such values to have meaning for us.

In precisely the same manner our knowledge of the world of matter leaves the way open for us to share the spirit of the universe, that is, to be aware of the God that the mystics declare they know. But one must not look to science for evidence of conscious motivation, such as love or hate, in the great powers that govern our existence and our actions. It is not in the character of science that it should reveal anything about such matters. Yet it is precisely this aspect of the world that gives us our ultimate sense of values. "Except ye become as little children, ye shall not enter into the kingdom of heaven." This is the exact parallel of the fact that while a babe knows the approval or disapproval of its mother even before it can speak, if one observes only with the sophisticated eye of science one can see in the mother's actions merely the consistent working of the immutable laws of physics. The feeling of pleasure or pain, the understanding of truth, the appreciation of beauty, sympathy with those who suffer and aspire and love—such are the things that give life its meaning, and of these the science of the physical world knows nothing.

Thus it is that the recent remarkable growth of science, in the very process of extending our knowledge of the physical world, has shown us more sharply what its limitations are. Physical science is concerned with the material world. It shows us the framework that is the basis of our lives. But it is not in the character of science that it shall be capable of opening to man a knowledge of his inmost soul.

## SCIENCE OPENS TO MAN NEW VISTAS
## OF WHAT HE MAY BECOME

The story is told that young King Solomon was given the choice between wealth and wisdom. When he chose wisdom, God was so pleased that he gave to Solomon not only wisdom but wealth also.

So it is with science. The most devoted followers of science for the most part have been those who have similarly loved knowledge for its own sake. Let us, however, not despise the practical gifts of science. With new knowledge has come increased power to meet man's needs, and health and prosperity have resulted. But this is not all. We find that if we are to make wise use of the gifts that science offers we must educate ourselves regarding man's nature and his possibilities. Becoming skilled in various specialties, we must learn to work together and to find our satisfactions in meeting others' needs. Thus the love of scientific knowledge brings with it food for our bodies and life for our souls.

In the days of the first Elizabeth, Sir Francis Bacon told his English compatriots what might be hoped for if science should be taken seriously. He pictured a "New Atlantis" in the South Pacific in which the most influential citizens were a group of scientific investigators. Their aim was to learn the inner workings of nature to the end that men might achieve all things possible.

Until the nineteenth century, one finds only here and there an isolated professional employed to advance the bounds of knowledge. Science was carried on by amateurs, to whom the understanding of the world was a goal of esthetic value. When in 1802, however, the Royal Institution of London was established with Sir Humphry Davy as its first director, followed by Michael Faraday and a series of other noted men, professional scientific and technological research had a firm beginning. Davy's experiments gave us the first practical electric light in the form of the arc lamp. Faraday discovered the laws of electromagnetism that are basic to electrical engineering.

Toward the close of the nineteenth century Thomas Edison introduced the research team, organized to attack specific new problems in applied science. The Germans took up the idea and in their chemical industry exploited it with remarkable success. George Ellery Hale, early in the twentieth century, applied the same idea in the organization of the Mount Wilson Solar Observatory. Thence the idea of organized research teams has spread, in the fields of both basic and applied science, until at the present moment there are nearly half a million qualified research men in the United States employed by thousands of different organizations for the primary purpose of finding new knowledge. This multiplication of research workers is a major reason why science has recently been making such rapid strides.

If we should liken the five thousand million years of the world's known existence to a cross-country flight from New York to San Francisco, a lifetime of seventy years would correspond to the last half-inch of that twenty-five-hundred-mile journey. Consider some of the developments that have occurred during this lifetime of one man: The world's use of electric power has been born and has grown to vital importance. The number of men employed to find new facts and to develop new industrial, business, and medical processes has multiplied a hundredfold. The top speed that man travels in normal passenger conveyances has increased tenfold, as has also the number of international organizations. To a new degree the world's people have become dependent on each other in their economic life. As measured in terms of the volume of published reports on advances in scientific knowledge, the information discovered in each ten years has been more than that discovered in all previous history. All except the most recalcitrant have, during this life span, come to understand that cooperation among nations must take the place of war for solving international disputes. During this brief period, as we have traversed the last half-inch in our twenty-five-hundred-mile flight, there has thus been added to the heritage of man something that is substantial in relation to his entire previous history.

This is what we mean by saying that we are changing rapidly. It is this striking fact that impels us to ask with new urgency, toward what destiny should we aspire?

## HOPE FOR HEALTH, FOOD, AND
## EDUCATION FOR ALL

Far more important to men and women than the pleasures of television or the motorcar is the fact that they can get the food and shelter and the medical care needed to keep themselves and their families in health and reasonable comfort. What happened to our health during the first half of this century is strikingly evident from our increased life expectancy. Not so striking, but of equal significance, is the fact that during this period of time our standard of living has continued to increase while the population of our nation doubled.

It is this demonstrated ability to maintain a rising standard of life within a population that is confined to a limited area that Arnold Toynbee described as the great historic event of our time. Never before has such a thing occurred. It has given new hope to men the world over that the specters of hunger, destitution, disease, and degrading ignorance may be banished forever.

What has made this continued improvement possible? Can we expect the rise in life span and in living standard to continue indefinitely?

It is evident that the advance in our scientific knowledge is an essential factor in this improvement. But it is equally evident that by themselves our scientific discoveries are not sufficient to account for this remarkable human phenomenon. In addition to the essential importance of the new scientific knowledge, the continuing advance of living standards requires factors other than science and technology that are present in the United States to an unusual degree. Of these factors two seem to me especially noteworthy. The first is the spirit of the American, who wants to do his part in making the life in his community what he thinks it ought to be. It is this spirit that has resulted in the rapid acceptance and development of new ideas. The second factor is our education, both formal and informal, for mutual understanding and widespread cooperative action. This training in cooperation has made possible the effective and stable operation of large-scale business and industry in organizations comprised of individuals who are for the most part highly specialized experts.

To my mind it is our faith in the value of working to make our world what we want it to be, inspired by a true concern for the welfare of our fellows, that is the basic and distinctive source of our nation's advancing health and prosperity.

It is not that such spirit is uniquely American, nor that without the possibilities opened by science our faith in the future could perform the miracle that we see here in progress. But it is a fact that this spirit of enterprise combined with a certain altruism is more than ordinarily present among our people. It is equally clear that this spirit has led us into a kind of widespread education that has enabled us relatively quickly and extensively to use the gifts of science.

The unusual development among our people of this faith in the feasibility of improving our lot is ascribed by some historians as due in large measure to our ten generations of experience as pioneers. In the frontier settlement one shaped his own world and built for the next generation. There was no other way to live. And this pattern of life was successful. The weight of tradition and the destruction from frequent wars that have too often frustrated such constructive efforts in the older societies of Europe and Asia have had little effect in our history. Thus when new possibilities are presented by technology, our thought is at once of how they can be used to improve our manner of life.

But there is a deeper basis for our desire to make life better. It is the drive of the same spirit that first sent the Pilgrim Fathers to our shores, and which continues to be active among us.

Certain it is that our Christian heritage has given Americans a strong incentive to make of their world the best that is possible. Recognition of the value of men and women and of the importance of service on their behalf has been influential in forming our nation's government, in developing our business enterprise, in founding our schools and colleges, and in stimulating our search for new knowledge. The gospel of service for one's neighbors was a seed planted by Christianity. This seed flourished in the soil of a new country where it was necessary for all to engage in hand labor. This has resulted in the general acceptance of the dignity of work, to the extent that the American accepts no substitute for one's efforts on behalf of one's fellows as a basis for reward and respect. As long as such a spirit is our inspiration, we can be confident that we shall educate ourselves and develop our science and technology as best we can toward meeting the needs of men and women.

The methods for finding new knowledge are now familiar. It would seem that these methods, if earnestly applied, are adequate to meet our essential physical requirements for an indefinite future. Even if conflict with a malevolent rival society should continue to drain from us a substantial portion of our strength, one can see ahead not only solutions of the problem of food for a growing population, but also means for identifying and solving social difficulties such as have caused earlier civilizations to decline.

The great question—in fact, it seems to me the only serious question—about whether we shall continue to develop toward the social order that we desire is whether we keep a vital will that in America people shall be able to live to their best.

To this question my considered answer is affirmative. Such an optimistic view comes from a balance of many factors.

The spirit of the present generation of young Americans seems to me fully as alert as that of its predecessors to the importance of keeping our civilization vigorously alive. This alertness is present in part because of the Russian challenge; but this challenge is calling forth a healthy response, and will apparently remain for some generations as a stimulus to do the best we can. Also, a steadily increasing fraction of our people is participating in the nation's religious life of which our American dream is a tangible expression.

## THE WILL TO GROW

But there is another basic reason for my optimism. The social forces that science and industry are bringing into being are providing new life for our American dream. As the counterpart to specialization there is increased stimulus toward working for each other's welfare. With our greater interdependence we feel an increasing need for humane goals on which we will unite. The conditions of life demand of us more education, not only in techniques and skills but also in human understanding. Travel becomes easier and more widespread. Ideas are more readily interchanged. There thus arises better acquaintance with our neighbors. Our own best development we see arising from our endeavor to bring into being the world of our dreams.

With this spirit alive, science offers us the means whereby our dreams can be realized. Let us not be discouraged by those who point to our failures. Never has the opportunity been so good for an American to grow to his fullest stature. Consider his seventy years of life expectancy as compared with his thirty years of a short century ago. Consider the five times larger portion of our young people graduating from college as compared with fifty years ago. Such things are those that spell human advance.

Thus, the hope for escape, as I see it, from the traditional decline and death of civilizations, is that our scientific methods should make it possible to identify the stages of our own decline and to take what precautions are needed to prevent it.

It is not that we do not have troubles. They are many and they are real. But each of our troubles represents something that we may hope to improve. If each of the evils that challenges us can provoke a suitable response, we will grow more and more strongly. And this applies to evils in the realm of morals as well as to those of war, disease, or want. The very troubles show us that there remains for us the joy of further great achievement.

## WHAT OF MAN'S DESTINY?

We find ourselves progressing in the task set by that pioneer of science, Pythagoras, when five hundred years before the time of Christ he asked his followers to study of what and how the world is made in order that they might find a better way of life. It was in the same spirit that Albert Einstein, speaking in this century to the engineers at California Institute of Technology, stated that a task worthy of a scientist is to help men and women to live more fully.

The thrilling practical discovery of the twentieth century is that man may reasonably hope to free himself from the curses of poverty, disease, and ignorance. And for this discovery thanks are due chiefly to science. It is reasonable to hope for continued improvement of man's lot, not only as to his physical needs, but also as to his human understanding.

Such advance will not come however as the automatic result of advancing science. High aspiration, guided by appreciation of the worth of one's fellows, is necessary if the powers of science are to meet the human needs that we see ahead. Because the desire to enable our fellows to live is so clearly demanded as a condition for survival in a society based on science, I am confident the spirit that has been effective in making possible our recent advances will itself continue to grow.

# Epilogue

*Lastly, I would address one general admonition to all; that they consider what are the true ends of knowledge, and that they seek it not either for pleasure of the mind, or for contention, or for superiority to others, or for profit, or fame, or power, or any of these inferior things; but for the benefit and use of life; and that they perfect and govern it in charity.*

Francis Bacon

# Notes

## Chapter 1

4:24   Among such studies is an unpublished analysis by Mr. Compton of biographical data from *American Men of Science.*

9:16   This witty defense of basic research, which originated with Benjamin Franklin, was repeated by Faraday as early as 1816, in a discussion of the new element chlorine.

9:37   The reader who would like further information about the early days of the Compton family may wish to consult James R. Blackwood: *The Comptons at Wooster* (Cambridge, Mass.: The M.I.T. Press, 1967), which gives an interesting account of the family's background and activities through 1913.

15:29   Speaking at the opening of the St. Louis Science Fair, on May 11, 1951, Mr. Compton referred to several of the scientific advances he had witnessed:

"A few days ago on this campus I heard Professor Bernardini of Columbia University tell a group of our physicists about his experiments with a beam of pi mesons produced by Columbia's giant cyclotron. Ten years ago in our studies of cosmic rays we had just become sufficiently confident of the existence of mesons to give them a name. The distinction between various types of mesons such as those that now are called the pi variety was not yet known. A meson was an object of wonder as it came into the earth from the upper atmosphere with its origin unknown. Now these rays are being produced and used in the laboratory. The speaker outlined how by their use important new theories could be developed and tested regarding the structure of the nucleus of the atom. He explained that the basic elements of matter (electrons, protons, and so on) could exist in a variety of energy states, and a new clue was found as to how these elemental particles are related to each other.

"A few weeks before in Philadelphia I had heard Edwin Hubble describe the observations with the great new two-hundred-inch telescope on Mount Palomar. He showed a photograph of the Andromeda nebula with its components separated into individual stars never before made visible. He showed photographs of portions of the sky dotted with multitudes of galaxies certain of which he explained were not less than four hundred million light-years away. He explained how one could now say with assurance that we have under observation a fair sample of all that we shall ever see in the universe. From this we may judge how big our universe is and perhaps make a reasonable guess as to how long it has been in substantially its present condition.

NOTE: The numbers printed in the left-hand margin give the text page and line references to which these notes pertain.

"It was only twenty-five years ago that Sir Arthur Eddington published his little book, *Stars and Atoms,* in which he called to the attention of the world of science the fact that stars owe their heat to the interactions of atomic nuclei. It was in part a result of this book that new laboratories were built in which within less than two decades nuclear energy was released. Now it is not the stars and atoms; it is galaxies of stars and the elemental particles of which the atoms are made. We feel with some confidence that we are at last finding the basic knowledge regarding the fundamentals, both large and small, of our universe. Here is the framework. The infinite task of the future of science is to build upon this framework a physical world that we can understand and in which we shall find our place.

"If physics and astronomy thus have before them an immense future, so likewise does the chemistry of living things. When I was a student we were only beginning to learn of vitamins and the essential part that these complex molecules have to play in building healthy bodies. Now we hear of enzymes and hormones. A generation ago enzymes were thought of as a vague kind of influence whose nature was unknown. Nowadays we crystallize enzymes and use them as catalysts to make little molecules organize themselves into big ones. We find the glands that produce the hormones and study how the hormones control the reactions brought about by the enzymes. The whole process of building molecules from simple forms into the more complex forms that go into the structure of a living cell begins to open before us. With X rays and electron microscopes structures of complex molecules such as proteins and viruses become apparent to us. Admittedly the chemistry of living things is complex, but this complexity is being rapidly reduced to order. Understanding of the physical basis of life has become a conscious goal."

16:40  The first Nobel prizes were awarded in 1901, at which time Roentgen was honored for his discovery. Mr. Compton discusses the significance of Roentgen's work in Chapter 3.

17:7  "A Study of the Wehnelt Electrolytic Interrupter," *Physical Review,* XXX: 2 (February 1910), 161–79.

17:31  In 1958 Mr. Compton commented as follows on this confirmation of Einstein's hypothesis: "The most convincing experimental evidence for the validity of Albert Einstein's quantum theory of the photoelectric effect was given in 1913. This evidence appeared in two nearly simultaneous papers, one by O. W. Richardson and K. T. Compton ("The Photoelectric Effect," *Philosophical Magazine,* XXVI [October 1913], 549–67), the other by Arthur L. Hughes, then working at Cambridge, England. The former paper was the sequel of [Karl] Compton's doctoral thesis ("Velocity of Electrons Liberated by Photoelectric Action," *Physical Review,* 1 [May 1913], 382–92, which he worked out under the direction of O. W. Richardson. (May 12, 1958, to *National Encyclopedia of American Biography.*)

20:14  "The Intensity of X-Ray Reflection, and the Distribution of the Electrons in Atoms," *Physical Review,* IX: 1 (January 1917), 29–57.

20:32  "A Sensitive Modification of the Quadrant Electrometer: Its Theory and Use," *Physical Review,* XIV: 2 (August 1919), 85–98.

22:4    When Arthur Compton received his Ph.D in physics in 1916, he became the third brother to receive a Princeton doctorate, Karl Compton having received the Ph.D. in physics in 1912 and Wilson Compton
in economics in 1915. They remain the only three brothers to have
earned Princeton doctorates. They later became the only three brothers simultaneously to head American colleges: Karl, Massachusetts Institute of Technology, 1930–48; Arthur, Washington University, 1945–
53; and Wilson, the State College of Washington, 1944–51.

In recognition of these and other distinctions, which gained them
the appellation of "America's first family of learning," Princeton University in 1964 named one of its new graduate dormitory quadrangles
Compton Court.

Preserved in the Princeton physics museum is a rotation ring that
Arthur Compton devised while a student to carry out an ingenious
new method that he invented for measuring the earth's rotation independent of astronomical observations. Karl Compton referred to this
device in an address at Washington University: "I recall an incident
during [Arthur's] last year as a graduate student at Princeton, where
I had just become an assistant professor. The head of our department
had become quite intrigued with my brother's method of measuring
the earth's rotation by use of fluid in a ring-shaped glass tube, and
had had the apparatus constructed for classroom demonstration. About
that time it happened that our laboratory was visited by the late Elmer
Sperry . . . who had developed the gyroscopic compass. Mr. Sperry
was invited to witness the operation of my brother's device, which had
been set up on a lecture table for demonstration. But Mr. Sperry
walked right past the door without even looking in, with the comment:
'This device is impossible. You have no idea how slowly the earth
revolves.' All of which illustrates the value of being young." (Commencement address, June 11, 1952.)

22:25   As instructor in physics, 1916–17.

23:32   The negative result was briefly reported (with Oswald Rognley) in
"The Nature of the Ultimate Magnetic Particle," *Science*, XLVI:
1191 (October 26, 1917), 415–16, and more fully in "Is the Atom the
Ultimate Magnetic Particle?" *Physical Review*, XV: 5 (November
1920), 464–76, in which other possible explanations of ferromagnetism
are discussed.

23:35   G. E. Uhlenbeck and S. Goudsmit, *Naturwissenschaften*, XIII (1925),
953; *Nature*, CXVII (1926), 264. In the latter the authors state: "So
far as we know, the idea of a quantised spinning of the electron was
put forward for the first time by A. H. Compton [*Journal of the Franklin Institute*, August 1921, p. 145], who pointed out the possible bearing of this idea on the origin of the natural unit of magnetism." [Mr.
Compton's paper concludes "that the electron itself, spinning like a
tiny gyroscope, is probably the ultimate magnetic particle."] "Without
being aware of Compton's suggestion, we have directed attention to
the possibility of applying the spinning electron to interpret a number
of features of the quantum theory of the Zeeman effect, and also of
the analysis of complex spectra in general."

24:15   The Westinghouse laboratory, one of the earliest industrial research laboratories to be organized, was established in 1904. Arthur Compton, who was employed as research engineer for two years (1917–19), was among the first employees of the laboratory.

25:2    Chapter 26, written while he was a member of the Westinghouse research staff, contains some of Mr. Compton's ideas on the importance of fundamental research.

25:26   The fellowship was one of the first National Research fellowships to be awarded. The National Research Council had been established in 1916 to organize scientific resources in the interest of national security and welfare. Robert A. Millikan was a member of the Council's organizing committee and later its first executive officer and director of research. In 1918, the president of the Rockefeller Foundation requested Millikan's advice on the strengthening of American science, and he proposed the establishment of an extensive fellowship program to enable young scientists of outstanding research ability to pursue further training. Millikan later referred to this program, which was financed by the Rockefeller Foundation and administered by the National Research Council, as "the most vital influence in the development of the United States into a country whose scientific output is now comparable to that of the other leading scientific countries." The fellows were originally required to study at American universities. Arthur Compton was one of the first two fellows permitted to pursue their studies outside the United States.

28:15   Mr. Compton's paper, in the form of a letter, was published as "The Distribution of Electrons in Atoms," *Nature*, XCV: 2378 (May 27, 1915), 343–4. It appeared in conjunction with a letter of W. H. Bragg, which included the comment: "I believe Mr. Compton is right in ascribing the rapid decline in the intensities of the X-ray spectra as we proceed to higher orders to the fact that the atom should not be treated as a point, but as a distribution of electrons in space. . . ."

28:17   *X-Rays and Electrons: An Outline of Recent X-Ray Theory* (New York: D. Van Nostrand; 1926). This book and its later revision (*X-Rays in Theory and Experiment* [with S. K. Allison; 1935]) have been considered the most authoritative discussions of Roentgen rays published in English until the present. The latter volume is still in use as a text in several universities; the earlier book also has significance as the first important work on modern physics to be published in the United States.

31:22   On May 4, 1966, Washington University dedicated its newly constructed Arthur Holly Compton Laboratory of Physics, which greatly expanded campus physics facilities. A five-level structure, the building provides more than 65,000 square feet of office, laboratory, and library space. The new building houses laboratories for research in cosmic radiation, high-energy particle physics and relativity, nuclear structure physics, solid-state physics, theoretical physics, optical coherence studies, and astrophysics. Occupancy of the new facility will enable the physics department to admit more students to both its graduate and undergraduate programs. The department presently numbers 19 faculty members, 3 postdoctoral research associates, 38 nonacademic staff members, 72 graduate students, and 50 undergraduate physics majors. In 1919, when Mr. Compton first accepted a position with the university, the physics department consisted of three persons.

32:30 Reginald J. Stephenson recalls that he came to know Mr. Compton, or "A.H." as he was commonly known among the students, when in 1931 he went as a graduate student to the University of Chicago: "It was there that I listened to him lecture on the scattering of X-rays with never a mention of their commonly accepted name, the Compton effect or Compton scattering. Few people outside the field of physics realize how the terms Compton effect, Compton wave length, Compton electrons, Compton absorption coefficient have come into common use. There are three principal means by which X-rays and gamma rays can lose energy when passing through materials. These are called the Photoelectric, the Compton, and the Pair production processes." (*Wooster Alumni Bulletin*, LXXVI: 7 [April 1962].)

33:7 When they occurred to him, it was Mr. Compton's habit to record the hunches that he might later investigate. One of the most interesting documents among his personal papers consists of the notes he made on shipboard en route home from England to take up his new duties at Washington University. On two pieces of the ship's stationery he jotted down some ideas about the research he planned to pursue, including a diagram of the equipment with which he later attained his striking experimental disclosure of the particle nature of the photon.

33:9 These remarks are based on two informal lectures, for college students and science teachers, presented at Washington University. The first, entitled "Waves, Particles, and Uncertainty," was presented on January 27, 1955; the other, "X-Rays as Particles and Waves," on December 12, 1961.

33:41 C. G. Barkla: "Note on the Energy of Scattered X-Radiation" (*Philosophical Magazine*, XXI [May 1911], 648–52); E. Rutherford, "The Scattering of $\alpha$ and $\beta$ Particles by Matter, and the Structure of the Atom" (ibid., 669–88).

34:28 In those days it was no small task to obtain suitable apparatus, and equipment manufacturers were not interested in Mr. Compton's designs. As a result, it was necessary to construct much of the equipment in the Washington University laboratories, including even the building of special X-ray tubes. Though unorthodox in design, the equipment proved to be more sensitive than that in use for similar experiments elsewhere.

36:17 "Secondary Radiations Produoced by X Rays," *Bulletin of the National Research Council*, IV: 20, Pt. 2 (October 1922), 56 pp.

38:8 Another by-product of great value to physics was the X-ray method of determining the charge on the electron.

39:33 The trip was made possible by a fellowship from the John Simon Guggenheim Memorial Foundation, which awarded its first fellowships in 1925.

41:12 This tale, which Mr. Compton told on numerous occasions, is not included here as it appears in full in Chapter 12, p. 142.

42:8 Arthur Compton enrolled for all the philosophy courses offered by the College of Wooster and received the philosophy prize for his outstanding work in the subject.

43:22   Chapter 14 gives a brief account of the world survey of cosmic rays and the data that were obtained.

43:24   Around 1900 several physicists were interested in the spontaneous ionization of the atmosphere. Their studies gradually made evident the existence of the cosmic rays, a highly penetrating radiation of unknown origin. During the early years of the century cosmic-ray research centered in the geophysical aspects of the phenomenon and constituted a comparatively minor field of physics research. Professor Compton was prominent among a number of investigators who began intensive studies of cosmic rays during the early 1930's to clarify their nature and enable them to be used as a powerful investigative tool. His chief contributions in this field were to establish the electrical composition of cosmic rays and the variation of cosmic rays with latitude and altitude, the strongest evidence in support of their extraterrestrial origin. In January 1936, Professor Compton summarized his cosmic-ray researches before a joint meeting of the American Physical Society and Section B of the American Association for the Advancement of Science. ("Recent Developments in Cosmic Rays," *Review of Scientific Instruments*, VII: 2 [February 1936], 71–81.).

44:15   The president of the National Academy of Sciences was Frank B. Jewett, then president of the Bell Telephone Laboratories. Through the initiative of Vannevar Bush, chairman of the National Defense Research Committee, Dr. Jewett was asked to appoint a committee to appraise the possible military value of nuclear energy. Arthur Compton was asked to head such a committee at a meeting at the National Academy in Washington in April 1941. Those present were Jewett, Bush, and Lyman J. Briggs, director of the National Bureau of Standards and chairman of the government's Advisory Committee on Uranium.

45:13   Various aspects of the wartime atomic energy program are discussed in Chapters 27, 28, 32, and 33.

48:36   Among the frequent opportunities for service to the nation that were presented to Mr. Compton during his tenure at Washington University was the repeated suggestion of his name as chairman of the Atomic Energy Commission. On one occasion he felt it necessary to issue a public statement of his position:

"There is in my opinion nothing more effective than a well-balanced education as a means for establishing a peaceful society in which free men and women can live satisfactory lives. The most strategic place that I know to develop a program of such peace-building education is at Washington University.

"If you take these two propositions, and add to them my own yen to do what I can to make the world what it ought to be, you will see how difficult it would be to persuade me to leave Washington University.

"The work of the Atomic Energy Commission is essential to the nation's safety and welfare, but it seems to me clear that I can do more toward these ends at Washington University than with the Atomic Energy Commission. This is in part because the students, the faculty, and the friends of the university are working together toward making our institution a center for preparing young men and women to find the opportunities and meet the responsibilities of the day." [Statement to the press, March 20, 1950.]

50:17  Mr. Compton was one of six university presidents who were invited by the Association of American Universities to attend the conference, which was held at the University of Delhi, December 12–22, 1949, under the sponsorship of the Indian Council on World Affairs. He was later elected chairman of the American delegation of about thirty persons representing education, industry, finance, journalism, and public affairs. This group of private citizens explored with an equal number of Indian representatives how increased scholarly, economic, cultural, and social relations might be fostered between the two countries on a personal and unofficial level.

50:39  Mr. Compton spoke at the dedication, in which Prime Minister Nehru also participated, on January 3, 1950. In his remarks Mr. Compton stressed the importance to India of a vigorous and healthy growth of science and its applications: "In science and in scientific education lies the hope of increasing the supply of goods from [India's] own resources that will fill the needs of her vast and growing population. Here is the way toward improved health, toward control of the growth of her population, and toward an understanding of her place in man's modern world. . . . I should like especially to emphasize the distinctive place in present-day science of the chemistry of life processes. With the possible exception of the physicist's study of the elemental particles . . . I know of no aspect of science that appears as promising for progress during the generation immediately before us as is our increasing knowledge of the chemical processes of growth. . . ."

52:2  The remarks Mr. Compton prepared for this occasion appear as Chapter 2 of this volume.

52:34  The first book of Herodotus tells of Solon's visit to King Croesus at Sardis. The king showed the wise Greek his treasures, expecting to be admired as the most fortunate of men. But Solon looked coldly at Croesus' display of wealth and declared: "You are very rich, and you rule a numerous people; but the question you asked me I will not answer, until I know that you have died happily. Great wealth can make a man no happier than moderate means, unless he has the luck to continue in prosperity to the end. . . . Now if a man thus favored dies as he has lived, he will be just the one you are looking for: the only sort of person who deserves to be called happy. But mark this: until he is dead, keep the word 'happy' in reserve. Till then, he is not happy, but only lucky." (*Herodotus: The Histories*, trans. with intro. by Aubrey de Selincourt [Penguin; 1954].)

Upon the death of his brother Karl, in 1954, Arthur Compton alluded to Solon's story in these words: "I have wondered why I have really not found myself sad on Karl's account for having been cut down at an all-too-young age. The loss is heavy, especially so to me myself, who relied on him in so many ways, including the need for . . . an understanding friend. I think the answer to my question is that of Solon. I truly see Karl's life as a remarkably happy one, full of the joy of doing his part. The close of his life was as he would have wanted it, in the fullness of the greatest service that he knew how to give."

## Chapter 2

53:8 In a letter to members of the Board of Directors of Washington University, dated April 10, 1953, Mr. Compton referred to his new task in this way:

> . . . ever since the recent war was drawing to a close, I have been eager to undertake a task of a scholarly nature for which my experience has seemed to give me certain special qualifications. This task has to do with the relations of science to human affairs. It includes such things as the effort to understand the distinctively human characteristics of man in light of science, and the adjustment of the individual to life in the complex society that science has helped to build. While what one man can do toward answering such questions is small, I consider the answers nevertheless vital to the continued success of the civilization we are building. Eight years ago, I turned away from the opportunity to work on these problems because I saw in helping to reorganize the work at Washington University an undertaking of such importance and urgency that it could not be refused.

Mr. Compton's resignation as chancellor became effective December 31, 1953, and his new appointment as Distinguished Service Professor of Natural Philosophy the following day.

53:13 See, for example, Chapter 43: "Man's Hopes and the New Need for Human Responsibility," presented in 1954.

53:21 The quotation is from *New Atlantis* [1627], the fable in which Francis Bacon described a society of scholars engaged in acquiring systematic knowledge of nature for the benefit of mankind, and which inspired formation of the Royal Society of London.

## Chapter 3

67:7 In Chapter 16, "Creativity in Science," Mr. Compton again discusses Roentgen's work. See also "Modern Physics and the Discovery of X Rays" (*Radiology*, XLV: 5 [November 1945], 534–8), an article published in observance of the fiftieth anniversary of Roentgen's discovery. An authoritative biography of Roentgen by Dr. Otto Glasser was published in the same year: *Dr. W. C. Röntgen* (Springfield, Ill.: Charles C. Thomas; 1945).

67:9 For a description of some of this work see Chapter 13, "What We Have Learned from Scattered X Rays."

67:14 *Secondary Radiations Produced by X Rays* (Princeton, N.J.: Van Nostrand; 1935).

68:14 Presented before the annual meeting of the American Association for the Advancement of Science in Indianapolis, Indiana, December 1937. This address, which was not published, was substantially the same as that included here.

72:6    This enumeration includes several of Mr. Compton's contributions to science. In an outline autobiography, revised in 1952, he listed his chief scientific accomplishments as follows: discovered and interpreted change in wavelength of X rays when scattered [Compton effect]; discovered total reflection of X rays; method of demonstrating earth's rotation; complete polarization of X rays (with C. F. Hagenow); first X-ray spectra from ruled gratings (with R. L. Doan); invented sodium vapor lamp; established variation of cosmic rays with latitude; electrical composition of cosmic rays; directed development of first atomic chain reaction and of first quantity production of plutonium.

## Chapter 4

73:5    This so-called Compton effect was one of the most important stimuli for the development of the quantum mechanics. At the same time, this effect had striking meaning for the work first of Schrödinger, then of Bohr. I have said that Compton's observations could be understood if one interpreted not only the scattering matter but also the light as being corpuscular. Schrödinger showed that one could also explain these observations if one understood not only that light but also that matter as a field is a wave phenomenon. With this, the two concepts —particle and field—are no longer ascribed to different physical entities—matter and light—but instead each entity admits both descriptions. This was finally understood by Bohr. (C. F. von Weizsäcker: "Gedenkworte für Arthur H. Compton," in *Reden und Gedenkworte*, Orden Pour le mérite für Wissenschaften und Künste [Heidelberg: Lambert Schneider; 1962], V, 113–16; translated by George E. Pake and used by permission of Professor Weizsäcker.)

Chapter 13 includes an explanation of the Compton effect. For a detailed technical explanation of the Compton effect and its implications for physics, see Robert S. Shankland: *Atomic and Nuclear Physics* (New York: Macmillan; 1955; 2nd edn., 1960). Professor Shankland has also written the article on the Compton effect that appears in the *Encyclopaedia Britannica* after 1958. Previously, the article was written by Professor Compton.

Morris H. Shamos has included annotated excerpts from two of Professor Compton's 1923 papers in *Great Experiments in Physics* (New York: Holt; 1960). This book, which is designed for the liberal arts student, explains and illustrates a number of the concepts that are essential to an understanding of contemporary ideas in physics.

## Chapter 5

75:10   The published conference proceedings contain a different version of Mr. Compton's talk, evidently due to use of a re-translation into English of the German translation of these remarks.

## Chapter 6

81:13   The lectures were translated by Carl Eckart and Frank C. Hoyt and published as *The Physical Principles of the Quantum Theory*. The volume includes a brief foreword by Mr. Compton. Aside from the technical journals, this is the earliest presentation in English of Heisenberg's work.

88:23 In *The Freedom of Man,* p. 11, Mr. Compton makes it clear that this is Dampier's conclusion: "From the standpoint of science, however, Dampier-Whetham considers the influence of Socrates and Plato as a world calamity. Except for them, he suggests that science might have reached its present stage of development two thousand years ago."

## Chapter 7

111:31 A Muslim university located in Aligarh, a small city in northern India near New Delhi.

## Chapter 8

115:10 See Chapter 43, "Man's Hopes and the New Need for Human Responsibility," for Mr. Compton's address opening the first conference.

Five working papers from the 1954 conference, including Mr. Compton's, appeared as "Science and Human Responsibility: A Round Table" in the *Journal of Public Law,* published by the Emory University Law School (IV: 2 [Fall 1955], 322–66).

Concurrently with the 1956–7 conferences, a series of twenty-five television interviews with individual participants was produced for the National Educational Television network. Transcripts of these interviews were published as *Science and Human Responsibility* (St. Louis: Washington University; 1960). The programs themselves are available on film through the Audio-Visual Center of the University of Indiana for use in the classroom or in adult discussion groups. Participants were: Harrison Brown, Harlan Cleveland, Everett R. Clinchy, Arthur H. Compton, Norman Cousins, Harold H. Fisher, Clarence Faust, Erich Fromm, John E. Hull, Robert M. Hutchins, Aldous Huxley, Julian Huxley, Barbara Ward Jackson, Frank C. Laubach, James S. McDonnell, Paul H. Nitze, Filmer S. C. Northrop, and Henry A. Wallace. Huston Smith served as the questioner in all the films.

122:36 The conference, called to discuss "Man Confronting Science," was held September 3–13, 1952, under the auspices of the Rencontres Internationales de Genève.

## Chapter 9

125:22 Niels Bohr's account of these discussions and their implications may be found in two volumes of his collected essays: *Atomic Physics and Human Knowledge* (New York: Wiley; 1958), and *Essays 1958–1962 on Atomic Physics and Human Knowledge* (New York: Interscience; 1963).

125:23 The most complete statement of Max Born's philosophic views is found in *Natural Philosophy of Cause and Chance* (New York: Dover; 1964). See also *Physics and Politics* (New York: Basic Books; 1962).

## Chapter 10

131:26 The handwritten original of this letter, preserved among the Compton papers at Washington University, bears the date March 24, 1908, an obvious but understandable error.

133:32 These were Mr. Compton's first published papers: "A Criticism of Mr. C. W. Williams's article: 'Concerning Aeroplanes,'" *Scientific American*, C: 7 (February 13, 1909), 135. Subsequently two further articles on airplanes were published: "Striving for Perfect Machine," *Aeronautics*, V: 2 (August 1909), 58 ff.; and "Aeroplane Stability," *Scientific American Supplement*, LXXII: 1858 (August 12, 1911), 100–2.

## Chapter 11

137:29 This statement is based on a calculation of the diffusion of nitrogen. A similar illustration has been used recently by Harlow Shapley, who explains in detail why a part of any ancient breath will now be found present anywhere in the atmosphere. Professor Shapley's computation appears in *The View from a Distant Star* (New York: Basic Books; 1963), pp. 95–8.

## Chapter 12

140:6 A more detailed explanation of the problem, especially as related to his own scientific work, appears in Chapter 13. The reader seeking further technical material may wish to consult "What Is Light?" a paper prepared for the *Sigma Xi Quarterly* (XVII: 1 [March 1929], 14–34) which attracted wide interest. The specialist may be interested in "X-Rays as a Branch of Optics," Arthur Compton's 1927 Nobel prize lecture (*J. O. S. A.* and *Review of Scientific Instruments*, XVI: 2 [February 1928], 71–87) and "The Corpuscular Properties of Light," his paper for the 1927 Solvay Conference (*Physical Review Supplement*, 1: 1 [July 1929], 74–89).

147:25 In 1927 Mr. Compton introduced the term *photon*, which immediately came into general use to describe the quantum of radiation associated with a single quantum of energy. He described his derivation of the term in this manner: "The first use that I know of this word was made by Dr. Gilbert N. Lewis, Professor of Chemistry at the University of California, to describe a unit of radiant energy which he considered to be indestructible as it moved from an emitting atom to an absorbing atom and moved as a part of that atom until again emitted. I saw in this name a word that would describe the corpuscular quantum of radiation that had been varyingly described as a light corpuscle or a needle ray." (Letter of August 11, 1949, to Samuel Glasstone, author of *Sourcebook on Atomic Energy*.)

148:19 This picture was altered in 1932 by James Chadwick's demonstration of the existence of the neutron, an elementary particle devoid of charge. In 1920 Rutherford had made the first suggestion of the existence of a neutral particle with the characteristics that are now known.

148:25 Davisson's work is discussed in greater detail in Chapter 22.

## Chapter 13

149:5 The reader with a knowledge of physics and an interest in its historical development is referred to the following papers by Arthur Compton in which he reviews his most notable X-ray work in greater technical detail: "The Scattering of X-Ray Photons," *American Journal of
Physics*, XIV: 2 (March–April 1946), 80–4; "The Scattering of X
Rays as Particles," *American Journal of Physics*, XXIX: 12 (December
1961), 817–20, "X-Rays as a Branch of Optics," *J. O. S. A.* and *Review of Scientific Instruments*, XVI: 2 (February 1928), 71–87
(Nobel lecture); and "Some Experimental Difficulties with the Electromagnetic Theory of Radiation," *Journal of the Franklin Institute*,
CCV: 2 (February 1928), 155–78. It is planned to include a complete bibliography in the edition of his scientific work that is now in
preparation. The most complete published bibliography presently
available appears in Poggendorff's Biographical Handbook (J. C. Poggendorff: *Biographisch-Literarisches Handwörtenbuch* [Berlin: Verlag
Chemie; 1936]).

## Chapter 14

157:1 Cosmic rays are elementary charged particles of extremely high energy
and penetrating power that travel in space at speeds approaching that
of light. Some of these rays enter the earth's atmosphere, where they
can be detected by delicate instruments. After a slow start in the early
years of the present century, cosmic-ray research has become one of
the most important fields of physics. This is because the cosmic rays
provide a valuable scientific tool for the study of such matters as
relativistic electromagnetic theory, the interchange of energy between
matter and radiation, elementary particles, and various cosmic phenomena. In a report on an international cosmic-ray symposium that
he organized in 1939, Arthur Compton stated that "in cosmic rays we
have the most effective tool for studying the components of atoms
and how their nuclei are put together. Just as when the study of X-ray
spectra helped us to solve the problems of the electronic atmosphere
of atoms, so, it is hoped, the study of cosmic-ray processes will clarify
our understanding of radio-activity and other nuclear processes, and
lead to the next great advance beyond the quantum theory." (*Scientific Monthly*, XLIX [September 1939], 280–4.)

157:2 The author's work in cosmic rays appears in the scientific literature in
a series of some sixty technical papers between 1930 and 1943. The
world survey of cosmic rays, which he directed in the early 1930's,
was one of the first scientific inquiries to engage the efforts of a group
of investigators organized on a global basis. The reader interested in
a technical description of this work is referred to two papers entitled
"A Geographic Study of Cosmic Rays," *Scientific Monthly*, XXXVI
(January 1933), 75–87; *Physical Review*, XLIII: 6 (March 15, 1933),
387–403. His major findings in the field of cosmic rays were summarized in "Recent Developments in Cosmic Rays" (*Review of Scientific Instruments*, VII: 2 [February 1936], 71–81).

157:10 "Data and Nature of Cosmic Rays," *Bell System Technical Journal*,

XI (January 1932), 148. Dr. Darrow, a member of the Bell Telephone Laboratories technical staff, was long engaged in preparing studies and analyses of especially significant research in physics. Since 1941 he has served as secretary of the American Physical Society.

## Chapter 15

172:24 In 1842 Doppler predicted that the color of a luminous body moving toward a stationary observer should appear different from its color when it is moving away from the observer, and he used this principle to explain the differences among the colors of the stars as due to their line of sight velocities. Within our galaxy most stars do not move fast enough relative to the velocity of light for Doppler's idea to be realized. In 1848 Fizeau suggested the use of sharp spectral lines to observe the Doppler shift in the radiation from stars. It was not until about 1870, however, that spectroscopy was sufficiently developed for the predicted shift to be detected. Since then this so-called Doppler effect has enabled the velocity of approach or recession of stars and other heavenly bodies to be calculated from the observed shifts of known spectral lines.

173:23 Now called "meson." The change in terminology is attributed to Werner Heisenberg, who pointed out that the Greek word *mesos* (in between), from which the name of the new particle was derived, has no "tr" in it. In 1939 a question of major disagreement at the Chicago cosmic-ray conference was that of the name to be applied to this particle of intermediate mass, variously called a heavy electron, a barytron, a yukon, a mesotron, a mesoton, and a meson. "Partly because the European investigators seemed unanimously to favor the word meson," Arthur Compton concluded, "the present writer is likewise adopting that word in order to prevent the confusion of tongues." (*Scientific Monthly*, XLIX [September 1939], 284.)

## Chapter 16

190:5 Julius Plücker was one of the leading scientists of his day; however, the reference to him as a glassblower was a natural one for Mr. Compton, who himself greatly enjoyed blowing glass.

190:40 This occurred during 1934–5, when Mr. Compton was in England as George Eastman Professor at Oxford University. Dr. Zay Jeffries of the General Electric Company has provided an account of this development (*loc. cit.*, Ch. 5).

## Chapter 17

193:6 "For his optical precision instrument and the spectroscopic and metrological investigations he has carried out with it."

193:6 "For his work on the elementary charge of electricity and on the photoelectric effect."

193:7 "For his discovery of the effect named after him." In conjunction with

Mr. Compton's article, which is reprinted here, there appeared also an article about him by Waldemar Kaempffert, science editor of *The New York Times.*

193:7   "For his work on the thermionic phenomenon and especially for the discovery of the law named after him."

196:37  Miller's results remained at variance with all other tests of the Michelson-Morley experiment for nearly thirty years. In 1955 Robert S. Shankland *et al.* subjected Miller's data to a new analysis and concluded that his results are not consistent with the ether theory but were due to unrecognized systematic errors in his data. ("New Analysis of the Interferometer Observations of Dayton C. Miller," *Review of Modern Physics*, XXVII: 2 [April 1955], 167–78.)

198:41  A slight upward revision of the quantitative value of the electronic charge has resulted from later X-ray techniques initiated at the University of Chicago.

## Chapter 19

205:8   The code name for the central laboratory responsible for the development of plutonium for use in the atomic bomb.

206:22  The first cosmic-ray readings on Mount Evans, made in September 1931 by Mr. Compton, were soon followed by others, leading to construction of a permanent laboratory in 1936. Mr. Stearns described the rigors of the early expeditions and the establishment of the laboratory in 1938 ("The Mount Evans Laboratory," *Science* [March 1938], pp. 242–8).

206:31  A memorial plaque to Mr. Stearns was publicly presented at the time of a cosmic-ray symposium held in 1949 at Echo Lake on Mount Evans.

## Chapter 21

216:2   A revealing comment in this connection appears in a note to Mr. Compton: "Cosmic rays, which it now looks as though every laboratory in the world is adopting as a major part of its research program, are after all only a minor element in the huge job which you have been so active in, of trying to do what you can to combat the dogmatism and the indifference of much too large a fraction of scientists in the face of the much greater problem of doing what we can to make a better world. You have been one of the most active and influential men in this effort, and I have admired and applauded your efforts. Your influence will, I have no doubt, carry farther in your new position than it could do in the one that you have left. More power to your elbow!" (Robert A. Millikan to AHC, June 28, 1948.)

## Chapter 23

224:31  As explained in Chapter 17 and elsewhere, the development of Lawrence's method of producing plutonium was assigned to Arthur Compton.

Chapter 24

229:31 The comparable figures now, including the 1965 awards, are: three hundred sixty-six individuals, nine institutions, and thirty-one countries.

229:32 There are at present two additional women Nobel laureates: Maria Goeppert Mayer (physics, 1963), and Dorothy Crowfoot Hodgkin (chemistry, 1964).

229:36 Mme Curie remains the only person to have been honored twice for contributions to science. Linus C. Pauling, who received the peace award in 1962, became the second person to receive two Nobel prizes. He had been awarded the chemistry prize in 1954.

229:39 The award of the Nobel peace prize to the German pacifist Carl von Ossietzky, an outspoken anti-Nazi who was then in prison, had provoked so much resentment in Germany that Hitler issued a decree forbidding Germans to accept Nobel prizes. Subsequently, a German scientist, Gerhard Domagk, was selected to receive the Nobel prize in medicine for 1939, but was forced to decline because of government pressure. Although his prize money reverted to the Nobel fund, he received his medal and diploma in Stockholm after the war. In 1945 Otto Hahn was awarded the 1944 physics prize and was able to receive it the next year.

A more recent example of government pressure occurred in the case of Boris Pasternak, the Russian writer who was selected to receive the 1958 prize in literature but who declined. His name remains listed among the Nobel laureates.

Enrico Fermi, who was chosen for the 1938 physics award, was given permission by the Italian government to travel to Sweden to receive his prize. He took advantage of this opportunity to flee fascist Italy with his family. Immediately after the ceremony in Stockholm, he sought refuge in the United States.

229:40 Eighty-seven Americans have now received Nobel prizes, sixty-seven for their achievements in science. A number of commentators have called attention to the increasing proportion of awards to American scientists as a rough index of the development and maturity of American science. The first American scientist to be honored by a Nobel prize was A. A. Michelson in 1907. By 1930 only five Americans had received Nobel awards in science; by 1940, fourteen; by 1950, twenty-nine; and by 1960, fifty-four. See espicially Bernard Jaffe: *Men of Science in America* (New York: Simon and Schuster; 1958).

230:4 The fifth St. Louisan was Mr. Compton, whose award was in physics. Arthur Kornberg, then of Stanford University, was honored in 1959 for scientific research he had performed in St. Louis. Thus seven recipients of the prize in science have carried on their award-winning investigations in St. Louis.

The distinguished historian Donald R. Fleming, in discussing the continental development of American science and culture, has called attention to the fact that the majority of American Nobel prize winners in science have been divided among the following institutions: California Institute of Technology, Columbia, Harvard, University of

California at Berkeley, and Washington University. See "The Big Money and High Politics of Science," *Atlantic*, CCXVI: 2 (August 1965), 41–5.

## Chapter 25

234:26 Jefferson Papers, Library of Congress, Vol. 231, p. 41473a, cited in Nathan Schachner: *Thomas Jefferson, A Biography* (New York: Appleton-Century-Crofts; 1951), p. 1008.

## Chapter 27

243:5 Those who would like to follow in greater detail the story of the nation's wartime atomic project may wish to consult the author's account of this development and his involvement in it: *Atomic Quest, A Personal Narrative* (New York: Oxford University Press; 1956). In this work Mr. Compton cites a number of additional sources of information about the project. *The New World*, by Richard G. Hewlett and Oscar E. Anderson, is the Atomic Energy Commission's official account of the atomic project (University Park: Pennsylvania State University Press; 1962). This volume, which was prepared with the help of a seven-member Historical Advisory Committee of which Mr. Compton was a member, contains an excellent note on published sources.

A statement entitled "Future of Atomic Energy," prepared by Arthur Compton and Zay Jeffries in 1946 for transmission by Bernard Baruch to the United Nations Atomic Energy Commission, was published as Chapter 1 of Volume II in *The International Control of Atomic Energy* (Washington, D.C.: Department of State Publication 2661; 1946). "Hiroshima Revisited" (*Science*, CXXXIV: 3486 [October 20, 1961], 1231–3), is an essay-review in which Mr. Compton discusses two of the many recent volumes dealing with aspects of military and peaceful use of atomic energy (*Japan Subdued* by Herbert Feis [Princeton, N.J.: Princeton University Press; 1961] and *The Impact of Atomic Energy* by Erwin Hiebert [Newton, Kansas: Faith and Life Press; 1961]).

243:14 The National Academy of Sciences Committee on the Military Uses of Atomic Energy originally consisted of the following membership, all physicists: Arthur H. Compton, chairman; William D. Coolidge, retired director of the General Electric research laboratory, vice chairman; Ernest O. Lawrence, University of California at Berkeley; J. C. Slater, Massachusetts Institute of Technology; H. J. Van Vleck, Harvard University. Later two engineers were added: L. W. Chubb of Westinghouse and O. E. Buckley of Bell Telephone Laboratories. By mid-October the committee was further strengthened by the addition of Warren K. Lewis, dean of American chemical engineers, George B. Kistiakowsky of Harvard, one of the nation's foremost explosives experts, and Robert S. Milliken of the University of Chicago, an authority on isotope separation.

Mr. Compton recorded in *Atomic Quest* (p. 59) that he presented the committee's report personally to Vannevar Bush on November 6, 1941.

243:16 The other members of the S-1 Committee were: James B. Conant, chairman; Lyman J. Briggs, Eger V. Murphree, Ernest O. Lawrence, and Harold C. Urey.

## Chapter 28

259:4 Henry L. Stimson: "The Decision to Use the Atomic Bomb," *Harper's Magazine,* CXCIV (February 1947), 101.

259:5 Arthur Compton has discussed in detail in *Atomic Quest* (Ch. 27) the factors given consideration at various levels of civilian and military authority in the decision to employ the atomic bomb in World War II. See especially pp. 219–85. See also Chapter 33 of the present volume.

## Chapter 29

263:fn. Edward A. Shils was at that time Professor of Social Science in the Committee on Social Thought at the University of Chicago; he served as special editor of the issue.

## Chapter 30

265:12 Arthur Compton was among the early critics of Senator Joseph McCarthy. On March 28, 1950, upon his return from a trip abroad, Mr. Compton released a statement concerning Senator McCarthy's attacks on the State Department, which included the following remarks:

> The tragedy of the present day is that those who should be our leaders are playing the Russian game. They are spreading the false belief that democracy is corrupt and ineffective. Actually faulty as it may be, it comes closer to what men need, and has greater strength and greater endurance than does any form of despotism, whether we call this monarchy, state socialism, fascism, or communism.
>
> The lethal character of such attacks is illustrated by Senator McCarthy's broadcast attack upon our State Department. Nothing could be more effective in destroying the influence of democracy abroad, or the spirit of loyal Americans who so believe in their freedom that they will devote their lives to its cause, than to know that those in high places will take every opportunity to block our nation's progress if it means their partisan gain.
>
> This is a time of war, a cold war it is true, but nevertheless a war to the death so far as concerns freedom.
>
> I have myself just returned from leading the American delegation to unofficial conferences with India and Pakistan. I know the sincerity of the efforts for democracy made by some of the principals of McCarthy's attack. I have felt the importance of the

reliance by other nations on their freedom to discuss the American situation as they know it.

I have no means of knowing whether the Senators now attacking the State Department understand the inevitable damage that their accusations cause to the position of democratic freedom in the world. I cannot know their motives. But if it should appear that there is indeed no substantial evidence for the accusations of disloyalty in which they are indulging they should be recognized by their fellow Americans as a major menace to their country.

268:17 Mr. Compton's own thinking at that time is reflected in the following comments to a member of the President's cabinet:

I have just completed a session with the other members of the Scientific Panel of the Interim Committee on Atomic Energy, writing a report on the technical prospects and requirements for the coming years. In our discussions there emerged certain broad implications of a nontechnical type. Though not explicitly stated in our report to the Interim Committee, these implications have been basic to our thinking. You can judge as to their value in shaping national policy. . . .

By a relatively modest development and production effort (of perhaps a billion dollars per year) we estimate that within ten years we can produce all the atomic weapons required, in conjunction with normal Army and Navy facilities, to destroy all major surface concentrations of industrial and military facilities throughout the world. I personally believe that the objective of American military preparations should be held to this limited goal. . . .

There is a reasonable chance that a concentrated scientific and technical effort, comparable with that spent on the development of the present atom bomb, could develop a super bomb which would exceed the atom bomb as greatly as that exceeds the "blockbusters." We [Compton, Fermi, Lawrence, Oppenheimer] feel that this development should *not* be undertaken, primarily because we should prefer defeat in war to a victory obtained at the expense of the enormous human disaster that would be caused by its determined use. . . .

The theoretical basis of the super bomb has arisen spontaneously with at least four persons working on our project who have independently brought the idea to me. This means that it will occur likewise to those in other nations engaged on similar developments. If developed here, other great powers must follow suit. . . .

We see great possibilities ahead if the vast strength of our nation is turned toward developing our peacetime economy. Atomic bombs may well be a source of pessimism if we insist on placing ourselves in a position where we cannot be seriously damaged by another nation. The rocket, the airplane, and the atomic bomb have combined to make impossible the attainment of such a goal. All the world thus faces a future in which sudden destruction is possible at any time, unless prevented by policing and by the cultivation of good will. . . .

It is obvious that I am in no position to indicate how these broad objectives are to be attained. Statesmen, military men, sociologists and economists, are needed for this purpose rather than physicists. As a scientist I have wanted, however, to point out that what seems to be our proper military task is reduced by recent developments to one that should require only limited effort. As a citizen, I have wanted to point out also that we are now ready to develop in our nation the strongest and most world-enriching civilization of all time.

We have the strength. I believe we can gain also the vision and the courage. (AHC to Henry A. Wallace, September 27, 1945.)

## Chapter 31

274:22 In July 1955, after eight years of refusal, the Department of State issued a passport to Professor Kamen. The department's action was in line with a ruling of the United States Circuit Court of Appeals that passports cannot arbitrarily be denied without substantial cause and without due process of law.

Professor Kamen attributes the successful outcome of his case to Arthur Compton's firmness in supporting and defending him. He has provided the following summary of the relevant events, in a letter to the editor of this volume dated October 26, 1965:

The moral courage needed to sustain adherence to ethical principles of fair play and justice is possessed by few individuals. Even fewer are also gifted intellectually. Arthur Compton was one of these very few—a fact better known the longer one knew him. I had unique opportunity to appreciate this fact especially because his unselfish efforts over nearly a decade of struggle were required to rescue me from the consequences of a miscarriage of Army justice. It is a long-awaited privilege, therefore, to contribute this all too brief and inadequate tribute.

In the context of Chapter 31, I may relate briefly the facts in my case, as supported conclusively by appropriate documentation, the presentation of which is precluded by lack of space.

I was asked to resign from the Manhattan Project at the University of California in Berkeley in July 1944. At that time, Arthur Compton was director of the Project at the University of Chicago and so was called in to review the action, although he was given no detailed bill of particulars. He knew me only as a student who had attended his lectures in an undergraduate course (electricity and magnetism) some ten years previously at the University of Chicago. He was obliged to concur with the action desired by the Army security officials but, together with Professor E. O. Lawrence —then my superior at Berkeley—was determined that my dismissal in no way should be construed as impugning my loyalty or integrity. A year later, when circumstance decreed that I accept a position at Washington University in St. Louis, and he found himself soon to be Chancellor there, Arthur Compton conferred with Professor Lawrence and ascertained that there existed no grounds for questioning my desirability as a member of the university faculty.

Nevertheless, the machinery of the security Program had been set in motion and I became a recurrent object of suspicion, especially as the atmosphere of the cold war intensified. On many occasions, mostly unknown to me, Chancellor Compton was called upon to defend my employment. All through the next ten years, he stood by me and fended off attacks which threatened to end my career. Thus, in 1948, I was plummeted into national notoriety when the Un-American Activities Committee in Washington subjected me to a grilling about the circumstances surrounding my departure from the Manhattan Project in 1944. The attendant publicity produced much anxiety among members of the university community and subjected Chancellor Compton to strong pressures from influential quarters who felt my continuance as a member of the faculty was inimical to the best interests of the university.

Later, in 1951, I was described in the Chicago *Tribune* and Washington *Times-Herald* as a paid employee of a foreign spy apparatus. The story was concocted from assertions made under the cloak of legislative immunity in the United States Senate. Again, Chancellor Compton found himself under pressures to terminate my employment. And, as before, he stood between me and my detractors and saved my career. In this action he again took the unpopular side of a controversy, placed his own prestige in jeopardy, and risked weakening his own image in many quarters.

As a result of the libel perpetrated in the press, I brought suit, and so inadvertently laid the stage for a most remarkable demonstration of qualities associated with high moral character and probity which Arthur Compton possessed in the fullest measure. Early in 1955 he was called upon to give a deposition concerning the facts of my unfortunate encounter with the security machinery of the Manhattan Project. For most of one day and far into the evening, he was subjected to a polite but merciless questioning by the defense attorneys, who sought to shake his recollection of events and thereby undermine confidence in his credibility. His performance on this occasion earned the unstinting admiration of all who attended the hearing as well as of the judge who later heard the deposition read at the trial. There is little doubt that the transcript of this deposition, which ran to over two hundred typed pages, was a very significant contribution to the fashioning of the jury verdict, which was unanimous in my favor.

One may say with Tom Paine, there are "times which try men's souls." Such times are surely typical when political disturbances result in excesses such as those of the McCarthy era and of the cold war immediately proceeding. Then it is that the existence of truly great humans, who can stand uncompromisingly and at whatever cost against hysterical or cynical persecution of innocents, is essential for the preservation of our national freedoms. That I can write these words today I owe to the fact that Arthur Compton lived as one of the society of these truly great.

274:25 This incident was more fully described in an interview with *Student Life,* the Washington University student newspaper (LXXV: 4 [October 6, 1953]), following Chancellor Compton's references, in a university assembly talk, to having felt "the stinging blows . . . of America's neo-fascists."

275:27 Information about the atomic project did leak to Russia from the United States, largely through the Canadian scientist Alan Nunn May, the German-born British scientist Klaus Fuchs, and Bruno Pontecorvo, the Italian who worked with Fuchs at the British atomic center at Harwell. These scientists were sent to the United States through official arrangements with our allies to assist in the atomic project. American policy at that time did not question the loyalty of men cleared to their own satisfaction by our British and Canadian allies. A detailed report of the backgrounds and espionage activities of Fuchs, May, and Pontecorvo has been compiled by the British journalist Alan Morehead in *The Traitors* (New York: Harper and Row; 1952; 2nd edn. 1963).

## Chapter 32

286:5 Membership of the committee is given in Notes for Chapter 27, p. 437.
286:11 The British report was prepared by the MAUD Committee, under the chairmanship of Sir George Thomson.
286:19 This committee was known as the S-1 Committee. See Notes for Chapter 27, p. 437, for its membership.
286:41 Company A is identified elsewhere as the Mallinckrodt Chemical Works. Mr. Compton recounts this story in greater detail in *Atomic Quest* (Ch. 27), pp. 93–6.
290:14 Discovered in 1938 by Otto Hahn and F. Strassmann and published in January 1939.
294:2 Significant progress has been made in engineering education in the years following World War II. "Inventing an Education for Engineers," by T. Keith Glennan of Case Institute of Technology, describes some of the changes that are creating a radically different kind of engineer (*Saturday Review,* XLVIII: 47 [November 20, 1965], 72–4 ff.).

## Chapter 33

304:29 Prominent among these was James Franck, Nobel prize-winning scientist and refugee from Nazi Germany, who headed the Metallurgical Project's committee on the social and political consequences of atomic energy. As the war approached its close his committee prepared what became known as the Franck Report, an appeal to the Secretary of War urging that atomic weapons not be used against Japan. After the war the Franck Report was published in condensed form in "Before Hiroshima," *Bulletin of Atomic Scientists,* 1 (May 1946), 1.

Mr. Compton discussed the Franck Report and various petitions and polls of the scientists in *Atomic Quest,* pp. 233–6 and 241–5. See also Farrington Daniels and A. H. Compton: "A Poll of Scientists at Chicago," *Bulletin of Atomic Scientists,* 4 (February 1948), 44.

In *The Peril and the Hope* (Chicago: University of Chicago Press; 1965) Alice Kimball Smith includes a detailed examination of the circumstances surrounding the preparation of the Franck Report (published in full in her book), as well as other attempts by the atomic scientists to influence governmental policy.

## Chapter 34

310:27  See pp. 401–2, Chapter 44, for Adams's statement.

312:7  Niels Bohr has discussed the relation of science to human affairs in some detail in *Atomic Physics and Human Knowledge* (Ch. 9), especially in "Atoms and Human Knowledge," pp. 83–93.

## Chapter 35

321:11  In a memorandum to the chairman of the United States delegation, Mr. Compton recommended a greater emphasis upon science activities: "Considering the present active world concern with the growth and use of science, not less than 30 per cent and perhaps as much as 50 per cent of the effort of Unesco should be spent in this direction. As the world's recognized leader in the field, it is necessary for the United States to work actively for such an increased emphasis on science and technological education if this work is to take its proper place in the Unesco program. . . . I hope it will not be considered presumptuous for me to point out that the personnel of the U. S. Government is not such as to make possible a true evaluation of the place of science in the national or international picture. As far as I know, there is not one individual with a background of science in the State Department, in the President's Cabinet, or in any other official position of influence at Washington." (AHC to William Benton, December 18, 1946.)

## Chapter 36

323:4  On March 1, 1954, the twenty-three crewmen of the *Fukuryu Maru No. 5,* a tuna trawler, were accidentally dusted with radioactive ash from the first test of a hydrogen bomb as they were fishing about eighty-five miles from Bikini Atoll, where the test was conducted.

325:16  The crewmen were hospitalized and treated for radiation sickness, and all but one recovered. The ship's radioman, Aikichi Kuboyama, died of liver disease on September 23. Medical opinion is divided about whether his death was due to radiation damage or to hepatitis caused by the frequent blood transfusions that were part of his treatment.

## Chapter 39

341:21  Two months earlier, Mr. Compton had prepared a brief review of Edward Teller and Albert Latter: *Our Nuclear Future* (New York: Criterion Books; 1958), a book that discusses nuclear weapons and the possible hazards attendant on their continued testing. See *Chicago Tribune,* March 23, 1958.

## Chapter 40

346:19 This position was developed by Mr. Compton in subsequent statements:

"I should not feel satisfied that we can maintain the armed strength necessary for defense if we should agree to stop tests of our tactical bombs. But, very possibly, such tests can be carried out underground. I do not believe that it would affect us more seriously than Russia to curtail our tests of the large-size nuclear bombs. In fact, if it should be good political strategy, I would see no great harm in announcing a unilateral cessation of nuclear tests in the large-weapon field." (AHC to Representative Carl T. Durham, May 27, 1958.)

"It has indeed been difficult to balance the relative importance of the health danger from fallout from nuclear tests as against the loss in defensive strength that may come from abandoning nuclear tests. Your suggestion of prohibiting tests in the atmosphere while permitting their continuance underground seems to me to supply a very satisfying answer. Those to whom the fallout seems to be a serious health hazard should be completely satisfied, because the fallout would no longer occur. Those who fear that prohibiting tests will endanger our military preparedness can have the assurance that when necessary such tests can be made, and our weapons can be maintained in working condition. . . .

"If the health dangers are as great as we are asked to believe (which I doubt, though I recognize the weight of expert opinion on the side of the danger), the explosions in the atmosphere should be stopped without further delay. I can see only good resulting from our taking such action unilaterally, followed by strong efforts to bring Russia and Britain to take similar action." (AHC to Senator Albert Gore, December 11, 1958.)

Also on December 11, 1958, he submitted the following draft resolution for consideration by a committee of the Metropolitan Church Federation of St. Louis:

"1. We commend the President of the United States for his action in suspending tests of nuclear explosions during the year ending November 1, 1959, and for negotiating patiently with Russia and Great Britain toward reaching a trustworthy agreement as to limitations under which such tests may be acceptable in view of the proper interests of the peoples of the world.

"2. In order to protect the people of the world from possible injury caused by radioactive contamination by the products of nuclear explosions, no tests of nuclear explosions shall be made by the United States in the earth's atmosphere, or under conditions such that radioactive contamination can reach the atmosphere in appreciable amounts, and further, continued care shall be taken to prevent contamination of the atmosphere as a result of any kind of industrial process using nuclear energy, and further,

"3. That the United States Government do all in its power to prevail upon Russia, Great Britain, and other nations of the world to join in similarly limiting their own nuclear activities."

## Chapter 40

351:9 A slightly different version of this talk appeared in *Scribner's Magazine*, CXCIX:6 (June 1936), 355–7.

## Chapter 41

367:31 Mr. Compton served as Protestant co-chairman of the National Conference of Christians and Jews from 1938 to 1947 and as a member of its board for a number of years thereafter.

## Chapter 42

369:6 A. J. Carlson: "Science and the Supernatural," *Scientific Monthly*, LIX:2 (August 1944), 85–95.

369:10 It will be evident that a single article cannot adequately convey Arthur Compton's religious views. The reader who seeks to understand them more fully may wish to consult *The Freedom of Man*, especially Chapters 4 and 5. He may also find interest in an address entitled "A Modern Concept of God" (Ch. 1 in *Man's Destiny in Eternity* [Boston: Beacon Press; 1949]), the first Garvin Lecture on God and Immortality, presented in 1940 at Lancaster, Pennsylvania. The address was originally published by the American Unitarian Association as "The Idea of God as Affected by Modern Knowledge" (Pamphlet 355). The meaning of "faith" was discussed by Mr. Compton in an essay-review of P. W. Bridgman's *The Way Things Are* (*Saturday Review*, XLII: 32 [August 8, 1959]).

## Chapter 43

379:4 The headnote to Chapter 8 gives additional details about the Science and Human Responsibility conferences.

379:4 Participants were as follows: Robert Lowry Calhoun, Langmead Casserley, Arthur H. Compton, Gerty T. Cori, Norman Cousins, Chester Davis, Fr. D. Dubarle, Merle Fainsod, Clarence Faust, Evarts A. Graham, Thomas S. Hall, E. Harris Harbison, Werner Heisenberg, Hu Shih, Norman Isaacs, Zay Jeffries, Howard Foster Lowry, Rollo May, Filmer S. C. Northrop, William Fielding Ogburn, Sarvepalli Radhakrishnan, Francis O. Schmitt, Huston Smith, Warren Spencer, Carl F. Taeusch, Paul A. Weiss, Gerald F. Winfield, and Quincy Wright.

385:5 This figure remains correct if one is concerned only with the visible universe in the immediate vicinity of our solar system. In the larger view, which would include not only our galaxy but external galaxies as well, the time-scale would be considerably longer, of the order of at least ten billion years according to currently accepted ideas.

386:11 The genes are contained in a complex nucleic acid molecule called deoxyribonucleic acid, or DNA.

396:6 The Indian leader is identified elsewhere as Jawaharlal Nehru, then Prime Minister of India.

398:33 At the conclusion of the 1954 conference, on October 28, the participants joined in the following statement:

The Conference on Science and Human Responsibility closes with firmly grounded hope. We recognize that not only great dangers but also great opportunities lie before us. An atmosphere of urgency has pervaded the Conference. We are presented with a deadline before which certain vital human questions must have answers, or disaster will overtake us. But we see progress toward these answers, in some cases rapid progress. The military stalemate and the technological relief of economic pressure are buying time to build a social structure which we dare hope will provide enduring peace with freedom.

A series of challenges with which mankind is faced has been brought sharply to our attention. Under conditions of relative peace, and with the aid of science and its use in industry and agriculture, we see the way of meeting to an increasing degree man's economic needs during the next few decades. For the longer future the world's prosperity will depend more upon the form of man's aspirations than upon the limitations of his technical knowledge.

The great strides of medicine during the past century continue unabated. These are giving new health and vigor to mankind. We face, however, the task of providing an adequate place in our society for more and more old people. The increasing control of infectious diseases and the mounting prevalence of mental disorders call for new approaches to the problems of health.

Recent developments in the field of law seem to place this vital regulator of society also at a point where one can now with greater confidence draft laws that will carry weight and will be enforceable. This gives new urgency to the efforts toward making adjustments that will give greater freedom to individual communities, and toward reaching agreements among nations which will be useful and enforceable.

A great challenge to every agency of communication and education is to develop an understanding among nations and among groups within each national community which will make feasible the adjustment and cooperation needed for their proper growth. Studies of the factors influencing attitudes have shown how such understanding and adjustment can be developed. Thus the way is open for an education that will ensure harmonious peace.

If a strong and enduring social order is to be attained, men must find meaning in their lives. This point has been emphasized by many participants. Such meaning implies objectives that are considered worthy, and the need for each person to work toward achieving these objectives. An objective that seems acceptable and of vital importance throughout the free world is that every person shall have an opportunity to grow to his fullest stature. This vision is taking form in such documents as the United Nations declaration of human rights.

Providing an opportunity for the full growth of every person is a challenge for every member of a family, for every citizen with respect to his community, for every government with respect to its

| 447 |

people, and for the international community of nations. We know the great sources of inspiration that can give the courage and the will to achieve this goal. Its attainment requires wise planning and creation of the necessary machinery. It appears to the members of this Conference that science is competent to find the knowledge, and that technology can create the machinery needed, to give every person his appropriate opportunity. Will men and women see in this task something of such importance that they will dedicate themselves to its achievement?

The really pressing question is, can these challenges be met in time? The trend toward a devastating third world war must not be permitted to pass the point of no return. Before we are smothered by the economic pressure of a mounting population the world must set its human sights, draw its plans, and put these plans in operation. The knowledge and the strength to meet these great challenges are available. Whether we shall do so depends upon the spirit that is within us.

## Chapter 44

403:26   The occasion was the presentation of the first Atoms for Peace award on October 24, 1957. See Chapter 34 for Mr. Compton's remarks at the award ceremony.

# Chronology of the Life
# of Arthur Holly Compton

1892   Born September 10, Wooster, Ohio.
     Son of Elias Compton, Professor of Philosophy, and Otelia Catherine Augspurger Compton.
     Brother of Karl Taylor (b. 1887), Mary Elesa (b. 1889), and Wilson Martindale Compton (b. 1890).

1895   *Wilhelm Roentgen discovers X rays.*

1896   First summer at Otsego Lake, Gaylord, Michigan, lifelong summer home.

1898–1905 Attends Wooster elementary and grammar school.

1899   Elias Compton appointed Dean of College of Wooster, a position held until 1921.

1900   *Max Planck advances hypothesis of the quantum as a discrete unit of energy.*

1905   *Albert Einstein postulates theory of light quanta to explain the photoelectric effect.*

1908–9  Elias Compton pursues postdoctoral studies in philosophy at British Museum in London.

1909   Publication of first articles, on airplanes.
     Graduates from Wooster Preparatory School.
     Builds 27-foot glider and flies in it successfully.

1911   *Ernest Rutherford discovers nucleus of the atom.*

1912   *Victor Hess establishes existence of cosmic rays.*

1913   Publishes first scientific paper of importance: "A Laboratory Method of Demonstrating the Earth's Rotation," *Science,* XXXVII: 960 (May 23, 1913), 803–6.
     B.Sc., College of Wooster.
      Letters in football, basketball, track; graduates third in class of eighty.
     Mary Compton marries C. Herbert Rice in Ludhiana, India, and begins missionary work.

1914   M.A., Princeton University.

1914–15 Assistant in Physics, Princeton University.

1915–16 Porter Ogden Jacobus Fellow, Princeton University, the fellowship awarded the graduate student of "highest scholarly excellence."

1916   Ph.D., Princeton University.
     Marries Betty Charity McCloskey of New Waterford, Ohio.
     Elected Fellow, American Physical Society.

1916–17  Instructor in Physics, University of Minnesota.

1917–19  Research Engineer, Lamp Division, Westinghouse Electric and
     Manufacturing Company, East Pittsburgh, Pennsylvania.

1917–18  Civilian Associate, United States Signal Corps, developing airplane
     instruments.

1918   June 12. Birth of son, Arthur Alan.

*1919*   *Ernest Rutherford achieves first artificial transmutation of matter.*

1919–20  National Research Council Fellow, Cavendish Laboratory, Cam-
     bridge, England.

1920–3   Wayman Crow Professor of Physics and Head of Department of
     Physics, Washington University.

1921–2   Summers. Visiting Lecturer, University of California at Berkeley.

1922–5   Chairman, National Research Council Committee on X Rays and
     Radioactivity.

1922   October. Publication of *Secondary Radiations Produced by X Rays*
     (National Research Council Bulletin, No. 20, Vol. IV, Part 2), an-
     nouncing the total reflection of X rays and first suggesting an
     interpretation of scattering as a quantum phenomenon.

1923   Appointed Professor of Physics, University of Chicago.
      Professor of Physics, 1923–9.
      Charles H. Swift Distinguished Service Professor, 1929–45.

1923–5   Member of Board of Editors, *Physical Review.*

1925   Elected to membership in American Philosophical Society.

1926   Publication of *X-Rays and Electrons* (New York: Van Nostrand).

1926–7   John Simon Guggenheim Fellow; Lecturer, Punjab University,
     Lahore, India.

1926–45  Consultant, General Electric Company, Nela Park, Cleveland,
     Ohio.

1927   Vice President, American Association for the Advancement of
     Science.
     Attends Fifth Solvay International Congress of Physics, Brussels,
     Belgium.
     Attends Volta Electrical Congress, Como, Italy.
      Rumford Gold Medal of American Academy of Arts and
      Sciences.
      Honorary degree of Doctor of Science, College of Wooster.
      Elected to membership in National Academy of Sciences.
      Nobel Prize for Physics.

1928   May 17. Birth of son, John Joseph.

Elias Compton retires as Professor of Philosophy.
> Elected Fellow of American Academy of Arts and Sciences.
> Gold Medal, Radiological Society of North America.
> Honorary degree of Doctor of Laws, Washington University.

1929     Appointed Charles H. Swift Distinguished Service Professor, University of Chicago.
Summer. Visiting Lecturer, Cornell University.
> Honorary degree of Doctor of Science, Ohio State University; Yale University.
> Elected Honorary member, Western Society of Engineers.

1929–32     Councillor, American Optical Society.

1929–49     Member of Board of Editors, *Reviews of Modern Physics.*

1930     Honorary degree of Doctor of Laws, University of California at Berkeley.

1931     Terry Lecturer, Yale University.
Elliott Lecturer, Western Theological Seminary.
Attends First International Conference on Nuclear Physics, Rome, Italy.

1931–4     Director, World Survey of Cosmic Rays.

1931–41     Research Associate (cosmic rays), Carnegie Institution of Washington.

1932     Otelia Compton receives honorary degree of Doctor of Laws, Western College for Women, Oxford, Ohio, for "her rich achievement as a wife, a mother, a friend of youth, a servant of the Church"; her son Arthur delivering the principal College Day Address.

1932–4     President, University of Chicago Settlement.

1933     Vice President, American Physical Society.

1933     Summer. Visiting Lecturer, Columbia University.
Scientific Director, Century of Progress Balloon Flight.
> Matteucci Gold Medal, Italian Academy of Arts and Sciences.

1933–44     Member of Advisory Editorial Board, *Journal of Chemical Physics.*

1934     President, American Physical Society.
Attends International Conference of Physics, London.
Attends First International Congress of Electro-Radio-Biology, Venice, Italy.
Commission for Relief of Belgium Lecturer, University of Brussels.
> Honorary degree of Doctor of Science, Princeton University.

1934–5     George Eastman Visiting Professor, Oxford University.
> Fellow, Balliol College; honorary degree of Master of Arts, Oxford University.

1934–48     General Chairman, Laymen's Missionary Movement.

1935     Publication of *X-Rays in Theory and Experiment,* with Samuel K.

Allison (New York: D. Van Nostrand Co.), revision of *X-Rays and Electrons*.
Publication of *The Freedom of Man* (New Haven, Conn.: Yale University Press), the Terry Lectures.
Loud Foundation Lecturer, University of Michigan.
Twentieth Guthrie Lecturer, Physical Society of London.
   Honorary degree of Doctor of Science, Brown University.

| | |
|---|---|
| 1936 | Honorary degree of Doctor of Science, Harvard University. |
| 1937–44 | Member of National Cancer Advisory Council. |
| 1937–49 | Vice President and member of Scientific Committee, Chicago Tumor Institute. |
| 1938 | May 2. Elias Compton dies. |
| *1938* | *Otto Hahn and F. Strassmann discover nuclear fission.* |
| 1938–47 | Protestant Co-Chairman, National Conference of Christians and Jews. |
| 1938–62 | Regent, Smithsonian Institution. |
| 1939 | Organizes first International Symposium on Cosmic Rays, University of Chicago.<br>Lowell Lecturer, Boston.<br>John Calvin McNair Lecturer, University of North Carolina.<br>   Otelia Compton chosen American Mother of the Year. |
| 1939–45 | Member of Board of Trustees, John Crerar Library, Chicago, Illinois. |
| 1940 | Publication of *The Human Meaning of Science* (Chapel Hill, N.C.: University of North Carolina Press), the McNair Lectures.<br>Walker-Ames Visiting Professor, University of Washington.<br>Presents the First Garvin Lecture on God and Immortality, Lancaster, Pennsylvania.<br>   Franklin Gold Medal of Franklin Institute.<br>   Hughes Medal of Royal Society of London. |
| 1940–5 | Chairman of Department of Physics and Dean of Physical Sciences, University of Chicago. |
| 1940–62 | Member of Board of Trustees, College of Wooster (Chairman, 1940–53). |
| 1941 | Chairman, National Academy of Sciences Committee to Evaluate Use of Atomic Energy in War. |
| 1941 | Director, University of Chicago South American Cosmic Ray Expeditions.<br>Attends International Symposium on Cosmic Rays, Rio de Janeiro, Brazil.<br>   Honorary degree of Doctor of Humane Letters, University of Tampa; Doctorate, University of San Marcos, Lima, Peru; Doctor of Science, University of St. Augustine, Arequipa, Peru. |

1941–5      Member of Board of Trustees, Museum of Science and Industry, Chicago.

1942–5      Director, United States Government's Plutonium Research Project.

1942      President, American Association for the Advancement of Science.
December 2. First self-sustaining nuclear chain reaction, Stagg Field, University of Chicago.
Honorary degree of Doctor of Letters, Jewish Theological Seminary of America.

1943      Annual Award of Jewish Education Committee.

1944      December 15. Otelia Compton dies.

1945      *August 6. First atomic bomb dropped on Hiroshima.*
*August 9. Atomic bomb dropped on Nagasaki.*

1945      *August 14. Japan surrenders.*
*September 2. Formal surrender of Japan and end of World War II.*
Franklin Medal, American Philosophical Society.
Washington Award, Western Society of Engineers.

1945–6      Chairman, Board of Governors, Argonne National Laboratory.

1945–53      Chancellor, Washington University.

1945–62      Member of Advisory Board, John Simon Guggenheim Memorial Foundation.

1946      Member of Civilian Advisory Committee to Secretary of the Navy.
Member of Scientific Panel and Adviser to the United States Representative, United Nations Atomic Energy Commission (Bernard Baruch).
Member of United States delegation to First General Conference of Unesco, Paris.
United States Government Medal for Merit.
St. Louis Award.
Honorary degree of Doctor of Laws, Lehigh University.

1946–8      Member of Presidential Commission on Higher Education.

1946–50      Member of United States National Commission for Unesco (Vice Chairman, 1946–7).

1946–52      Member of Committee for Economic Development.

1946–53      Member of Naval Research Advisory Committee (Chairman, 1952–3).
Member of Board of Trustees, Carnegie Foundation for the Advancement of Teaching.

1947      Twentieth Steinmetz Memorial Lecturer, Schenectady Section of American Institute of Electrical Engineers.
Adviser to United States delegation to Second General Conference of Unesco, Mexico City.
Elected Honorary member, New York Academy of Sciences.
Gold Medal of French Academy with palm, with honorary

titles of Officer of Academy and Officer of Public Instruction of French government.

Grande Médaille, Association des Ingénieurs Docteurs de France.

Officer of the Legion of Honor of the Republic of France.

1947–50    Member of Board of Directors, National Conference of Christians and Jews. Subsequent terms: 1951–4; 1955–8.

Member of Advisory Committee of Presbyterian Board of Christian Education.

1947–53    Member of Board of Directors, St. Louis Symphony Society.

1947–56    Member of Board of Trustees, Jefferson National Expansion Memorial Association.

1948–51    Vice President, American Philosophical Society.

1948–53    Member of Board of Trustees, Institute of International Education.

Member of Board of Directors, St. Louis Metropolitan Y.M.C.A.

Honorary Chairman, Laymen's Missionary Movement.

1948–62    Member of Advisory Board, *Bulletin of Atomic Scientists.*

Elder, Second Presbyterian Church, St. Louis.

1949    Forbes-Hawkes Lecturer, University of Miami.

Visiting Lecturer, Jewish Theological Seminary.

Chairman, American delegation to India-America Relations Conference, University of Delhi, New Delhi, India.

Honorary degree of Doctor of Science, Capital University; University of the Punjab, Lahore, Pakistan; Doctor of Laws, Texas Christian University.

1950    Honorary degree of Doctor of Science, University of Aligarh, Aligarh, India.

1950–5    General Chairman, World Brotherhood.

1950–62    Member of College of Electors, Hall of Fame.

1951    Vice President, American Association for the Advancement of Science.

Centennial Award of Northwestern University.

Honorary degree of Doctor of Laws, Baylor University.

Chevalier et Compagnon Honoraire de la Croix de Lorraine et de la Résistance, Republic of France.

1951–2    Vice President, Metropolitan Church Federation of St. Louis.

1951–3    Member of Educational Policies Commission.

Member of National Commission on Accrediting (representative of Association of American Universities).

1952    Member of Committee on Academic Freedom, Association of American Universities.

Attends Conference on "Man Confronting Science," Rencontres Internationales de Genève.

| | |
|---|---|
| 1952 | Honorary degree of Doctor of Science, University of Chicago; Doctor of Laws, Westminster College.<br>Freedoms Foundation Award.<br>Popular Mechanics Hall of Fame. |
| 1952–3 | Civilian Aide to the Secretary of the Army. |
| 1952–5 | Chairman, Board of Trustees, St. Louis Educational Television Commission. |
| 1953 | Attends Conference on Science and Freedom, University of Hamburg, Germany.<br>First DeGolyer Lecturer, University of Oklahoma.<br>Honorary degree of Doctor of Science, Coe College.<br>Award of Merit, St. Louis Chapter of Hadassah. |
| 1953–62 | Honorary Trustee, Museum of Science and Industry, Chicago. |
| 1954 | Heads four-month World Brotherhood Mission to Asia and Europe.<br>Organizes first Conference on Science and Human Responsibility, Washington University.<br>June 22. Karl Compton dies. |
| 1954–6 | Member of Permanent Commission on Interchurch Relations of Presbyterian Church, U.S.A. |
| 1954–61 | Distinguished Service Professor of Natural Philosophy, Washington University. |
| 1954–62 | National Board Member, National Book Committee. |
| 1955 | Attends Fourth International Congress on Peace and Christian Civilization, Florence, Italy.<br>Attends Second International Convention of World Brotherhood, Brussels, Belgium.<br>Hill Foundation Lecturer, St. Olaf College.<br>Montgomery Lecturer, University of Nebraska.<br>Dedication of Otelia Compton Hall, women's residence, College of Wooster.<br>Order "Pour le Mérite," Federal Republic of Germany.<br>Medal of Honor of the Theodore Roosevelt Association. |
| 1955–6 | Member of Board of Trustees, Federal Union, Inc. |
| 1955–7 | Executive Director, St. Louis Educational Television Station KETC. |
| 1955–62 | Member of Board of Trustees, Atoms for Peace Awards, Inc.<br>Honorary Trustee, Institute of International Education.<br>Co-Chairman (for North America), World Brotherhood.<br>Member of Board of Trustees, Fisk University. |
| 1955–62 | Member of Board of Directors, Urban League of St. Louis.<br>Honorary Trustee, Committee for Economic Development. |
| 1956 | Tenth Charles Schwab Memorial Lecturer, American Iron and Steel Institute. |

Publication of *Atomic Quest, A Personal Narrative* (New York: Oxford University Press).
Member of President's Committee on Civilian National Honors.
  Honorary degree of Doctor of Laws, Michigan State University.

1956–9    Member of Board of Trustees, Brookings Institution.
Member of Board of Visitors, United States Air Force Academy.

1957    Heads three-month World Brotherhood Mission to Asia and Europe.
Röntgen-Plakette of Röntgen-Museums, Remscheid-Lennep, Germany.
Honorary degree of Doctor of Science, Brandeis University; Lake Forest College.
Pioneer in Brotherhood Award, World Brotherhood.

1957–62    Chairman, Board of Trustees, American-Philippine Science Foundation.

1957–62    Member of Board of Trustees, Roger Williams Straus Memorial Foundation, Inc.

1958–62    Member of Atomic Energy Commission Historical Advisory Commission.
Honorary member of Board of Directors, Washington University.
Consultant, University of California Radiation Laboratory.

1959    Elected to Ohio Teen Age Hall of Fame.

1959–62    Member of Advisory Council, McDonnell Aircraft Corporation.

1960–2    Consultant, Mallinckrodt Chemical Works.

1961    June 27. Mary Compton Rice dies.
Attends Oxford Conference on Tensions in Development, Oxford, England.

1961–2    Professor-at-Large, Washington University, University of California at Berkeley. A similar appointment at the College of Wooster was terminated by death.
Humanities Award of *St. Louis Globe-Democrat*.

1962    March 15. Dies in Berkeley, California.

❖ ❖ ❖

*Honorary fraternity memberships:*
Phi Beta Kappa
Sigma Xi
Kappa Delta Pi
Gamma Alpha
Pi Kappa Pi

*Foreign academic affiliations, as honorary member or fellow:*
Academy of Sciences of Lisbon (1953)
Austrian Academy of Sciences (1935)
Association des Ingénieurs-Docteurs de France (1949)

Bavarian Academy of Sciences (1932)
Brazilian Academy of Sciences (1941)
Cambridge Philosophical Society (1954)
Chemical Society of Peru (1941)
Chinese Physical Society (1943)
Indian Academy of Sciences (1935)
National Academy of Exact Sciences of Lima (1941)
National Academy of Peiping (1948)
National Academy of Sciences of India (1955)
National Institute of Sciences of India (1957)
Norwegian Academy of Sciences (1946)
Société Philomatique de Paris (1938)
Prussian Academy of Sciences (1932)
Reale Accademia dei Lincei, Rome (1925)
Royal Akademie, Amsterdam (1938)
Royal German Academy of Sciences (1934)
Royal Irish Academy (1946)
Royal Society of Canada (1946)
Royal Society of Sciences, Uppsala (1938)
Royal Society of New Zealand (1934)
Swedish Academy of Sciences

❋　❋　❋

1963　March 15. Presentation of Arthur Compton's personal papers to Washington University, and dedication of the Arthur Holly Compton Memorial Alcove in the John M. Olin Library.

1964　May 9. Dedication of Compton Court, graduate quadrangle at Princeton University, in honor of the three Compton brothers, Karl, Wilson, and Arthur.

1966　May 4. Dedication of the Arthur Holly Compton Laboratory of Physics, Washington University.

Establishment by the American Nuclear Society of the Arthur Holly Compton Award for outstanding contributions to education in the fields of science and engineering germane to nuclear energy.

# Scientific Bibliography

### 1909

1. "A Criticism of Mr. C. W. Williams' Article, 'Concerning Aeroplanes,'" *Fly*, I (Feb. 1909), 13.
2. "Comparison of Wright and Voisin Aeroplanes," *Scientific American*, C: 7 (Feb. 13, 1909), 135 (L).
3. "Striving for Perfect Machine," *Aeronautics*, V: 2 (Aug. 1909), 58 ff.

### 1911

4. "Aeroplane Stability," *Scientific American Supplement*, LXXII: 1858 (Aug. 12, 1911), 100–2.

### 1913

5. "A Laboratory Method of Demonstrating the Earth's Rotation," *Science*, XXXVII: 960 (May 23, 1913), 803–6.

### 1914

6. "New Light on the Structure of Matter," *Scientific American Supplement*, LXXVIII: 2009 (July 4, 1914), 4–6.

### 1915

7. "A Determination of Latitude, Azimuth, and the Length of the Day Independent of Astronomical Observations," *Physical Review*, V: 2 (Feb. 1915), 109–17; also in *Popular Astronomy*, XXIII: 4 (Apr. 1915), 199–207.
8. "Watching the Earth Revolve," *Scientific American Supplement*, LXXIX: 2047 (Mar. 27, 1915), 196–7.
9. "An Agglomeration Theory of the Variation of the Specific Heat of Solids with Temperature," *Physical Review*, V: 4 (Apr. 1915), 338–9 (A).
10. "What Is Matter Made Of?," *Scientific American*, CXII: 20 (May 15, 1915), 451–2.
11. "The Distribution of the Electrons in Atoms," *Nature*, XCV: 2378 (May 27, 1915), 343–4 (L).
12. "The Variation of the Specific Heat of Solids with Temperature," *Physical Review*, VI: 5 (Nov. 1915), 377–89.

### 1916

13. "A Physical Study of the Thermal Conductivity of Solids," *Physical Review*, VII: 3 (Mar. 1916), 341–8.
14. "On the Location of the Thermal Energy of Solids," *Physical Review*, VII: 3 (Mar. 1916), 349–54.
15. "The X-Ray Spectrum of Tungsten," *Physical Review*, VII: 4 (Apr. 1916), 498–9 (A).

16. "A Recording X-Ray Spectrometer, and the High Frequency Spectrum of Tungsten," *Physical Review*, VII: 6 (June 1916), 646–59.

### 1917
17. "The Intensity of X-Ray Reflection, and the Distribution of the Electrons in Atoms," *Physical Review*, IX: 1 (Jan. 1917), 29–57. (Ph.D. thesis, Princeton University.)
18. "The Reflection Coefficient of Monochromatic X Rays from Rock Salt and Calcite," *Physical Review*, X: 1 (July 1917), 95–6 (A).
19. "The Nature of the Ultimate Magnetic Particle" (with Oswald Rognley), *Science*, XLVI: 1191 (Oct. 26, 1917), 415–16.

### 1918
20. "The Size and Shape of the Electron," *Journal of the Washington Academy of Sciences*, VIII: 1 (Jan. 4, 1918), 1–11.
21. "The Nature of the Ultimate Magnetic Particle" (with Oswald Rognley), *Physical Review*, XI: 2 (Feb. 1918), 132–4 (A).
22. "The Size and Shape of the Electron," *Physical Review*, XI: 4 (Apr. 1918), 330 (A).
23. "The Non-Molecular Structure of Solids," *Journal of the Franklin Institute*, CLXXXV: 6 (June 1918), 745–74.
24. "Note on the Grating Space of Calcite and the X-Ray Spectrum of Gallium," *Physical Review*, XI: 6 (June 1918), 430–2.

### 1919
25. "An Addition to the Theory of the Quadrant Electrometer" (with K. T. Compton), *Physical Review*, XIII: 4 (Apr. 1919), 288 (A).
26. "The Law of Absorption of High Frequency Radiation," *Physical Review*, XIII: 4 (Apr. 1919), 296 (A).
27. "The Size and Shape of the Electron: I. The Scattering of High Frequency Radiation," *Physical Review*, XIV: 1 (July 1919), 20–43.
28. "A Sensitive Modification of the Quadrant Electrometer: Its Theory and Use" (with K. T. Compton), *Physical Review*, XIV: 2 (Aug. 1919), 85–98.
29. "The Size and Shape of the Electron: II. The Absorption of High Frequency Radiation," *Physical Review*, XIV: 3 (Sept. 1919), 247–59.
30. "Radio-activity and Gravitation" (E. Rutherford with A. H. Compton), *Nature*, CIV: 2617 (Dec. 25, 1919), 412 (L).

### 1920
31. "A Photoelectric Photometer," *Transactions of the American Illuminating Engineering Society*, XV (Feb. 10, 1920), 28–33.
32. "Cathode Fall in Neon" (with C. C. Van Voorhis), *Physical Review*, XV: 6 (June 1920), 492–7.
33. "Radioactivity and the Gravitational Field," *Philosophical Magazine*, XXXIX: 234 (June 1920), 659–62.
34. "Is the Atom the Ultimate Magnetic Particle?" (with Oswald Rognley), *Physical Review*, XVI: 5 (Nov. 1920), 464–76.

### 1921
35. "The Absorption of Gamma Rays by Magnetized Iron," *Physical Review*, XVII: 1 (Jan. 1921), 38–41.

36. "Classical Electrodynamics and the Dissipation of X-Ray Energy," *Washington University Studies*, VIII: 2 (Jan. 1921), 93–129.
37. "Possible Magnetic Polarity of Free Electrons," *Philosophical Magazine*, XLI: 242 (Feb. 1921), 279–81.
38. "The Elementary Particle of Positive Electricity," *Nature*, CVI: 2678 (Feb. 24, 1921), 828 (L).
39. "The Degradation of Gamma-Ray Energy," *Philosophical Magazine*, XLI: 245 (May 1921), 749–69.
40. "The Wavelength of Hard Gamma Rays," *Philosophical Magazine*, XLI: 245 (May 1921), 770–7.
41. "The Magnetic Electron," *Journal of the Franklin Institute*, CXCII: 2 (Aug. 1921), 145–55.
42. "Secondary High Frequency Radiation," *Physical Review*, XVIII: 2 (Aug. 1921), 96–7 (A).
43. "The Polarization of Secondary X Rays" (with C. F. Hagenow), *Physical Review*, XVIII: 2 (Aug. 1921), 97–8 (A).
44. "The Width of X-Ray Spectrum Lines," *Physical Review*, XVIII: 4 (Oct. 1921), 322 (A).
45. "A Possible Origin of the Defect of the Combination Principle in X Rays," *Physical Review*, XVIII: 4 (Oct. 1921), 336–8 (A).
46. "The Softening of Secondary X Rays," *Nature*, CVIII: 2716 (Nov. 17, 1921), 366–7 (L).

1922
47. "The Width of X-Ray Spectrum Lines," *Physical Review*, XIX: 1 (Jan. 1922), 68–72.
48. "The Spectrum of Secondary X Rays," *Physical Review*, XIX: 3 (Mar. 1922), 267–8 (A).
49. "The Intensity of X-Ray Reflection from Powdered Crystals" (with Newell L. Freeman), *Nature*, CX: 2749 (July 8, 1922), 38 (L).
50. "Total Reflection of X Rays from Glass and Silver," *Physical Review*, XX: 1 (July 1922), 84 (A).
51. "Secondary Radiations Produced by X Rays," *Bulletin of the National Research Council*, Vol. IV, Pt. 2 (Oct. 1922), 56 pp.
52. "Radiation a Form of Matter," *Science*, LVI: 1460 (Dec. 22, 1922), 716–17 (L).

1923
53. "A Quantum Theory of the Scattering of X Rays by Light Elements," *Physical Review*, XXI: 2 (Feb. 1923), 207 (A).
54. "The Luminous Efficiency of Gases Excited by Electric Discharge" (with C. C. Van Voorhis), *Physical Review*, XXI: 2 (Feb. 1923), 210 (A).
55. "A Quantum Theory of the Scattering of X Rays by Light Elements," *Physical Review*, XXI: 5 (May 1923), 483–502.
56. "Wavelength Measurements of Scattered X Rays," *Physical Review*, XXI: 6 (June 1923), 715 (A).
57. "The Total Reflexion of X Rays," *Philosophical Magazine*, XLV: 270 (June 1923), 1121–31.
58. "Recoil of Electrons from Scattered X Rays," *Nature*, CXII: 2812 (Sept. 22, 1923), 435 (L).

59. "Absorption Measurements of the Change of Wavelength Accompanying the Scattering of X Rays," *Philosophical Magazine,* XLVI: 275 (Nov. 1923), 897–911.
60. "The Spectrum of Scattered X Rays," *Physical Review,* XXII: 5 (Nov. 1923), 409–13.
61. "The Quantum Integral and Diffraction by a Crystal," *Proceedings of the National Academy of Sciences,* IX: 11 (Nov. 15, 1923), 359–62.

1924
62. "A Quantum Theory of Uniform Rectilinear Motion," *Physical Review,* XXIII: 1 (Jan. 1924), 118 (A).
63. "Scattering of X-Ray Quanta and the J Phenomena," *Nature,* CXIII: 2831 (Feb. 2, 1924), 160–1 (L).
64. "A Measurement of the Polarization of Secondary X Rays" (with C. F. Hagenow), *Journal of the Optical Society of America and Review of Scientific Instruments,* VIII: 4 (Apr. 1924), 487–91.
65. "The Recoil of Electrons from Scattered X Rays" (with J. C. Hubbard), *Physical Review,* XXIII: 4 (Apr. 1924), 439–49.
66. "The Wavelength of Molybdenum Kα Rays Scattered by Light Elements" (with Y. H. Woo), *Physical Review,* XXIII: 6 (June 1924), 763 (A).
67. "A General Quantum Theory of the Wavelength of Scattered X Rays," *Physical Review,* XXIII: 6 (June 1924), 763 (A).
68. "The Wavelength of Molybdenum Kα Rays When Scattered by Light Elements" (with Y. H. Woo), *Proceedings of the National Academy of Sciences,* X: 6 (June 1924), 271–3.
69. "The Scattering of X Rays," *Journal of the Franklin Institute,* CXCVIII: 1183 (July 1924), 57–72.
70. "A General Quantum Theory of the Wavelength of Scattered X Rays," *Physical Review,* XXIV: 2 (Aug. 1924), 168–76.
71. "The Scattering of X Rays," *Radiology,* III (Dec. 1924), 479–85.

1925
72. "Measurements of the Beta Rays Excited by Hard X Rays" (with Alfred W. Simon), *Physical Review,* XXV: 1 (Jan. 1925), 107 (A).
73. "Tests of the Effect of an Enclosing Box on the Spectrum of Scattered X Rays" (with J. A. Bearden and Y. H. Woo), *Physical Review,* XXV: 2 (Feb. 1925), 236 (A).
74. "The Effect of a Surrounding Box on the Spectrum of Scattered X Rays" (with J. A. Bearden), *Proceedings of the National Academy of Sciences,* XI: 2 (Feb. 1925), 117–19.
75. "Measurement of β Rays Associated with Scattered X Rays" (with Alfred W. Simon), *Physical Review,* XXV: 3 (Mar. 1925), 306–13.
76. "The Density of Rock Salt and Calcite" (O. K. DeFoe with Arthur H. Compton), *Physical Review,* XXV: 5 (May 1925), 618–20.
77. "The Grating Space of Calcite and Rock Salt" (with H. N. Beets and O. K. DeFoe), *Physical Review,* XXV: 5 (May 1925), 625–9.
78. "On the Mechanism of X-Ray Scattering," *Proceedings of the National Academy of Sciences,* XI: 6 (June 15, 1925), 303–6.
79. "Directed Quanta of Scattered X Rays" (with Alfred W. Simon), *Physical Review,* XXVI: 3 (Sept. 1925), 289–99.

80. "X-Ray Spectra from a Ruled Reflection Grating" (with R. L. Doan), *Proceedings of the National Academy of Sciences*, XI: 10 (Oct. 15, 1925), 598–601.

81. "Light Waves or Light Bullets?," *Scientific American*, CXXXIII: 4 (Oct. 1925), 246–7.

### 1926
82. "Diffraction of X Rays by a Ruled Metallic Grating" (R. L. Doan with A. H. Compton), *Physical Review*, XXVII: 1 (Jan. 1926), 104–5 (A).

83. "Electron Distribution in Sodium Chloride," *Physical Review*, XXVII: 5 (Apr. 1926), 510–11 (A).

### 1927
84. "Röntgenstrahlen als Teilgebiet der Optik," *Zeitschrift für technische Physik*, VII: 12 (Dec. 1927), 530–7; "X Rays as a Branch of Optics," *Journal of the Optical Society of America and Review of Scientific Instruments*, XVI: 2 (Feb. 1928) 71–87; also in *Les Prix Nobel en 1927* (Les Conférences Nobel; Stockholm: P. A. Norstedt & Fils; 1928). (Nobel lecture, Dec. 12, 1927.)

85. "Coherence of the Reflected X Rays from Crystals" (G. E. M. Jauncey with A. H. Compton), *Nature*, CXX: 3024 (Oct. 15, 1927), 549 (L).

### 1928
86. "On the Interaction Between Radiation and Electrons," *Physical Review*, XXXI: 1 (Jan. 1928), 59–65; also in *Atti del Congresso Internazionale dei Fisici* (Sept. 1927), V, I (Bologna, 1928), 161–70.

87. "An Attempt to Find a Unidirectional Effect of X-Ray Photons" (with K. N. Mathur and H. R. Sarna), *Physical Review*, XXXI: 1 (Jan. 1928), 159 (A).

88. "Some Experimental Difficulties with the Electromagnetic Theory of Radiation," *Journal of the Franklin Institute*, CCV: 2 (Feb. 1928), 155–78.

89. "The Spectrum and State of Polarization of Fluorescent X Rays," *Proceedings of the National Academy of Sciences*, XIV: 7 (July 15, 1928), 549–53.

90. "Discordances entre l'expérience et la Théorie Electromagnetique du Rayonnement," Ch. ii in *Electrons et Photons*, report of 5ᵉ Conseil de Physique, Institut Solvay, Brussels, 1927 (Paris: Gautier-Villars; 1928), 55–104; "The Corpuscular Properties of Light," *Naturwissenschaften*, XVII: 26 (June 28, 1929), 507–15; *Physical Review Supplement and Reviews of Modern Physics*, I: 1 (July 1929), 74–89.

### 1929
91. "What Is Light?," *Sigma Xi Quarterly*, XVII: 1 (Mar. 1929), 14–34; repr. in *Scientific Monthly*, XXVIII (Apr. 1929), 289–303; *Proceedings of Ohio State Educational Conference*, XXXV: 3 (Sept. 15, 1930), 401–20 (with alterations); *Smithsonian Report for 1929*, Publication No. 3038 (Washington, 1930), 215–28; *Journal of Chemical Education*, VII: 12 (Dec. 1930), 2769–87.

92. "An Attempt to Detect a Unidirectional Effect of X Rays" (with K. N. Mathur and H. R. Sarna), *Indian Journal of Physics*, III: 4 (May 1929), 463–6.

93. "A New Wavelength Standard for X Rays," *Journal of the Franklin Institute*, CCVIII: 5 (Nov. 1929), 605–16.

94. "The Efficiency of Production of Fluorescent X Rays," *Philosophical Magazine*, VIII: 54 (Dec. 1929), 961–77.

95. "What Things Are Made Of: Part I," *Scientific American*, CXL: 2 (Feb. 1929), 110–13; "Part II," CXL: 3 (Mar. 1929), 234–6.

96. "Compton Effect," *Encyclopaedia Britannica*, 14th edn. (1929–58).

### 1930

97. "The Efficiency of X-Ray Fluorescence," *Physical Review*, XXXV: 1 (Jan. 1930), 127–8 (A).

98. "The Determination of Electron Distributions from Measurements of Scattered X Rays," *Physical Review*, XXXV: 8 (Apr. 15, 1930), 925–38.

99. "Scattering of X Rays and the Distribution of Electrons in Helium," *Physical Review*, XXXV: 11 (June 1, 1930), 1427–8.

100. "Are Planets Rare?," *Science*, LXXII: 1861 (Aug. 29, 1930), 219 (L).

101. "Looking Inside the Atom: X-Ray Scattering and the Structure of Atoms," *Technology Review*, XXXIII: 1 (Oct. 1930), 19 ff.

### 1931

102. "Electron Distribution in Argon, and the Existence of Zero Point Energy," *Physical Review*, XXXVII: 1 (Jan. 1, 1931), 104 (A).

103. "The Optics of X Rays," *Journal of the Optical Society of America*, XXI: 2 (Feb. 1931), 75–89.

104. "Precision Wavelength Measurement with the Double Crystal X-Ray Spectrometer," *Physical Review*, XXXVII: 12 (June 15, 1931), 1694 (A).

105. "A Precision X Ray Spectrometer and the Wavelength of Mo K$\alpha_1$," *Review of Scientific Instruments*, II: 7 (July 1931), 365–76.

106. "The Uncertainty Principle and Free Will," *Science*, LXXIV: 1911 (Aug. 14, 1931), 172.

107. "Assault on Atoms," *Proceedings of the American Philosophical Society*, LXX: 3 (1931), 215–29; repr. in *Smithsonian Report for 1931*, Publication No. 3150 (Washington, 1932), 287–96.

108. "Ionization as a Function of Pressure and Temperature" (with R. D. Bennett and J. C. Stearns), *Physical Review*, XXXVIII: 8 (Oct. 15, 1931), 1565–6 (L).

109. "The Constancy of Cosmic Rays" (R. D. Bennett with J. C. Stearns and A. H. Compton), *Physical Review*, XXXVIII: 8 (Oct. 15, 1931), 1566 (L).

### 1932

110. "Comparison of Cosmic Rays in the Alps and the Rockies," *Physical Review*, XXXIX: 1 (Jan. 1, 1932), 190 (A).

111. "Ionization by Penetrating Radiation as a Function of Pressure and Temperature" (with R. D. Bennett and J. C. Stearns), *Physical Review*, XXXIX: 6 (Mar. 15, 1932), 873–82.

112. "Variation of the Cosmic Rays with Latitude," *Physical Review*, XLI: 1 (July 1, 1932), 111–13 (L).

113. "Diurnal Variation of Cosmic Rays" (R. D. Bennett with J. C. Stearns and A. H. Compton), *Physical Review*, XLI: 2 (July 15, 1932), 119–26.

114. "Use of Argon in the Ionization Method of Measuring Cosmic Rays" (with John J. Hopfield), *Physical Review*, XLI: 4 (Aug. 15, 1932), 539 (L).
115. "Progress of Cosmic-Ray Survey," *Physical Review*, XLI: 5 (Sept. 1, 1932), 681–2 (L).
116. "Studies of Cosmic Rays," *Carnegie Institution of Washington Year Book No. 31, 1931–2* (Dec. 9, 1932), 331–3.
117. "Sea Level Intensity of Cosmic Rays in Certain Localities from 46° South to 68° North Latitude," *Physical Review*, XLII: 6 (Dec. 15, 1932), 904 (A).

1933
118. "A Geographic Study of Cosmic Rays," *Scientific Monthly*, XXXVI (Jan. 1933), 75–87.
119. "Some Evidence Regarding the Nature of Cosmic Rays," *Physical Review*, XLIII: 5 (Mar. 1, 1933), 382 (A).
120. "A Geographic Study of Cosmic Rays," *Physical Review*, XLIII: 6 (Mar. 15, 1933), 387–403.
121. "A Positively Charged Component of Cosmic Rays" (Luis Alvarez with A. H. Compton), *Physical Review*, XLIII: 10 (May 15, 1933), 835–6 (L).
122. "The Significance of Recent Measurements of Cosmic Rays," *Science*, LXXVII: 2003 (May 19, 1933), 480–2.
123. "Nature of Cosmic Rays," *Nature*, CXXXI: 3316 (May 20, 1933), 713–15.
124. "The Secret Message of the Cosmic Ray," *Scientific American*, CXLIX: 1 (July 1933), 5–7.
125. "An Improved Cosmic-Ray Meter" (with J. J. Hopfield), *Review of Scientific Instruments*, IV: 9 (Sept. 1933), 491–5.
126. "Studies of Cosmic Rays," *Carnegie Institution of Washigton Year Book No. 32, 1932–3* (Dec. 15, 1933), 334–9.
127. "Nature of Cosmic Rays," Ch. xxiv in *The Science of Radiology*, O. Glasser, ed. (Springfield, Ill.: Thomas; 1933), 398–411; repr. in part from *Physical Review*, XLIII: 6 (Mar. 1933), 387–403, and *Scientific Monthly*, XXXVI (Jan. 1933), 75–87.
128. "Progress of World-Survey of Cosmic Rays," *Transactions of the American Geophysical Union*, 14th annual meeting (1933), 154–8.

1934
129. "Scientific Work in the 'Century of Progress' Stratosphere Balloon," *Proceedings of the National Academy of Sciences*, XX: 1 (Jan. 1934), 79–81.
130. "Further Geographic Studies of Cosmic Rays" (with J. M. Benade and P. G. Ledig), *Physical Review*, XLV: 4 (Feb. 15, 1934), 294–5 (A).
131. "Cosmic-Ray Ionization at High Altitudes" (with R. J. Stephenson), *Physical Review*, XLV: 7 (Apr .1, 1934), 441–50.
132. "Cosmic-Ray Ionization in a Heavy Walled Chamber at High Altitudes" (with R. J. Stephenson), *Physical Review*, XLV: 8 (Apr. 15, 1934), 564 (A).
133. "Interpretation of Data from World Cosmic-Ray Survey," *Science*, LXXIX: 2052 (Apr. 27, 1934), 378 (A).
134. " 'Appearance' of Atoms as Observed with X Rays" (with E. O. Wollan), *Science*, LXXIX: 2052 (Apr. 27, 1934), 379–80 (A).

135. "A Precision Recording Cosmic-Ray Meter" (with E. O. Wollan, R. D. Bennett, and A. W. Simon), *Physical Review*, XLV: 10 (May 15, 1934), 758 (A).

136. "The Appearance of Atoms as Determined by X-Ray Scattering" (E. O. Wollan with A. H. Compton), *Journal of the Optical Society of America*, XXIV: 9 (Sept. 1934), 229–33.

137. "Composition of Cosmic Rays (with H. A. Bethe)," *Nature*, CXXXIV: 3393 (Nov. 10, 1934), 734–5 (L).

138. "Studies of Cosmic Rays," *Carnegie Institution of Washington Year Book*, No. 33, 1933–4 (Dec. 14, 1934), 316–21.

139. "Magnitude of Cosmic-Ray Bursts," *Nature*, CXXXIV: 3400 (Dec. 29, 1934), 1006 (L).

140. "A Precision Recording Cosmic-Ray Meter (with E. O. Wollan and R. D. Bennett)," *Review of Scientific Instruments*, V: 12 (Dec. 1934), 415–22.

1935

141. "Incoherent Scattering and the Concept of Discrete Electrons," *Physical Review*, XLVII: 5 (Jan. 15, 1935), 203 (A).

142. "Incoherent Scattering and the Concept of Discrete Electrons," *Physical Review*, XLVII: 5 (Mar. 1, 1935), 367–70.

143. "The Composition of Cosmic Rays," *Proceedings of the American Philosophical Society*, LXXV: 4 (Apr. 20, 1935), 251–74.

144. "Cosmic Rays," *Nature*, CXXXV: 3418 (May 4, 1935), 695–8; *Scientific American*, CLIII: 3 (Sept. 1935), 133.

145. "An Apparent Effect of Galactic Rotation on the Intensity of Cosmic Rays" (with Ivan A. Getting), *Physical Review*, XLVII: 11 (June 1, 1935), 817–21.

146. "An Attempt to Analyse Cosmic Rays," *Proceedings of the Physical Society (London)*, XLVII: 261 (July 1, 1935), 747–73.

147. "Studies of Cosmic Rays," *Carnegie Institution of Washington Year Book*, No. 34, 1934–5 (Dec. 13, 1935), 336–40.

148. "A Study of Cosmic-Ray Bursts at Different Altitudes" (with Ralph D. Bennett), *Papers and Discussions of the International Conference on Physics*, London, 1934, Vol. I. *Nuclear Physics* (London Physical Society, 1935), 225.

1936

149. "Recent Developments in Cosmic Rays," *Review of Scientific Instruments*, VII: 2 (Feb. 1936), 71–81.

150. "Scattering of X Rays by a Spinning Electron," *Physical Review*, L: 9 (Nov. 15, 1936), 878–81.

151. "Studies of Cosmic Rays," *Carnegie Institution of Washington Year Book*, No. 35, 1935–6 (Dec. 11, 1936), 343–6.

152. "Cosmic Rays as Electrical Particles," *Physical Review*, L: 12 (Dec. 15, 1936), 1119–30.

1937

153. "An Energy Distribution Analysis of Primary Cosmic Rays," *Physical Review*, LI: 1 (Jan. 1, 1937), 59 (A).

154. "Effect of Galactic Rotation on Cosmic Rays," *Science*, LXXXV: 2192 (Jan. 1, 1937), 25 (A).

155. "Variations of Cosmic Rays with Latitude on the Pacific Ocean" (with R. N. Turner), *Physical Review*, LI: 11 (June 1, 1937), 1005 (A).

156. "On the Origin of Cosmic Rays" (with P. Y. Chou), *Physical Review*, LI: 12 (June 15, 1937), 1104 (L).

157. "Cosmic Rays on the Pacific Ocean" (with R. N. Turner), *Physical Review*, LII: 8 (Oct. 15, 1937), 799–814.

158. "Studies of Cosmic Rays," *Carnegie Institution of Washington Year Book*, No. 36, 1936–7 (Dec. 10, 1937), 356–8.

### 1938

159. "An Alternative Interpretation of Jauncey's 'Heavy Electron' Spectra," *Physical Review*, LIII: 5 (Mar. 1, 1938), 431 (L).

160. *Chart of Electromagnetic Radiations* (Chicago: W. M. Welch Scientific Co., 1938).

### 1939

161. "Significance of Sidereal Time Variations of Cosmic Rays" (with P. S. Gill), *Physical Review*, LV: 2 (Jan. 15, 1939), 233 (A).

162. "Cosmic-Ray Intensity and the Thermal Expansion of the Atmosphere" (with M. Schein and P. S. Gill), *Science*, LXXXXIX: 2314 (May 5, 1939), 398 (A).

163. "Time Variations of Cosmic Rays," *Journal of the Franklin Institute*, CCXXVII: 5 (May 1939), 607–20.

164. "Cosmic Rays on the Pacific Ocean" (with P. S. Gill), *Reviews of Modern Physics*, XI: 3–4 (July–Oct. 1939), 136.

165. "Recurrence Phenomena in Cosmic-Ray Intensity" (A. T. Monk with A. H. Compton), *Reviews of Modern Physics*, XI: 3–4 (July–Oct. 1939), 173–9.

166. "Chicago Cosmic-Ray Symposium," *Scientific Monthly*, XLIX (Sept. 1939), 280–4.

### 1940

167. "What We Have Learned from Scattered X Rays," *Journal of the Franklin Institute*, CCXXX: 2 (Aug. 1940), 149–57.

168. "Physical Differences Between Types of Penetrating Radiation," *American Journal of Roentgenology and Radium Therapy*, XXXIV: 2 (Aug. 1940), 270–5; *Radiography* (excerpt), VII (May 1941), 69–73.

169. "Effect of an Eclipse on Cosmic Rays," *Physical Review*, LVIII: 9 (Nov. 1, 1940), 841 (L).

170. "Report on Cosmic-Ray Research at the University of Chicago," *Carnegie Institution of Washington Year Book*, No. 39, 1939–40 (Dec. 13, 1940), 116–21.

171. "Studies of Cosmic Rays at High Altitudes," *American Philosophical Society Year Book*, 1940 (report as recipient of Grant No. 427 from the Penrose Fund), 147–9.

### 1941

172. "Recurrence Pulses in Cosmic-Ray Intensity" (with A. T. Monk), *Physical Review*, LIX: 1 (Jan. 1, 1941), 112 (A).

173. "Protons as Primary Cosmic Rays" (with Marcel Schein), *Science*, XCIII: 2419 (May 9, 1941), 436 (A).

174. "Recent Studies of Cosmic Rays at High Altitudes," *Science*, XCIII: 2420 (May 16, 1941), 462 (A).

175. "Report on Cosmic-Ray Research at the University of Chicago," *Carnegie Institution of Washington Year Book*, No. 40, 1940–1 (Dec. 12, 1941), 121–6.

1942

176. "Report on Cosmic-Ray Research at the University of Chicago," *Carnegie Institution of Washington Year Book*, No. 41, 1941–2 (Dec. 18, 1942), 90–4.

1943

177. "On the Fluctuations of Cosmic Rays," *Anais da Academia Brasileira de Ciências* (1943), 59–66.

1945

178. "Modern Physics and the Discovery of X Rays," *Radiology*, XLV: 5 (Nov. 1945), 534–8.

1946

179. "The Scattering of X-Ray Photons," *American Journal of Physics*, XIV: 2 (Mar.–Apr. 1946), 80–4.

1952

180. "Man's Awareness and the Limits of Physical Science," *Science*, CXVI: 3020 (Nov. 14, 1952), 519 (A).

1956

181. "The World of Science in the Late Eighteenth Century and Today," *Proceedings of the American Philosophical Society*, C: 4 (Aug. 1956), 296–303.

1961

182. "The Scattering of X Rays as Particles," *American Journal of Physics*, XXIX: 12 (Dec. 1961), 817–20.

# Index

Adams, James Truslow, 310; quoted, 377; *Epic of America*, 401, 402, 403

Addams, Jane, 230

Adenauer, Konrad, 335

AEC: *see* Atomic Energy Commission

Aepinus, Franz Maria, 105

aeronautics, 9, 12–15, 131–5

Air Force Academy, United States, 131

Ahmad, Nazir, 40; quoted, 41, 142

Alaska, 161, 162

alchemy, development of, 92

Alembert, Jean Le Rond d', 94, 108

Alexander III (the Great), 89, 355

al-Ghazali: *see* Ghazali, Abu Mohammed al-

Aligarh University (India), 111

Allen, Frederick Lewis: *The Big Change*, 333 and *n.*

alpha particles, research on, 185–6; *see also* atom

Alvarez, Luis Walter, 25

American Association for the Advancement of Science, 342, 369

American Philosophical Society, 101, 217, 222, 226, 234, 317

American Physical Society, 32, 36, 38, 342

American Telephone and Telegraph Co., 162

Ampère, André Marie, 241

Anaxagoras, 111, 116, 363

Anderson, Carl, 173

Aquinas, Thomas, 93, 113

*Arabian Nights,* 92

Archimedes: principle of hydrostatics, 90; laws of the lever and of pulleys, 90

Aristarchus, 7, 90

Aristotle, 8, 86, 88, 89, 93, 101, 108, 109, 110, 112, 117, 170; quoted, 177, 395; 361

Army, United States, 189, 266, 282, 288, 289, 291–2, 293, 294, 295

*Art of Scientific Investigation, The: see* Beveridge, W. I. B.

Arthur, James, 164

artificial transmutation of matter, 29, 252; *see also* Rutherford, Sir Ernest

Ashby, Eric, 276

Astor, David, 405

astrology, development of, 85, 89

astronomy: in ancient times, 85, 92; modern, 168, 222, 414

*Atlantic Monthly, The,* 115, 121

atom(s): electronic structure of, 22–4, 28, 32–4, 37–8, 152; discovery of nucleus of, 29, 126, 185; and Compton effect, 32 *ff.;* 37, 38, 94, 95, 119; chain reaction, 120, 187, 188, 189, 243; early AHC talk on (*1931*), 136–9; 159, 160, 162; radioactive, 166, 171; size of, 185–6; atomic number, 34, 151, 186, 203; Bohr's theory of the structure of, 186, 203; peaceful uses of, 251–6

# A Note About the Author

ARTHUR HOLLY COMPTON was born in Wooster, Ohio, in 1892. He received his B.S. from Wooster College and his M.A. and Ph.D. from Princeton University. His busy life was filled with major scientific attainments and honors, and in 1927 he was awarded the Nobel prize for physics for his test of the particle nature of the photon. He was a student and colleague of the great figures from Rutherford to Fermi, led the field in cosmic-ray researches here and abroad, and directed the work at Chicago that resulted in the first atomic chain reaction. Dr. Compton was an educator as well as a scientist; before his death in 1962, he had been Chancellor at Washington University in St. Louis. Not the least of Dr. Compton's contributions as educator was his unparalleled ability to speak and write simply and clearly about scientific and social subjects to his non-scientific fellow citizens.

# A Note on the Type

*The text of this book is set in Caledonia, a Linotype face designed by W. A. Dwiggins. This type belongs to the family of printing types called "modern face" by printers—a term used to mark the change in style of type-letters that occurred about 1800. Caledonia borders on the general design of Scotch Modern, but is more freely drawn than that letter.*

*The book was composed by Brown Bros. Linotypers, Inc., New York, New York, printed and bound by The Haddon Craftsmen, Inc., Scranton, Pennsylvania.*